Don Lavery
- The University of Chicago
- 1948 -

AN INTRODUCTION TO
ABSTRACT ALGEBRA

AN INTRODUCTION TO
ABSTRACT ALGEBRA

BY

CYRUS COLTON MAC DUFFEE
Professor of Mathematics at the University of Wisconsin

Don Lavory

NEW YORK

JOHN WILEY & SONS, Inc.

LONDON: CHAPMAN & HALL, Limited

PREFACE

The phenomenal development in algebra which has occurred in recent years has been largely the result of a changed point of view toward the subject, the displacement of formalism by generalization and abstraction. The maxim so often emphasized by the late E. H. Moore that the existence of parallel theories indicates an underlying unifying theory has been thoroughly vindicated in modern algebra. Number theory, group theory, and formal algebra have been unified and abstracted to produce what is now known as abstract algebra.

But abstract theorems are empty words to those who are not familiar with the concrete facts which they generalize. One of the major problems in teaching abstract algebra, and one which must be fairly met, is to give to the student a selected body of facts from number theory, group theory, etc., so that he will have the background to understand and appreciate the generalized results. Without this background, the game of playing with postulates becomes absurd.

The present book is designed primarily to be used as a textbook by beginning graduate students in American universities. It presupposes the traditional course in theory of equations, and nothing more except some mathematical maturity. Most of the material is classical, but it is believed that the selection and method of presentation are such as to orient the student and to lead him most rapidly to an ability to read and understand the more advanced books and the literature of modern algebra.

The method of presentation has been guided by pedagogical as well as logical considerations. The abstract point of view is developed gradually. Special cases are first discussed, and when an abstract idea is presented, concrete instances of it are already at hand. The degree of complexity increases gradually from the system of rational integers to linear associative algebras. Incidentally, the Kronecker program of developing all number systems from the rational integers has been carried through.

It has been my experience that the book contains enough material for a year's work. It is recommended that the students do not attempt to read too rapidly, and that all problems be worked. The problems furnish the laboratory material for the course, the concrete instances of the abstract theorems.   The student's ability to solve the problems is the crucial test of his mastery of the text.

All the material of this book has been used in mimeographed form at the University of Wisconsin, and the first five chapters have been used at the Ohio State University.   That students of the first-year graduate level can use the book successfully has thus been demonstrated.

To those students who have contributed to the preparation of this book by their interest and unsparing criticism, I owe much.   I am particularly indebted to Dr. C. J. Everett, Jr., who has read both the manuscript and the proofs.   Finally, acknowledgment is due to Professor C. G. Latimer for the use of his notes in the preparation of the sections on the number theory of quaternions.

C. C. MacDuffee

Madison, Wisconsin
February 1, 1940

CONTENTS

INTRODUCTION TO ABSTRACT ALGEBRA

CHAPTER I

THE THEORY OF NUMBERS

1. The positive integers. At the foundation of mathematics are the *positive integers* or *natural numbers*

$$1, 2, 3, 4, \cdots.$$

The set of positive integers has been characterized by Peano by the following properties (or axioms, or postulates):

(1.1)   There is a positive integer **1**.

(1.2)   Every positive integer a has a *consequent* a^+.

If a^+ is the consequent of a, we call a the *antecedent* of a^+.

(1.3)   The integer 1 has no antecedent.

(1.4)   If $a^+ = b^+$, then $a = b$.

(1.5)   Every set of positive integers which contains 1 and the consequent of every number of the set contains all the positive integers.

This last postulate is the property of the positive integers which enables us to prove theorems by induction. If a theorem holds for the integer 1, and if the statement of the theorem for every a^+ is a logical consequence of the statement of the theorem for a, then the theorem is true for every positive integer.

The integer 1 and the relation "consequent" are said to be *undefined*. It is evident that the process of defining mathematical concepts in terms of simpler ones must lead ultimately to concepts which cannot be defined in terms of simpler ones, and hence cannot be explicitly defined. They are not, however, truly undefined, for they are implicitly defined by the postulates which they are assumed to satisfy.

Addition of two positive integers is defined by the equations

(1.6) $$a + 1 = a^+,$$

(1.7) $$a + b^+ = (a + b)^+,$$

for every a and b of the set.

Since every number except 1 is of the form b^+, addition is thus defined uniquely for every two positive integers.

Theorem 1.1.   Addition is associative, namely

$$(a + b) + c = a + (b + c).$$

By (1.7) and (1.6),

$$(a + b) + 1 = a + (b + 1),$$

so the theorem holds for $c = 1$.   Also

$$(a + b) + c^+ = [(a + b) + c]^+.$$

The induction hypothesis, i.e., the statement of the theorem for c, gives

$$(a + b) + c^+ = [a + (b + c)]^+,$$

and, by two applications of (1.7), we obtain

$$(a + b) + c^+ = a + (b + c)^+ = a + (b + c^+).$$

The proof is thus complete.

Theorem 1.2.   Addition is commutative, namely

$$a + b = b + a.$$

We shall first prove that

$$a + 1 = 1 + a.$$

This is obvious for $a = 1$.   By the induction hypothesis

$$a^+ + 1 = (a + 1) + 1 = (1 + a) + 1.$$

By Theorem 1.1, we have

$$a^+ + 1 = 1 + (a + 1) = 1 + a^+.$$

Thus our theorem is true for every a when $b = 1$.

By (1.7)

$$a + b^+ = a + (b + 1) = (a + b) + 1.$$

By Case I of our theorem and the induction hypothesis this is equal to

$$1 + (a + b) = 1 + (b + a).$$

By Theorem 1.1 and Case I we have

$$(1 + b) + a = (b + 1) + a = b^+ + a.$$

This completes the proof.

Theorem 1.3.   If $a + b = a + c$, then $b = c$.

Consider first the case where $a = 1$. If $1 + b = 1 + c$, then by Theorem 1.2

$$b + 1 = c + 1,$$

whence $b = c$ by (1.4).

Now suppose that

$$a^+ + b = a^+ + c.$$

From Theorems 1.2 and 1.1,

$$(a + 1) + b = (a + 1) + c,$$
$$(1 + a) + b = (1 + a) + c,$$
$$1 + (a + b) = 1 + (a + c).$$

By the first case of our theorem,

$$a + b = a + c,$$

whence $b = c$ by the induction hypothesis.

We now define another operation called *multiplication* by the following properties:

(1.8) $$a \cdot 1 = a,$$

(1.9) $$a \cdot b^+ = ab + a.$$

Every number except 1 is the consequent of some number, and so multiplication is defined uniquely for every two numbers.

Theorem 1.4. Multiplication is left-distributive with respect to addition:

$$a(b + c) = ab + ac.$$

By (1.9) and (1.8), this is true for $c = 1$. Furthermore, by (1.7) and (1.9),

$$a(b + c^+) = a(b + c)^+ = a(b + c) + a.$$

Now by the induction hypothesis and Theorem 1.1 and (1.9), this equals

$$(ab + ac) + a = ab + (ac + a) = ab + ac^+.$$

Theorem 1.5. $1 \cdot a = a$ *and* $b^+ a = ba + a$.

The first result is evident for $a = 1$ from (1.8). Then, by Theorem 1.4,

$$1 \cdot a^+ = 1(a + 1) = 1 \cdot a + 1 \cdot 1 = 1 \cdot a + 1.$$

By the induction hypothesis this is equal to

$$a + 1 = a^+,$$

so the first statement is proved.

Now, by (1.8),

$$b^+ \cdot 1 = b^+ = b + 1 = b \cdot 1 + 1,$$

so the second part of the theorem is true for $a = 1$. By (1.9) and the induction hypothesis,

$$b^+ a^+ = b^+ a + b^+ = ba + a + b + 1 = ba + b + a + 1$$
$$= ba^+ + a^+.$$

Theorem 1.6. Multiplication is associative: $ab \cdot c = a \cdot bc$.

By (1.8),

$$(ab)1 = ab = a(b1),$$

so the theorem holds for $c = 1$. By (1.9),

$$ab \cdot c^+ = ab \cdot c + ab.$$

By the induction hypothesis and Theorem 1.4, this is equal to

$$a \cdot bc + ab = a(bc + b) = a(bc^+),$$

which proves the theorem.

Theorem 1.7. Multiplication is commutative: $ab = ba$.

Take $b = 1$. Then $a \cdot 1 = a = 1 \cdot a$ by (1.8) and Theorem 1.5. By (1.9),

$$ab^+ = ab + a,$$

which by the induction hypothesis and Theorem 1.5 gives

$$ab^+ = ba + a = b^+ a.$$

Corollary 1.7. Multiplication is right-distributive with respect to addition: $(b + c)a = ba + ca$.

EXERCISES

1. Prove Corollary 1.7 by paralleling the proof of Theorem 1.4.
2. Show that the set of all numbers

$$1, \ 1^+ = 2, \ 2^+ = 3, \ 3^+ = 4, \ \cdots,$$

each of which is obtainable from 1 in a finite number of steps, satisfies (1.5) and hence constitutes the set of all positive integers.

3. If $a = b + c$, then $a > b$ and $b < a$. Prove that:

(a) For every two positive integers a and b, one and only one of the relations

$$a < b, \quad a = b, \quad a > b$$

holds.

    (*b*) If $a < b$ and $b < c$, then $a < c$.

    (*c*) If $a < b$, then $a + c < b + c$.

    (*d*) If $a < b$, then $ac < bc$.

    4. Prove that $ab = ac$ implies $b = c$.

    5. Prove that, in every non-empty set of positive integers, there is a smallest, i.e., an integer s such that $s < b$ for every $b \neq s$ in the set.

    6. Prove that there is no number x such that $a < x < a + 1$.

    7. Prove that, if $a < b$, $a + 1 \leqq b$.

2. The rational integers. We shall now define the set of positive and negative integers and zero in terms of pairs of positive integers. Consider the set of all pairs (a, b) of positive integers, and define

$$(a, b) = (c, d)$$

to mean that $a + d = c + b$.

    Theorem 2.1.   Equality of pairs is:

    (*a*) *Reflexive:* $(a, b) = (a, b)$.

    (*b*) *Symmetric: if* $(a, b) = (c, d)$ *then* $(c, d) = (a, b)$.

    (*c*) *Transitive: if* $(a, b) = (c, d)$ *and* $(c, d) = (e, f)$,   *then* $(a, b) = (e, f)$.

    These three properties are the fundamental properties of an equals relation, without which the term "equality" would be inappropriate.

    Since $a + b = a + b$, (*a*) holds.   If $a + d = c + b$, then $c + b = a + d$, so (*b*) holds.   To prove (*c*), suppose that

$$a + d = c + b, \qquad c + f = e + d.$$

Then

$$a + d + f = c + b + f = b + e + d$$

by the associative and commutative laws for positive integers, and by Theorem 1.3

$$a + f = b + e$$

so that $(a, b) = (e, f)$.

    We now define *addition* of these pairs as follows:

(2.1) $$(a, b) + (c, d) = (a + c, b + d).$$

We define *multiplication* thus:

(2.2) $$(a, b) \times (c, d) = (ac + bd, ad + bc).$$

    Theorem 2.2.   Addition and multiplication are associative and commutative, and multiplication is distributive with respect to addition.

The associative laws follow from the corresponding laws for positive integers thus:

$$[(a, b) + (c, d)] + (e, f) = ([a + c] + e, [b + d] + f)$$
$$= (a + [c + e], b + [d + f])$$
$$= (a, b) + [(c, d) + (e, f)].$$

The remainder of the proof of this theorem is left as an exercise. If two sets of numbers

$$a, b, c, d, \cdots, \qquad \alpha, \beta, \gamma, \delta, \cdots$$

correspond biuniquely, say

$$a \leftrightarrow \alpha, \qquad b \leftrightarrow \beta, \qquad c \leftrightarrow \gamma, \cdots,$$

so that $a = b$ implies $\alpha = \beta$, and conversely, and so that

$$a + b \leftrightarrow \alpha + \beta, \qquad ab \leftrightarrow \alpha\beta,$$

these two sets are abstractly identical as far as properties involving addition and multiplication are concerned. We say that they are *isomorphic* relative to addition and multiplication.

Theorem 2.3. The number pairs (a, b) where $a > b$ are isomorphic with the positive integers.

If $a > b$, we can write $a = n + b$, by Ex. 3, § 1. Moreover, $(n + b, b)$ is independent of b, for

$$(n + b) + c = (n + c) + b,$$

so that

$$(n + b, b) = (n + c, c).$$

The correspondence

$$(n + b, b) \leftrightarrow n$$

is an isomorphism with respect to addition and multiplication. First,

$$(n + b, b) = (m + c, c)$$

if and only if $n + b + c = m + c + b$, that is, if and only if $n = m$. Second, if

$$(n + b, b) \leftrightarrow n, \qquad (m + c, c) \leftrightarrow m,$$

$$(n + b, b) + (m + c, c) = (m + n + b + c, b + c) \leftrightarrow m + n,$$

$$(n + b, b) \times (m + c, c) = (nm + nc + mb + bc + bc, nc + bc + mb + bc) \leftrightarrow mn.$$

Because of this isomorphism, we shall now use the notation n for the number pair $(n + b, b)$, and say that the rational integers *contain* the positive integers as a subset. More precisely, it is true only that the rational integers contain a subset isomorphic with the positive integers.

From the definition of equality, it follows that the number (a, a) is independent of a. We shall call this number *zero*, and denote it by 0.

Theorem 2.4. For every number pair (a, b),

$$(a, b) + 0 = (a, b), \qquad (a, b) \times 0 = 0.$$

For

$$(a, b) + (c, c) = (a + c, b + c) = (a, b),$$

$$(a, b) \times (c, c) = (ac + bc, ac + bc) = (c, c).$$

By Ex. 3, § 1, every number pair (a, b) is of one of the three types

$$a > b, \qquad a = b, \qquad a < b.$$

We have discussed the first two types. A number (a, b) of the third type can be written $(a, a + n)$, in which form it is clearly independent of a.

Evidently

$$(n + b, b) + (a, a + n) = 0,$$

for $n + b + a = b + a + n$. We shall use the symbol ^{-}n to denote the pair $(a, a + n)$, and call it a *negative number*. We have proved

Theorem 2.5. $n + {}^{-}n = 0$.

The set of pairs (a, b) subject to the definitions of equality, addition, and multiplication of this paragraph constitute the set $[Ra]$ of *rational integers*. They are composed of the positive integers, the negative integers, and zero.

A solution of the equation

(2.3) $$x + b = a$$

is called a *difference* $a - b$, and the operation of forming $a - b$ from a and b is called *subtraction*. It is an inverse of addition.

Theorem 2.6. The difference of two rational integers exists uniquely.

By Theorem 2.5,

$$(a + {}^{-}b) + b = a + ({}^{-}b + b) = a + 0 = a,$$

so that $a + {}^{-}b$ satisfies (2.3). Conversely, let x_1 be any solution of (2.3). Then

$$a + {}^{-}b = (x_1 + b) + {}^{-}b = x_1 + (b + {}^{-}b) = x_1,$$

so that $a + {}^{-}b$ is the only solution.

We can now dispense with the notation $a + {}^-b$, and write $a - b$ instead. In particular, we write $-b$ for ${}^-b$.

EXERCISES

1. Complete the proof of Theorem 2.2.
2. Prove that the product of two negative numbers is positive, and that the product of a positive number and a negative number is negative.
3. Extend Theorem 1.3 to $[Ra]$.
4. Show that Ex. 4, § 1, can be extended to $[Ra]$ only with the provision that $a \neq 0$.

3. Divisors. In the rest of this chapter we shall use the word *number* to indicate a rational integer.

Though every number has an inverse with respect to addition (Theorem 2.5), it is not true that every number has an inverse with respect to multiplication. Such an inverse, if it exists, is called a *reciprocal*, and only 1 and -1 have reciprocals in $[Ra]$. These numbers are called *units*.

If there exists a number x such that

$$xa = b,$$

then a is called a *divisor* of b. This fact can be expressed by saying that a *divides* b, written $a \mid b$. If a does not divide b, we write $a \nmid b$. The units are divisors of every number.

The number 0 also has distinctive properties relative to multiplication, for, if a is any number (Theorem 2.4),

$$a \times 0 = 0.$$

Thus every number divides 0.

If a is neither 0 nor a unit, and if there exists a number x neither 0 nor a unit such that $xa = b$, then a is called a *proper divisor* of b. A number not 0 or a unit having no proper divisors is called a *prime*. Numbers having proper divisors are called *composite* numbers.

Thus the rational integers fall into mutually exclusive classes:

1. Zero.   3. Primes.
2. The units $+1$ and -1.   4. Composite numbers.

If $a \mid b$ and $a \mid c$, then a is a *common divisor* of b and c. A number d is called a *greatest common divisor* of two or more numbers if:

(1) it is a common divisor of these numbers, and if
(2) every common divisor of these numbers divides d.

The abbreviation g.c.d. is used to denote the greatest common divisor. In the remainder of this chapter we shall use the notation (b, c) to denote the positive g.c.d. of b and c. Thus

$$(12, -18, 60) = 6.$$

Note that the term "greatest common divisor" is used in a technical sense, for -6 is also a g.c.d. of 12, -18, 60. The positive g.c.d. of several integers is, however, the greatest of their common divisors.

If $a \mid c$, then c is called a *multiple* of a. If $a \mid c$ and $b \mid c$, then c is a *common multiple* of a and b. A number m is called a *least common multiple* (l.c.m.) of two or more numbers if:

(1) it is a common multiple of the numbers, and if
(2) it divides every common multiple of the numbers.

Thus 60 is a l.c.m. of 15, 20, and 30. So is -60. We may use the notation

$$60 = [15, 20, 30].$$

Theorem 3.1. Let a be non-negative and b positive. There exist two non-negative integers q and r such that

$$a = bq + r, \qquad\qquad 0 \leqq r < b.$$

If $a = 0$, take $q = r = 0$.
Suppose $a > 0$. If $a = 1$ and $b = 1$, take $q = 1$ and $r = 0$. If $a = 1$ and $b > 1$, take $q = 0$ and $r = 1$. Thus the theorem holds for $a = 1$. From the induction hypothesis $a = bq + r$, we have

$$a + 1 = bq + r + 1.$$

If $r + 1 < b$, the theorem holds for $a + 1$ and b. If $r + 1$ is not less than b, $r + 1 = b$ by Ex. 7, § 1, so that

$$a + 1 = bq + b = b(q + 1).$$

Thus the step-up from a to $a + 1$ can always be made.

The process of determining the q and r for a given a and b is known as the *division transformation*. It is a tentative process in that it involves a certain amount of guessing, but in practice it presents no difficulty. A tentative process which demands but a finite number of trials is generally accepted as a legitimate method in number theory if the process can be carried out in a reasonable length of time. Ordinary division, as we are accustomed to call the division transformation, is such a process.

Theorem 3.2. If $a = bq + r$, then every g.c.d. of a and b is a g.c.d. of b and r, and vice versa.

Let d be a g.c.d. of a and b, and d_1 a g.c.d. of b and r. Since d divides the left member of $a - bq = r$, d divides r and hence is a common divisor of b and r. Hence $d \mid d_1$. Similarly d_1 divides the right member of $a = bq + r$ and hence divides a. Hence $d_1 \mid d$. If $d_1 = kd$, $d = ld_1$, then $kl = 1$ so that $k = l = \pm 1$ and $d = \pm d_1$.

Theorem 3.3. *Every pair of numbers not both 0 have a positive g.c.d.*

If either a or b is 0, the other is their g.c.d. We can without loss of generality assume that a and b are positive and $a > b$. Let

$$a = bq + r, \qquad\qquad 0 \leqq r < b.$$

By Theorem 3.2, $(a, b) = (b, r)$. Now set

$$b = rq_1 + r_1, \qquad\qquad 0 \leqq r_1 < r,$$

so that $(a, b) = (b, r) = (r, r_1)$. Continue in this manner as long as a non-zero remainder is obtained. There must be some k for which

$$r_{k-2} = r_{k-1}q_k + r_k, \qquad\qquad r_k \neq 0,$$

$$r_{k-1} = r_k q_{k+1},$$

for the sequence

$$r > r_1 > r_2 > \cdots > 0$$

can have but a finite number of members. Then r_k is a g.c.d. of a and b.

Theorem 3.4. *If $d = (a, b)$, there exist rational integers p and s such that*

$$d = pa + sb.$$

In the proof of Theorem 3.3, a chain of equations,

$$r_k = -q_k r_{k-1} + r_{k-2},$$

$$r_{k-1} = -q_{k-1}r_{k-2} + r_{k-3},$$

$$\cdot \quad \cdot \quad \cdot \quad \cdot \quad \cdot \quad \cdot \quad \cdot$$

$$r_1 = -q_1 r + b,$$

$$r = -qb + a,$$

was obtained. By eliminating in succession $r_{k-1}, r_{k-2}, \cdots, r$, we obtain

$$d = r_k = pa + sb.$$

If d_1 is any g.c.d. of a and b, $d_1 \mid d$ and $d \mid d_1$, and so, as in the proof of Theorem 3.2, $d_1 = \pm d$. Thus the theorem holds for every g.c.d.

EXERCISES

1. The following proof that the number of primes is infinite is credited to Euclid. Let p be any prime; form the product of all the primes from 2 to p and add 1. Then the number

$$2 \cdot 3 \cdot 5 \cdot 7 \cdot 11 \cdots p + 1$$

has no prime factor $\leq p$. Complete the proof.

2. Prove that the q and r in Theorem 3.1 are unique.

3. Find the positive g.c.d. of 3961 and 952, and express it linearly in terms of the given numbers.

4. Express $(147, 64)$ in the form $147p + 64s$.

5. Let* $\mathfrak{J}$ denote the set of all numbers $xa + yb$ where a and b are given numbers not both 0, and x and y range over all rational integers. Directly from the definition of g.c.d., prove the existence of (a, b) by showing that the smallest positive integer in $\mathfrak{J}$ fulfills the definition.

HINT: Let d be this smallest positive integer. Set $a = qd + r$, $0 \leq r < d$. Then r is in $\mathfrak{J}$.

4. Unique Factorization. Two numbers are called *relatively prime* if their greatest common divisors are ± 1. Thus 1 is relatively prime to every number, even to itself.

If a and b are relatively prime, there exist by Theorem 3.4 two numbers p and s such that

$$pa + sb = 1.$$

Theorem 4.1. If a number a divides a product bc and is prime to b, then it divides c.

If a is prime to b (i.e., if a and b are relatively prime) we have, on multiplying the last equation by c,

$$pac + sbc = c.$$

Since a divides bc, it divides the entire left member, and therefore divides c.

Corollary 4.1. If a prime p divides $b_1 b_2 \cdots b_k$ it divides one of the factors.

If b_1 is not a multiple of p it is prime to p so that $p \mid b_2 \cdots b_k$. If in the latter case b_2 is not a multiple of p, it is prime to p, so that $p \mid b_3 \cdots b_k$. If, finally, p does not divide $b_1, b_2, \cdots, b_{k-1}$, it must divide b_k.

Theorem 4.2. Every positive composite number is expressible as a product of positive primes, and, except for the order of the factors, this representation is unique.

* $\mathfrak{J}$ is German I. Consult page 297 for the script equivalent.

This important theorem is known as the *fundamental theorem of arithmetic.*

That at least one representation exists of every positive composite number as a product of positive primes is fairly evident. If c is composite, there exist integers a and b, neither 0 nor a unit, such that $c = ab$. If a or b is composite, it can be factored. We continue to replace each factor of c by its factors until no further factoring is possible. Since c is finite, this stage will be reached in a finite number of steps. Thus we have

$$c = p_1 p_2 \cdots p_h,$$

where the p's are positive primes.

Now suppose that

$$c = q_1 q_2 \cdots q_k$$

is a second such representation. Then

$$p_1 p_2 \cdots p_h = q_1 q_2 \cdots q_k.$$

Since p_1 is a prime dividing $q_1 q_2 \cdots q_k$, it divides some q_i (Corollary 4.1). Since q_i is also a positive prime, $p_1 = q_i$. By a rearrangement of the order of the q's if necessary, we may assume that $p_1 = q_1$. Then, since $p_1 \neq 0$,

$$p_2 p_3 \cdots p_h = q_2 q_3 \cdots q_k.$$

As before, p_2 divides one of the remaining q's, say q_2, and hence equals it. We proceed until all the p's or all the q's are exhausted. It is now evident that $h = k$, for otherwise we should have a product of primes equal to 1.

It follows from this theorem that every number n having the distinct prime factors $p_1, p_2, \cdots, p_k$ can be written uniquely,

$$n = p_1^{\alpha_1} p_2^{\alpha_2} \cdots p_k^{\alpha_k}.$$

EXERCISES

1. Show that all the divisors of n are given by

$$p_1^{\beta_1} p_2^{\beta_2} \cdots p_k^{\beta_k}, \quad 0 \leqq \beta_i \leqq \alpha_i, \ (i = 1, 2, \cdots, k),$$

where it is understood that $p_i^0 = 1$.

2. In how many different ways can n be separated into a product of two relatively prime factors?

3. Show that the sum of the divisors of n is

$$\frac{p_1^{\alpha_1+1} - 1}{p_1 - 1} \frac{p_2^{\alpha_2+1} - 1}{p_2 - 1} \cdots \frac{p_k^{\alpha_k+1} - 1}{p_k - 1}.$$

4. Let $d = (a, b)$, $a = hd$, $b = kd$. Show that h and k are relatively prime. Show that $[a, b] = hkd$.

5. Congruences. If $m \mid a - b$, in other words if there exists a number k such that $a - b = km$, we say that a is *congruent* to b *modulo m*. In notation,

$$a \equiv b \quad \mod m.$$

The number m is called the *modulus* of the congruence.

The relation of congruence is strikingly similar to the ordinary relation of equality. Indeed, in an abstract sense, congruence is a type of equality.

Theorem 5.1.   Congruence modulo m is

(a) *Reflexive.*   ($a \equiv a \mod m$.)
(b) *Symmetric.*   (If $a \equiv b$, then $b \equiv a \mod m$.)
(c) *Transitive.*   (If $a \equiv b$ and $b \equiv c$, then $a \equiv c \mod m$).

Since $m \mid a - a = 0$, (a) is proved.

If $a \equiv b$, $a - b = km$, so that $b - a = -km$, or $b \equiv a \mod m$. This proves (b).

The proof of (c) is left as an exercise.

Having proved Theorem 5.1, we can manipulate the congruence relation as if it were equality.

It is, however, necessary to reëxamine the operations of addition and multiplication to see whether they are well defined relative to congruence.

Theorem 5.2.   The sum (difference) of two numbers is a unique number modulo m.

That is, if, in the sum $a + c$, a is replaced by a number congruent to a, or c is replaced by a number congruent to c, or if both replacements are made, $a + c$ will be replaced by a number congruent to it. Suppose that

$$a \equiv b, \quad c \equiv d \quad \mod m.$$

Then

$$a - b = k_1 m, \quad c - d = k_2 m,$$

$$(a + c) - (b + d) = (k_1 + k_2)m,$$

$$(a - c) - (b - d) = (k_1 - k_2)m.$$

Hence

$$a + c \equiv b + d, \quad a - c \equiv b - d \quad \mod m.$$

Theorem 5.3. The product of two numbers is a unique number modulo m.

Suppose that

$$a \equiv b, \quad c \equiv d \quad \mod m.$$

Then

$$a = b + k_1 m, \qquad c = d + k_2 m,$$

$$ac = bd + (k_1 d + bk_2 + k_1 k_2 m)m,$$

$$ac \equiv bd \qquad \text{mod } m.$$

Theorem 5.4. If $ac \equiv bc \bmod m$ and $m = dm_1$, where $d = (c, m)$, then $a \equiv b \bmod m_1$.

Let $m = dm_1$, $c = dc_1$. By assumption we have

$$dc_1(a - b) = kdm_1,$$

and since $d \neq 0$,

$$c_1(a - b) = km_1.$$

Since c_1 is prime to m_1 (Ex. 4, § 4), it must divide k by Theorem 4.1. Set $k = c_1 k_1$, and divide out the c_1. This gives

$$a - b = k_1 m_1,$$

thus proving the theorem.

Corollary 5.4. If $ac \equiv bc \bmod m$, and if c is prime to m, then $a \equiv b \bmod m$.

Theorem 5.5. If $p(x)$ is any polynomial with rational integral coefficients, and if $a \equiv b \bmod m$, then $p(a) \equiv p(b) \bmod m$.

Since $p(x)$ is built from x and the rational integers by the operations of addition, subtraction, and multiplication, this theorem follows from Theorems 5.2 and 5.3.

EXERCISES

1. Every number can be written as a polynomial in powers of 10 with coefficients ≥ 0 and ≤ 9. Apply Theorem 5.5 to prove that the remainder obtained upon dividing any number by 9 (or 3) is the same as the remainder obtained upon dividing the sum of its digits by 9 (or 3).

This is known as the rule of casting out nines.

2. Show that the remainder obtained upon dividing any number by 11 is the same as the remainder obtained upon dividing by 11 the following number: the units digit minus the tens digit plus the hundredths digit minus the thousandths digit, etc.

3. Obtain a criterion for the division of a number by 7.

4. Show by an example that $(c, m) = 1$ is a necessary part of the hypothesis of Corollary 5.4.

5. With a minimum of labor, find the first ten powers of 7 modulo 11. HINT: $7^2 = 49 \equiv 5$, so $7^3 \equiv 35 \equiv 2$, etc.

6. Prove that congruence modulo 0 is ordinary equality.

6. The linear congruence. A number x_1 satisfies the linear congruence

(6.1) $ax \equiv b \qquad \text{mod } m$

if $ax_1 \equiv b \bmod m$. If x_1 is a number satisfying (6.1), then every number congruent to x_1 modulo m also satisfies it, by Theorem 5.5. We shall say that the set of numbers congruent to x_1 modulo m constitute *a solution* of the congruence. Any one number of a complete solution will be said to *represent* the solution.

Thus the solution of

$$2x \equiv 3 \qquad \text{mod } 5$$

is $x \equiv 4 \bmod 5$. Each of the numbers $4, 24, -6$ represents this solution.

Theorem 6.1. Every solution of (6.1) is represented by one and only one number x_0 in the interval $0 \leqq x_0 < |m|$.

From the equation

$$x_1 = qm + x_0, \qquad\qquad 0 \leqq x_0 < |m|,$$

it follows that every solution is represented by a number in the interval. There cannot be in this interval two distinct numbers which are congruent modulo m, for their difference, being in absolute value $< |m|$, could not be divisible by m.

If m is small, the easiest way to solve a congruence is simply to try each of the numbers $0, 1, 2, \cdots, |m| - 1$ in turn. Each of these numbers which satisfies the congruence represents a solution, and there are no others.

The complete theory of the linear congruence is contained in

Theorem 6.2. The congruence

$$ax \equiv b \qquad \text{mod } m$$

has a solution if and only if $(a, m) \mid b$. If it does, there is a unique solution modulo $m_1 = m/d$, and therefore d solutions modulo m.

We shall divide the argument into four steps. Let $(a, m) = d$.

  I. If there is a solution, $d \mid b$.
  II. If $d \mid b$, there is a solution.
  III. If x_0 is a solution, so is $x_0 + km_1$ for every k.
  IV. Every solution occurs among those obtained in Step III.

Proof of I. If x_1 is a solution of (6.1),

$$ax_1 - km = b.$$

Since $d = (a, m)$ divides the left member of this equation, it divides b.

Proof of II. If $d \mid b$, set $b = b_1 d$. Also set $a = a_1 d$ and $m = m_1 d$. Then a_1 is prime to m_1, so that

$$1 = pa_1 + sm_1$$

for some integers p and s which we know how to determine. Then

$$b = pb_1 da_1 + sb_1 dm_1$$
$$= pb_1 a + sb_1 m.$$

That is, pb_1 satisfies the congruence.

Proof of III. Suppose that x_0 is a solution. Then, for every k, $x_0 + km_1$ is a solution, for we find, upon substituting $x_0 + km_1$ into the given congruence,

$$a(x_0 + km_1) = ax_0 + a_1 dkm_1 = ax_0 + a_1 km$$
$$\equiv ax_0 \equiv b \qquad \text{mod } m.$$

Proof of IV. We show that every solution x_1 is congruent to x_0 modulo m_1, and so is contained among the solutions obtained above. If

$$ax_0 \equiv b, \quad ax_1 \equiv b \qquad \text{mod } m,$$

it follows from Theorems 5.1 and 5.4 that

$$x_0 \equiv x_1 \qquad \text{mod } m_1.$$

If two numbers are in the relation

$$aa' \equiv 1 \qquad \text{mod } m,$$

each is called a *reciprocal* of the other modulo m. We have

Corollary 6.2. A number has a reciprocal if and only if it is prime to the modulus. The reciprocal if it exists is unique.

EXERCISES

1. Determine the number of solutions of: (*a*) $3x \equiv 5$ mod 7; (*b*) $4x \equiv 5$ mod 6; (*c*) $10x \equiv 15$ mod 35.

2. By trial, solve

$$3x \equiv 9 \qquad \text{mod } 14.$$

3. By the method used in Step II of the proof of Theorem 6.2, find the solution of

$$64x \equiv 51 \qquad \text{mod } 147.$$

(See Ex. 4, § 3.)

4. A step-by-step method essentially similar to the method used in Ex. 3 but frequently shorter is as follows. If $7x \equiv 15$ mod 16, then, for some k,

$$7x = 15 + 16k.$$

We desire k so that
$$15 + 16k \equiv 0 \qquad \text{mod } 7.$$

This last congruence is equivalent to
$$2k \equiv -1 \equiv 6 \qquad \text{mod } 7,$$
so that $k \equiv 3 \text{ mod } 7$. Then
$$7x \equiv 15 + 16 \cdot 3 \equiv 63 \qquad \text{mod } 16,$$
$$x \equiv 9 \qquad \text{mod } 16.$$

Apply this method repeatedly to solve the congruence of Ex. **3**.

7. Simultaneous congruences in one unknown with different moduli.

Theorem 7.1. A necessary and sufficient condition in order that two congruences
$$x \equiv a_1 \qquad \text{mod } m_1, \qquad\qquad x \equiv a_2 \qquad \text{mod } m_2$$
have a common solution is that
$$a_1 \equiv a_2 \qquad \text{mod } d, \qquad\qquad d = (m_1, m_2).$$
There is then just one solution in the interval $0 \leqq x < [m_1, m_2]$.

If x_1 satisfies both congruences,
$$x_1 = a_1 + k_1 m_1 = a_2 + k_2 m_2,$$
so that
(7.1) $$a_1 - a_2 \equiv k_2 m_2 \qquad \text{mod } m_1.$$

If, conversely, such a k_2 exists, then $x_1 = a_2 + k_2 m_2$ is a solution of both congruences. But, by Theorem 6.2, k_2 exists if and only if $d \mid a_1 - a_2$, and if this condition is satisfied, k_2 is unique modulo m_1/d. Thus there is just one value of x_1 in every interval $0 \leqq x_1 < m_1 m_2/d$. But by Ex. 4, § 4, $m_1 m_2/d = [m_1, m_2]$.

Theorem 7.2. A necessary and sufficient condition in order that n congruences
$$x \equiv a_1 \text{ mod } m_1, \qquad x \equiv a_2 \text{ mod } m_2, \cdots, \qquad x \equiv a_n \text{ mod } m_n$$
have a common solution is that
$$(m_i, m_j) \mid a_i - a_j \qquad\qquad\qquad i \neq j.$$
There is then just one solution in the interval
$$0 \leqq x < [m_1, m_2, \cdots, m_n].$$

The necessity of the condition is obvious, since, if two congruences are inconsistent, the whole system is inconsistent.

Consider the case $n = 3$. By hypothesis

$$(m_1, m_2) \mid a_1 - a_2, \qquad (m_1, m_3) \mid a_1 - a_3, \qquad (m_2, m_3) \mid a_2 - a_3.$$

By Theorem 7.1 the first two congruences have a solution

$$x \equiv b \qquad \text{mod } [m_1, m_2].$$

This congruence will have a solution in common with $x \equiv a_3$ mod m_3 if and only if

$$(m_3, [m_1, m_2]) \mid b - a_3.$$

Let p^α be the highest power of the prime p which divides $(m_3, [m_1, m_2])$, and write

$$b - a_3 = b - a_1 + a_1 - a_3 = b - a_2 + a_2 - a_3.$$

Since $p^\alpha \mid (m_3, [m_1, m_2])$, it divides both m_3 and $[m_1, m_2]$, and hence either m_1 or m_2. If $p^\alpha \mid m_1$, then $p^\alpha \mid (m_1, m_3)$. But $(m_1, m_3) \mid a_1 - a_3$, so $p^\alpha \mid a_1 - a_3$. Now $b - a_1 \equiv 0$ mod m_1, so $p^\alpha \mid b - a_1$. Hence $p^\alpha \mid b - a_3$. A similar argument shows that, if $p^\alpha \mid m_2$, then also $p^\alpha \mid b - a_3$. Thus every prime power factor of $(m_3, [m_1, m_2])$ divides $b - a_3$, and, since these prime power factors are relatively prime in pairs,

$$(m_3, [m_1, m_2]) \mid b - a_3.$$

Thus

$$x \equiv b \qquad \text{mod } [m_1, m_2], \qquad\qquad x \equiv a_3 \qquad \text{mod } m_3$$

have a common solution.

The theorem for a general n follows immediately, for, if $x \equiv a_1$ mod m_1 and $x \equiv a_2$ mod m_2 are replaced by the equivalent congruence $x \equiv b$ mod $[m_1, m_2]$, the hypothesis of the theorem continues to hold for the new system of $n - 1$ congruences.

Since $[m_3, [m_1, m_2]] = [m_1, m_2, m_3]$, etc., the solution is unique modulo $[m_1, m_2, \cdots, m_n]$.

Corollary 7.2. The Chinese Remainder Theorem. If every pair of moduli m_i, m_j consists of relatively prime numbers, the system of congruences

$$x \equiv a_1 \quad \text{mod } m_1, \qquad x \equiv a_2 \quad \text{mod } m_2, \cdots, \qquad x \equiv a_n \quad \text{mod } m_n$$

has a unique solution modulo $m_1 m_2 \cdots m_n$.

EXERCISES

1. Solve $x \equiv 3$ mod 5, $\quad x \equiv 4$ mod 7. HINT: Use (7.1).
2. Solve $x \equiv 4$ mod 9, $\quad x \equiv 7$ mod 12.
3. Solve $x \equiv 2$ mod 3, $\quad x \equiv 5$ mod 7, $\quad x \equiv 5$ mod 8.
4. Solve $x \equiv 5$ mod 12, $\quad x \equiv 4$ mod 17, $\quad x \equiv 10$ mod 25.

5. A band of 13 pirates obtained a certain number of gold coins. They tried to distribute them equitably, but found they had 8 left. Two pirates died of smallpox; then after distributing the coins there were 3 left. Thereupon they shot 3 more pirates, but still there was a remainder of 5 coins. How many coins were there?

8. Simultaneous congruences in several unknowns with the same modulus.

The theory of simultaneous congruences is similar to the theory of simultaneous equations, but there are some points of difference which need to be carefully noted.

Consider the set of k congruences in n unknowns,

$$a_{11}x_1 + a_{12}x_2 + \cdots + a_{1n}x_n \equiv c_1,$$

$$a_{21}x_1 + a_{22}x_2 + \cdots + a_{2n}x_n \equiv c_2,$$

(8.1)

$$a_{k1}x_1 + a_{k2}x_2 + \cdots + a_{kn}x_n \equiv c_k \qquad \text{mod } m.$$

To condense the notation, write

$$l_i = a_{i1}x_1 + a_{i2}x_2 + \cdots + a_{in}x_n - c_i.$$

Theorem 8.1. If, in the system of congruences (8.1), $l_i \equiv 0$ is replaced by

$$b_1 l_1 + b_2 l_2 + \cdots + b_k l_k \equiv 0,$$

where b_i is prime to m, the resulting system is equivalent to the given one.

That every solution of (8.1) is a solution of the new system is obvious. Let $(x_1', x_2', \cdots, x_n')$ be a solution of the new system. It makes

$$l_1 \equiv l_2 \equiv \cdots \equiv l_{i-1} \equiv l_{i+1} \equiv \cdots \equiv l_k \equiv 0 \qquad \text{mod } m,$$

and also makes

$$b_1 l_1 + b_2 l_2 + \cdots + b_k l_k \equiv b_i l_i \equiv 0 \qquad \text{mod } m.$$

Since b_i is prime to m, $l_i \equiv 0 \bmod m$ by Theorem 5.4.

If the multiplier b_i is not prime to m, extraneous solutions will be introduced.

Solution of congruences by determinants is suggested by Theorem 8.1. Consider the system

$$\begin{cases} 2x + y - z \equiv 5, \\ 3x - 2y + z \equiv 4, \\ x + 2y - 3z \equiv 6 \qquad \text{mod } 9. \end{cases}$$

The determinant of the system is

$$\begin{vmatrix} 2 & 1 & -1 \\ 3 & -2 & 1 \\ 1 & 2 & -3 \end{vmatrix} \equiv 1 \qquad \text{mod } 9,$$

while the cofactors of the elements of the first column are

$$\begin{vmatrix} -2 & 1 \\ 2 & -3 \end{vmatrix} \equiv 4, \qquad -\begin{vmatrix} 1 & -1 \\ 2 & -3 \end{vmatrix} \equiv 1, \qquad \begin{vmatrix} 1 & -1 \\ -2 & 1 \end{vmatrix} \equiv 8 \qquad \text{mod } 9.$$

Hence multiply the first congruence by 4, the second by 1, the third by 8, and obtain

$$x \equiv 0 \qquad \text{mod } 9.$$

As it is not always true that all the cofactors are prime to the modulus, it is possible to introduce solutions by using the method of determinants without regard for the precaution of Theorem 8.1.

EXERCISES

1. Complete the solution of the above system modulo 9.
2. Solve:
$$\begin{cases} 3x + 5y + z \equiv 4, \\ 2x + 3y + 2z \equiv 7, \\ 5x + y + 3z \equiv 6 \qquad \text{mod } 12. \end{cases}$$

3. A practical secret code makes use of congruences. The key consists of a matrix such as

$$\begin{bmatrix} 2 & 1 & -1 \\ 3 & -2 & 1 \\ 1 & 2 & -3 \end{bmatrix} \qquad \text{mod } 29,$$

and a correspondence such as

$$\begin{array}{ccccccc} - & a & b & c \cdots z & * & . \\ 0 & 1 & 2 & 3 \cdots 26 & 27 & 28. \end{array}$$

The word *victor* may be put into code as follows. By the correspondence, *victor* corresponds to 22, 9, 3, 20, 15, 18. Set $x = 22, y = 9, z = 3$, and substitute into the congruences determined by the key matrix. These give

$$2x + y - z \equiv 21,$$

$$3x - 2y + z \equiv 22,$$

$$x + 2y - 3z \equiv 2 \qquad \text{mod } 29.$$

Similarly the next three numbers $x = 20, y = 15, z = 18$ give 8, 19, 25. The code message is *uvbhsy*.

Decode -*cp-tifgj*.

9. Residue classes. All numbers which are congruent modulo m to a given number r constitute the *residue class* $[r]$. Evidently each number in the class serves to determine the class. Since every number is congruent to one of the m numbers $0, 1, 2, \cdots, \mid m \mid - 1$, every number lies in one of the classes

$$[0], [1], \cdots, [\mid m \mid - 1].$$

No number lies in more than one class, since every two numbers in the set $0, 1, \cdots, \mid m \mid - 1$ are incongruent modulo m.

A set of numbers $r_1, r_2, \cdots, r_m$ one of which lies in each residue class constitutes a *complete set of residues* modulo m. The set $0, 1, \cdots, \mid m \mid - 1$ is called the *complete set of least positive residues*.

Every number of the class $[r]$ is of the form

$$r + km \qquad\qquad k = 0, \pm 1, \pm 2, \cdots,$$

so that every number of the class $[r]$ is relatively prime to m if and only if r is prime to m. If r is prime to m, we shall say that the class $[r]$ is prime to m.

The number of residue classes prime to m is called the *totient* or *indicator* or *Euler φ-function* of m, written $\varphi(m)$. It may be also defined as the number of integers in the interval $0, 1, \cdots, \mid m \mid - 1$ which are prime to m. Note that $\varphi(1) = 1$. The totient is of fundamental importance in number theory.

A set of numbers $r_1, r_2, \cdots, r_{\varphi(m)}$ one of which lies in each class prime to m constitutes a *reduced set of residues* modulo m. If each r lies in the interval $0 \leq r < \mid m \mid$, the set is the *reduced set of least positive residues*.

Theorem 9.1. The numbers of every two complete (or reduced) sets of residues modulo m are congruent to each other in some order.

That is, if $r_1, r_2, \cdots, r_m$ and $s_1, s_2, \cdots, s_m$ are two complete sets of residues, each residue class contains just one r (say r_i) and one s (say s_{α_i}). Hence

$$r_i \equiv s_{\alpha_i} \qquad \mod m, \qquad\qquad i = 1, 2, \cdots, m,$$

where $\alpha_1, \alpha_2, \cdots, \alpha_m$ is some permutation of $1, 2, \cdots, m$. The proof is similar for reduced sets.

Theorem 9.2. A necessary and sufficient condition that a set of numbers constitute a complete set of residues modulo m is that no two of them be congruent to each other, and that they be m in number.

Since no two are congruent, each must lie in a different residue class.

As there are just m residue classes, there must be exactly one of the set in each class. We prove similarly

Theorem 9.3. A necessary and sufficient condition that a set of numbers constitute a reduced set of residues modulo m is that each be prime to m, that no two be congruent to each other, and that they be $\varphi(m)$ in number.

EXERCISES

1. Find $\varphi(5)$, $\varphi(6)$, $\varphi(8)$.
2. Show that $\varphi(12) = \varphi(4) \cdot \varphi(3) \neq \varphi(6) \cdot \varphi(2)$.
3. If p is a prime, $\varphi(p^n) = p^n - p^{n-1}$.
4. The divisors of 12 are 1, 2, 3, 4, 6, 12. Show that

$$\varphi(1) + \varphi(2) + \varphi(3) + \varphi(4) + \varphi(6) + \varphi(12) = 12.$$

5. Find five values of x such that $\varphi(x) = 24$.

10. Properties of the totient.

Theorem 10.1. If m_1 and m_2 are relatively prime,

$$\varphi(m_1 m_2) = \varphi(m_1) \cdot \varphi(m_2).$$

Let h be a number in the interval $0 \leq h < |m_1 m_2|$. Two numbers r_1 and r_2 are determined uniquely by the relations

$$h \equiv r_1 \qquad \text{mod } m_1 \qquad\qquad 0 \leq r_1 < |m_1|,$$
$$h \equiv r_2 \qquad \text{mod } m_2 \qquad\qquad 0 \leq r_2 < |m_2|.$$

Conversely let r_1 and r_2 be any two numbers satisfying the above inequalities. By Theorem 7.1 there exists exactly one number h in the interval $0 \leq h < |m_1 m_2|$ satisfying the above congruences. Thus there is a biunique correspondence between the numbers h and the number pairs (r_1, r_2).

Now h is prime to $m_1 m_2$ if and only if it is prime to both m_1 and m_2, for a prime factor of h must divide either m_1 or m_2 by Corollary 4.1. Moreover h is prime to m_1 if and only if r_1 is prime to m_1, and h is prime to m_2 if and only if r_2 is prime to m_2. Thus there are exactly as many numbers h which are prime to $m_1 m_2$ as there are number pairs (r_1, r_2) with r_1 prime to m_1 and r_2 prime to m_2. But there are just $\varphi(m_1)$ choices for r_1 and $\varphi(m_2)$ choices for r_2. Hence there are $\varphi(m_1) \cdot \varphi(m_2)$ such pairs.

Theorem 10.2. If $p_1, p_2, \cdots, p_k$ are the distinct prime factors of m,

$$\varphi(m) = m \left(1 - \frac{1}{p_1}\right)\left(1 - \frac{1}{p_2}\right) \cdots \left(1 - \frac{1}{p_k}\right).$$

We prove first that, if p is a prime,

$$\varphi(p^\alpha) = p^\alpha\left(1 - \frac{1}{p}\right).$$

Every number in the interval $0 \leqq h < p^\alpha$ is either prime to p^α or a multiple of p. The multiplies of p are

$$0,\, p,\, 2p,\, \cdots,\, (p^{\alpha-1} - 1)p,$$

and are $p^{\alpha-1}$ in number. Hence the number of h's which are prime to p is

$$\varphi(p^\alpha) = p^\alpha - p^{\alpha-1} = p^\alpha\left(1 - \frac{1}{p}\right).$$

Since m can be written $p_1^{\alpha_1}p_2^{\alpha_2} \cdots p_k^{\alpha_k}$ (Theorem 4.2), where the prime powers are relatively prime in pairs, we have by Theorem 10.1

$$\varphi(m) = p_1^{\alpha_1}\left(1 - \frac{1}{p_1}\right) p_2^{\alpha_2}\left(1 - \frac{1}{p_2}\right) \cdots p_k^{\alpha_k}\left(1 - \frac{1}{p_k}\right)$$

$$= m\left(1 - \frac{1}{p_1}\right)\left(1 - \frac{1}{p_2}\right) \cdots \left(1 - \frac{1}{p_k}\right).$$

Theorem 10.3. *If $d_1, d_2, \cdots, d_r$ are the different divisors of m, then*

$$\varphi(d_1) + \varphi(d_2) + \cdots + \varphi(d_r) = m.$$

Consider first the number p^α, whose divisors are $1, p, p^2, \cdots, p^\alpha$. Now

$$\varphi(1) + \varphi(p) + \varphi(p^2) + \cdots + \varphi(p^\alpha)$$

$$= 1 + \left(1 - \frac{1}{p}\right)(p + p^2 + \cdots + p^\alpha),$$

$$= 1 + \frac{p - 1}{p}\, p\, \frac{p^\alpha - 1}{p - 1} = p^\alpha.$$

For $m = p_1^{\alpha_1}p_2^{\alpha_2}\cdots p_k^{\alpha_k}$, where the p's are distinct primes,

$$m = \sum_{i_1=0}^{\alpha_1}\varphi(p_1^{i_1}) \sum_{i_2=0}^{\alpha_2}\varphi(p_2^{i_2}) \cdots \sum_{i_k=0}^{\alpha_k}\varphi(p_k^{i_k})$$

$$= \sum_{i_1,\, i_2,\, \cdots,\, i_k} \varphi(p_1^{i_1})\cdot\varphi(p_2^{i_2}) \cdots \varphi(p_k^{i_k}),$$

which by Theorem 10.1 is equal to

$$\sum_{i_1,\, i_2,\, \cdots,\, i_k} \varphi(p_1^{i_1}p_2^{i_2} \cdots p_k^{i_k}).$$

This is the sum of the totients of all the divisors of m. (See § 4, Ex. 1.)

1. Find $\varphi(49)$, $\varphi(81)$, $\varphi(1728)$.

2. Let k be the product of the distinct prime factors common to m_1 and m_2. Show that

$$\varphi(m_1 m_2) = k \cdot \varphi(m_1) \cdot \varphi(m_2)/\varphi(k).$$

3. Verify Theorem 10.3 for $m = 70$.

4. If $n > 1$, the sum of the numbers $< n$ and prime to n is $\frac{1}{2}n\varphi(n)$.

5. We say that ω is a primitive nth root of unity if ω^n is the lowest power of ω which equals 1. Show that among the distinct powers of ω exactly $\varphi(n)$ are primitive.

11. The Theorems of Fermat and Euler.

Theorem 11.1. (*Euler.*) *If a is prime to m,*

$$a^{\varphi(m)} \equiv 1 \qquad \text{mod } m.$$

Let $\varphi(m) = k$, and let $r_1, r_2, \cdots, r_k$ be a reduced set of residues modulo m. Consider the set of numbers

$$(11.1) \qquad\qquad ar_1, ar_2, \cdots, ar_k.$$

They are all prime to m, since a and all the r's are prime to m. They are incongruent to each other, since

$$ar_i \equiv ar_j \qquad \text{mod } m \qquad\qquad\qquad (i \neq j)$$

would imply

$$r_i \equiv r_j \qquad \text{mod } m \qquad\qquad\qquad (i \neq j)$$

by Corollary 5.4. Hence the numbers (11.1) also constitute a reduced set of residues by Theorem 9.3.

Since both the set $(r_1, r_2, \cdots, r_k)$ and the set (11.1) are reduced sets of residues, they are congruent to each other in some order, by Theorem 9.1. That is,

$$ar_i \equiv r_{\alpha_i} \qquad \text{mod } m \qquad\qquad (i = 1, 2, \cdots, k),$$

where $\alpha_1, \alpha_2, \cdots, \alpha_k$ is a permutation of $1, 2, \cdots, k$. Then by Theorem 5.3.

$$a^k r_1 r_2 \cdots r_k \equiv r_{\alpha_1} r_{\alpha_2} \cdots r_{\alpha_k}$$

$$\equiv r_1 r_2 \cdots r_k \qquad \text{mod } m.$$

Since each r_i is prime to m, it follows from Corollary 5.4 that

$$a^k \equiv 1 \qquad \text{mod } m.$$

Corollary 11.1. *The Theorem of Fermat.* *If p is a prime and a not a multiple of p, then*

$$a^{p-1} \equiv 1 \qquad \text{mod } p.$$

Theorem 11.2. *If p is a prime,*

$$a^p \equiv a \qquad \text{mod } p.$$

This congruence can be written

$$a(a^{p-1} - 1) \equiv 0 \qquad \text{mod } p.$$

If a is prime to p, the second factor is congruent to 0. If a is not prime to p, it is a multiple of p, in which case the first factor is congruent to 0.

If a is prime to m, then $a^{\varphi(m)-1}$ is the reciprocal of a modulo m, by Theorem 11.1. Thus the solution of the congruence

$$ax \equiv b \qquad \text{mod } m \qquad\qquad (a, m) = 1$$

can be written explicitly

$$x \equiv ba^{\varphi(m)-1} \qquad \text{mod } m.$$

Theorem 11.3. *For every polynomial f(x), every prime p, and every integer m,*

$$f(x^{p^m}) \equiv [f(x)]^{p^m} \qquad \text{mod } p.$$

It is here to be understood that the coefficients of the powers of x in $f(x)$ are integers modulo p, but that x is an indeterminate. The above congruence means that coefficients of corresponding powers of x on the respective sides of the congruence are congruent modulo p.

Suppose that

$$f(x) = a_0 + a_1 x + a_2 x^2 + \cdots + a_{k-1}x^{k-1} + a_k x^k.$$

By the multinomial theorem

$$[f(x)]^p = \sum_{q_0 + \cdots + q_k = p} \frac{p!}{q_0! q_1! \cdots q_k!} a_0^{q_0} \cdots a_k^{q_k} x^{q_1 + 2q_2 + \cdots kq_k}.$$

As the multinomial coefficients are rational integers, each factor of the denominator is canceled by a factor of the numerator. But except for those terms having one of the q's equal to p (and the other q's therefore equal to 0) there is a prime p in the numerator which cannot be canceled by any factor of the denominator. Hence all multinomial coefficients are $\equiv 0$ mod p except those having a q equal to p. Thus

$$[f(x)]^p \equiv a_0^p + a_1^p x^p + \cdots + a_k^p x^{kp} \qquad \text{mod } p.$$

But by Theorem 11.2,
$$a_i^p \equiv a_i \qquad \text{mod } p,$$
so that

(11.2) $\qquad [f(x)]^p \equiv a_0 + a_1 x^p + \cdots + a_k x^{kp} \equiv f(x^p) \qquad \text{mod } p.$

This proves the theorem for $m = 1$.

We complete the proof by induction. Since x is an indeterminate, we may replace x by $x^{p^{m-1}}$ in (11.2), obtaining

(11.3) $\qquad [f(x^{p^{m-1}})]^p \equiv f(x^{p^m}) \qquad \text{mod } p.$

We assume for the induction proof that

$$f(x^{p^{m-1}}) \equiv [f(x)]^{p^{m-1}} \qquad \text{mod } p,$$

which evidently holds for $m = 1$, and in fact has just been proved for $m = 2$. Raise each side to the pth power:

$$[f(x^{p^{m-1}})]^p \equiv [f(x)]^{p^m} \qquad \text{mod } p.$$

Now by (11.3)

$$f(x^{p^m}) \equiv [f(x)]^{p^m} \qquad \text{mod } p,$$

which completes the proof.

EXERCISES

1. Verify that $5^6 \equiv 1 \bmod 7$.
2. Verify that $3^{\varphi(8)} \equiv 1 \bmod 8$, also $3^{\varphi(70)} \equiv 1 \bmod 70$.
3. Prove that $(x - y)^{p^m} \equiv x^{p^m} - y^{p^m} \bmod p$ for every m.
4. Prove that $(\Sigma x_i)^p \equiv \Sigma x_i^p \bmod p$ $(i = 1, \cdots, n)$, where $x_1, \cdots, x_n$ are indeterminates. Extend to exponent p^m.

12. The derivative. The derivative with respect to x of a polynomial

$$f(x) \equiv a_0 + a_1 x + a_2 x^2 + \cdots + a_n x^n \qquad \text{mod } m$$

is by definition

$$f'(x) \equiv a_1 + 2a_2 x + \cdots + n a_n x^{n-1} \qquad \text{mod } m.$$

Theorem 12.1. The derivative of an integer is congruent to 0. The derivative of x is congruent to 1. The derivative of a sum is congruent to the sum of the derivatives. The derivative of a product $f(x) \cdot g(x)$ is congruent to

$$f'(x) \cdot g(x) + f(x) \cdot g'(x).$$

The first three statements are evident. To prove the fourth, set

$$f(x) \equiv \sum_{i=0}^{l} a_i x^i, \qquad g(x) \equiv \sum_{j=0}^{n} b_j x^j,$$

$$f(x) \cdot g(x) \equiv \sum_{i=0}^{l} \sum_{j=0}^{n} a_i b_j x^{i+j} \qquad \text{mod } m.$$

Then the derivative of $f(x) \cdot g(x)$ is

$$\sum_{i=0}^{l} \sum_{j=0}^{n} (i+j) a_i b_j x^{i+j-1} \equiv \sum_{i=0}^{l} i a_i x^{i-1} \sum_{j=0}^{n} b_j x^j + \sum_{i=0}^{l} a_i x^i \sum_{j=0}^{n} j b_j x^{j-1}$$

$$\equiv f'(x) \cdot g(x) + f(x) \cdot g'(x) \qquad \text{mod } m.$$

Theorem 12.2. *If $u = g(x)$, then the derivative of $f(u)$ considered as a polynomial in x is $f'(u) \cdot g'(x)$.*

By repeated applications of Theorem 12.1 we can show that the derivative of u^i is $i u^{i-1} g'(x)$. Then the derivative of

$$f(u) \equiv \sum_{i=0}^{n} a_i u^i \qquad \text{mod } m$$

considered as a function of x is

$$\sum_{i=0}^{n} a_i [i u^{i-1} g'(x)] \equiv \sum_{i=0}^{n} i a_i u^{i-1} g'(x)$$

$$\equiv f'(u) \cdot g'(x) \qquad \text{mod } m.$$

Theorem 12.3. *If $(x - x_1)^h$ is the highest power of $x - x_1$ which divides $f(x)$, and if $(m, h) = 1$, then $(x - x_1)^{h-1}$ is the highest power of $x - x_1$ which divides $f'(x)$.*

Let $f(x) \equiv (x - x_1)^h g(x)$. Then, by Theorems 12.1 and 12.2,

$$f'(x) \equiv (x - x_1)^h g'(x) + h(x - x_1)^{h-1} g(x)$$

$$\equiv (x - x_1)^{h-1} [(x - x_1) \cdot g'(x) + h \cdot g(x)],$$

so that $(x - x_1)^{h-1} \,|\, f'(x)$. Now if $(x - x_1)^h$ is the highest power of $x - x_1$ which divides $f(x)$, $x - x_1 \nmid g(x)$, and since $(m, h) = 1$, $x - x_1 \nmid [(x - x_1)g'(x) + h \cdot g(x)]$. Thus $(x - x_1)^{h-1}$ is the highest power of $x - x_1$ which divides $f'(x)$.

1. Find the derivative of

$$8x^5 + 4x^4 - 3x^3 + 3x^2 + 3x + 6 \quad \text{mod 7.}$$

2. Find the derivative of

$$x^p - x \quad \text{mod } p.$$

3. Prove by induction that the derivative of u^i where $u = g(x)$ is $iu^{i-1}g'(x)$.

4. Find in two ways the derivative of

$$(x - 3)^3 \quad \text{mod 5.}$$

5. Find in two ways the derivative of

$$(x^2 + 3x + 1)(2x^2 + x + 4) \quad \text{mod 5.}$$

13. Congruences. A polynomial is of degree n modulo m if the coefficient of x^n is $\not\equiv 0$ mod m, while the coefficient of every higher power of x is $\equiv 0$ mod m. The degree of every number except 0, considered as a polynomial in x, is 0, while 0 has no degree.

Theorem 13.1. If the coefficients of $f(x)$ and $g(x)$ are integers, and if the leading coefficient of $g(x)$ is prime to m, then two polynomials $q(x)$ and $r(x)$ exist with integral coefficients such that

$$f(x) \equiv q(x) \cdot g(x) + r(x) \quad \text{mod } m,$$

where either $r(x) \equiv 0$ or else the degree of $r(x)$ is less than the degree of $g(x)$.

In other words, the ordinary process of long division exists for such polynomials. This process is evident from the example modulo 7:

$$
\begin{array}{l}
f(x) = 5x^5 + 5x^4 + 2x^3 + 2x^2 + 2x + 1 \quad \big|\ 3x^3 + x^2 + 2x + 5 = g(x) \\
\qquad\ \ 5x^5 + 4x^4 + \ \ x^3 + 6x^2 \qquad\qquad\quad \big|\ 4x^2 + 5x + 1 = q(x) \\
\hline
\qquad\qquad\quad x^4 + \ \ x^3 + 3x^2 + 2x + 1 \\
\qquad\qquad\quad x^4 + 5x^3 + 3x^2 + 4x \\
\hline
\qquad\qquad\qquad\qquad 3x^3 + \qquad\ 5x + 1 \\
\qquad\qquad\qquad\qquad 3x^3 + \ \ x^2 + 2x + 5 \\
\hline
\qquad\qquad\qquad\qquad\qquad\ 6x^2 + 3x + 3 = r(x).
\end{array}
$$

The leading coefficient 3 of $g(x)$ is prime to the modulus 7, so that every congruence $3y \equiv a$ mod 7 has a solution. Since 4 is a solution of $3y \equiv 5$, the first coefficient of $q(x)$ is 4. Since 5 is a solution of $3y \equiv 1$, the second coefficient is 5, etc.

Theorem 13.2. *If the congruence* $f(x) \equiv 0$ *modulo* p, *where* p *is a prime, has the distinct solutions* $x_1, x_2, \cdots, x_k$, *then*

$$f(x) \equiv q(x) \cdot (x - x_1)(x - x_2) \cdots (x - x_k) \qquad \text{mod } p.$$

By Theorem 13.1 we can write

$$f(x) \equiv q_1(x) \cdot (x - x_1) + R \qquad \text{mod } p,$$

where R is 0 or of degree 0. But the substitution of x_1 for x shows that $R \equiv 0 \bmod p$, so that

$$f(x) \equiv q_1(x) \cdot (x - x_1) \qquad \text{mod } p.$$

Now let x_2 be a root of the congruence distinct from x_1. Then

$$0 \equiv f(x_2) \equiv q_1(x_2) \cdot (x_2 - x_1) \qquad \text{mod } p.$$

Since $x_2 - x_1 \not\equiv 0 \bmod p$, it is prime to p, so that by Corollary 5.4, $q_1(x_2) \equiv 0 \bmod p$. As before,

$$q_1(x) \equiv q_2(x) \cdot (x - x_2),$$

$$f(x) \equiv q_2(x) \cdot (x - x_1)(x - x_2) \qquad \text{mod } p,$$

and so on for each of the k distinct solutions.

Corollary 13.2. $\quad x^{p-1} - 1 \equiv (x - 1)(x - 2) \cdots (x - p + 1),$

$$x^p - x \equiv x(x - 1)(x - 2) \cdots (x - p + 1) \qquad \text{mod } p.$$

We saw, if x_1 is a root of $f(x) \equiv 0 \bmod p$, that

$$f(x) \equiv q_1(x) \cdot (x - x_1) \qquad \text{mod } p.$$

It may happen that x_1 is a root of the congruence $q_1(x) \equiv 0 \bmod p$, in which case we can write

$$f(x) \equiv q_2(x) \cdot (x - x_1)^2 \qquad \text{mod } p.$$

In this case we say that x_1 is a *double root* of the congruence $f(x) \equiv 0 \bmod p$. More generally, if

$$f(x) \equiv q_h(x) \cdot (x - x_1)^h \qquad \text{mod } p,$$

where x_1 is not a root of $q_h(x) \equiv 0 \bmod p$, we say that x is a *multiple root* of $f(x) \equiv 0 \bmod p$ of *multiplicity* h.

The extension of Theorem 13.2 to include the case of multiple roots is now evident, and we can state

Theorem 13.3. *If the congruence $f(x) \equiv 0$ modulo p, where p is a prime, has the solutions $x_1, x_2, \cdots, x_k$, where x_i is of multiplicity h_i, then*

$$f(x) \equiv q(x) \cdot (x - x_1)^{h_1}(x - x_2)^{h_2} \cdots (x - x_k)^{h_k} \qquad \mod p,$$

where $q(x) \equiv 0$ has no solution.

Corollary 13.31. *A congruence with a prime modulus cannot have more solutions than its degree.*

Reference to Theorem 12.3 yields

Corollary 13.32. *If $p \nmid h$, a root of $f(x) \equiv 0 \mod p$ of multiplicity h is a root of $f'(x) \equiv 0 \mod p$ of multiplicity $h - 1$.*

If only the distinct roots of a congruence are required, the following theorem is useful.

Theorem 13.4. *If $f(x) \equiv 0 \mod p$ is a congruence of degree n, and if p is a prime, then there exists a congruence $r(x) \equiv 0 \mod p$ which vanishes identically or is of degree $r < p$ whose distinct roots coincide with the distinct roots of $f(x) \equiv 0 \mod p$.*

For, by Theorem 13.1, we may write

$$f(x) \equiv g(x) \cdot (x^p - x) + r(x) \qquad \mod p,$$

where $r(x) \equiv 0$ or else is of degree $r < p$. If x_1 is a root of $f(x) \equiv 0$ mod p, then $x_1^p - x_1 \equiv 0 \mod p$ by Theorem 11.2, whence $r(x_1) \equiv 0$ mod p. Conversely, every root of $r(x) \equiv 0 \mod p$ is a root of $f(x) \equiv 0$ mod p.

The multiplicity of x_1 as a root of $f(x) \equiv 0 \mod p$ may, however, not to be the same as its multiplicity as a root of $r(x) \equiv 0 \mod p$.

Theorem 13.5. *If $d \,|\, p - 1$, the congruence*

$$x^d \equiv 1 \qquad \mod p$$

has exactly d solutions.

Set $p - 1 = hd$ and write

$$x^{p-1} - 1 = (x^d - 1)(x^{(h-1)d} + x^{(h-2)d} + \cdots + x^d + 1).$$

By Corollary 11.1 the congruence

$$x^{p-1} - 1 \equiv 0 \qquad \mod p$$

is satisfied by the $p - 1$ incongruent numbers $1, 2, \cdots, p - 1$. Since at most $(h - 1)d = p - 1 - d$ of these are zeros of the second factor above (Corollary 13.31), the remaining d of them must be zeros of $x^d - 1$, by Corollary 4.1.

Theorem 13.6. *If a number satisfies the two congruences*

$$x^a \equiv 1, \quad x^b \equiv 1 \qquad \mathrm{mod}\ p,$$

it also satisfies

$$x^d \equiv 1 \qquad \mathrm{mod}\ p, \qquad\qquad d = (a, b)$$

By an interchange of a and b, if necessary, we can find s and t both positive so that $d = sa - tb$. Then

$$x^d \equiv x^{sa-tb} \qquad \mathrm{mod}\ p.$$

But $1 \equiv x^{tb} \bmod p$. Hence, multiplying,

$$x^d \equiv x^{sa} \equiv 1 \qquad \mathrm{mod}\ p.$$

The solution of a congruence with a prime modulus is a basic problem of considerably difficulty, and as a rule one can do little more than try the least positive residues of the modulus in turn. When one solution x_1 is found, the congruence can be depressed by dividing out $(x - x_1)$. Some theory can be developed for congruences of degree ≤ 4, but the solution of higher congruences, like the solution of equations of higher degree, is a tentative process. In the solution of congruences, however, one has the advantage of having a finite number of trials to make.

In the following paragraphs the solution of a congruence modulo m will be reduced to the solution of congruences with prime moduli.

EXERCISES

1. Reduce $x^7 + 2x^6 + 8x^5 + x + 3 \equiv 0 \bmod 5$ to a congruence of degree < 5.

2. Use synthetic division modulo 5 to find the roots of the original congruence of Ex. 1, also of the reduced congruence.

3. Prove that, if $p \nmid \alpha$, a root of multiplicity α of the g.c.d. of $f(x)$ and $f'(x)$ is a root of $f(x) \equiv 0 \bmod p$ of multiplicity $\alpha + 1$.

4. Show that

$$8x^5 + 4x^4 - 3x^3 + 3x^2 + 3x + 6 \equiv 0 \qquad \mathrm{mod}\ 7$$

has a multiple root. [Use the Euclid algorithm on $f(x)$ and $f'(x)$.]

5. Find all congruences

$$x^2 + px + q \equiv 0 \qquad \mathrm{mod}\ 5$$

which have no solution.

6. Prove Wilson's Theorem: A necessary and sufficient condition that n be prime is that

$$1 \cdot 2 \cdot 3 \cdots (n - 1) + 1 \equiv 0 \qquad \mathrm{mod}\ n.$$

HINT: Set $x = 0$ in Corollary 13.2. The prime 2 needs separate consideration.

14. Congruences modulo m. We shall now show how the solving of a congruence

(14.1) $\quad f(x) = a_n x^n + a_{n-1} x^{n-1} + \cdots + a_1 x + a_0 \equiv 0 \qquad \text{mod } p^{i+1}$

can be made to depend upon the solving of the same congruence modulo p^i. By taking $i = 1, 2, \cdots, \alpha - 1$ successively, we arrive at a solution of (14.1) modulo p^α.

Theorem 14.1.   If $f(x)$ is of degree n,

$$f(x + y) \equiv f(x) + f'(x)y + \frac{f''(x)}{2!} y^2 + \cdots + \frac{f^{(n)}(x)}{n!} y^n \qquad \text{mod } m.$$

The expression $f''(x)$ means the derivative of $f'(x)$, $f'''(x)$ means the derivative of $f''(x)$, etc.

If $f(x)$ is of degree n mod m, it is clear that it is possible to write

$$f(x + y) \equiv g_0(x) + g_1(x) \cdot y + g_2(x) \cdot y^2 + \cdots + g_n(x) \cdot y^n \qquad \text{mod } m.$$

Upon setting $y \equiv 0$, we see that $f(x) \equiv g_0(x)$. Now, by Theorem 12.2, the derivative of $f(x + y)$ with respect to y is

$$f'(x + y) \equiv g_1(x) + 2g_2(x) \cdot y + \cdots + n \cdot g_n(x) \cdot y^{n-1} \qquad \text{mod } m,$$

whence, upon setting $y = 0$, we obtain

$$f'(x) \equiv g_1(x).$$

By taking the second derivative, we obtain

$$f''(x) \equiv 2g_2(x),$$

and so on.

Theorem 14.2.   Let $f(x_1) \equiv 0 \bmod p^i$. Let h be a solution of

$$f(x_1) \equiv hp^i \qquad \text{mod } p^{i+1},$$

and let y be a solution of

$$f'(x_1) \cdot y + h \equiv 0 \qquad \text{mod } p.$$

Then $x_1 + p^i y$ is a solution of $f(x) \equiv 0 \bmod p^{i+1}$.

Suppose that x_1 is a solution of $f(x) \equiv 0 \bmod p^i$. All solutions of $f(x) \equiv 0 \bmod p^{i+1}$ are evidently solutions modulo p^i, but the converse is not true. Thus the solutions modulo p^{i+1} are of the form $x_1 + p^i y$ where y is to be determined.

By Theorem 14.1 we may write

$$f(x_1 + p^i y) \equiv f(x_1) + f'(x_1) \cdot p^i y + \frac{f''(x_1)}{2!} p^{2i} y^2 + \cdots$$

$$\equiv f(x_1) + f'(x_1) \cdot p^i y \qquad \text{mod } p^{i+1}.$$

Since the g.c.d. p^i of p^i and p^{i+1} divides $f(x_1)$, the congruence

$$f(x_1) \equiv h p^i \qquad \text{mod } p^{i+1}$$

has a solution h. Then

$$f(x_1 + p^i y) \equiv h p^i + f'(x_1) \cdot p^i y \equiv p^i (h + f'(x_1) y) \qquad \text{mod } p^{i+1}$$

Hence p^{i+1} will divide $f(x_1 + p^i y)$ if and only if p divides $h + f'(x_1) \cdot y$, that is, if y is a solution of

$$f'(x_1) \cdot y + h \equiv 0 \qquad \text{mod } p.$$

In case $f'(x_1)$ is not divisible by p, this congruence has a single solution, and every root of (14.1) modulo p^i determines one root modulo p^{i+1}. In case $p \mid f'(x_1)$, each root modulo p determines p roots or no root modulo p^{i+1} according as $p \mid h$ or $p \nmid h$.

The solution of a congruence

$$(14.2) \qquad f(x) \equiv a_n x^n + a_{n-1} x^{n-1} + \cdots + a_1 x + a_0 \equiv 0 \qquad \text{mod } m$$

where m is composite depends directly upon the solution of the same congruence modulo a prime power. For if

$$m = p_1^{\alpha_1} p_2^{\alpha_2} \cdots p_k^{\alpha_k},$$

where the p's are distinct primes, every solution of (14.2) is a solution of each of the congruences

$$(14.3) \qquad f(x) \equiv 0 \qquad \text{mod } p_i^{\alpha_i} \qquad (i = 1, 2, \cdots, k);$$

and conversely a common solution of each of these congruences will satisfy (14.2), since the prime powers are relatively prime in pairs.

Suppose that

$$x \equiv r_{11}, \qquad x \equiv r_{21}, \qquad \cdots \qquad x \equiv r_{k1},$$

$$x \equiv r_{12}, \qquad x \equiv r_{22}, \qquad \cdots \qquad x \equiv r_{k2},$$

$$\cdots \cdots \cdots \cdots \cdots \cdots \cdots \cdots \cdots \cdots \cdots$$

$$x \equiv r_{1h_1}, \ \text{mod } p_1^{\alpha_1}, \quad x \equiv r_{2h_2} \ \text{mod } p_2^{\alpha_2}, \quad \cdots \quad x \equiv r_{kh_k} \ \text{mod } p_k^{\alpha_k}$$

are all the solutions of (14.3). Select one r from each column and apply Corollary 7.3. The result is a solution of (14.2), and all solutions of (14.2) are obtainable in this way.

If m is composite, a congruence may have more solutions than its degree. Hence if x_1 is a solution, it is not permissible to depress the congruence by dividing out $x - x_1$ and consider only the quotient.

Also note that

$$x^2 + x \equiv x(x + 1) \equiv (x + 4)(x + 3) \qquad \text{mod } 6.$$

Thus a polynomial is not uniquely factorable into linear factors modulo 6. This example shows that Theorem 4.2 is not trivial.

EXERCISES

1. Solve $x^3 + x^2 - 4x - 4 \equiv 0 \bmod 25$.
2. Solve $2x^3 + x^2 - 7x + 3 \equiv 0 \bmod 27$. Factor in two ways.
3. Solve $x^3 + x^2 - 4x - 4 \equiv 0 \bmod 15$.
4. Solve $x^5 - 6x^4 + 8x^3 - 4x^2 + 7x + 2 \equiv 0 \bmod 20$.
5. Find two polynomials $p(x)$ and $s(x)$ such that

$$p(x) \cdot f(x) + s(x) \cdot g(x) \equiv 1 \qquad \text{mod } 5,$$

where

$$f(x) = x^3 + x^2 + 3x, \quad g(x) = 3x^2 + 2x + 4.$$

15. Primitive roots. We have seen (Theorem 11.1) that for every a prime to m,

$$a^{\varphi(m)} \equiv 1 \qquad \text{mod } m.$$

For every such a there is, therefore, a least exponent $e \leq \varphi(m)$ such that

$$a^e \equiv 1 \qquad \text{mod } m.$$

The number a is said to *belong* to the exponent e modulo m. If a belongs to $\varphi(m)$, it is called a *primitive root* modulo m.

Theorem 15.1. If a belongs to e modulo m, and if $a^k \equiv 1 \bmod m$, then $e \mid k$.

For we may write
$$k = qe + r \qquad\qquad 0 \leq r < e.$$
Then
$$a^k = a^{qe+r} = (a^e)^q a^r \equiv a^r \qquad \text{mod } m,$$

so that $a^r \equiv 1 \bmod m$. Since e was minimal, $r = 0$.

Corollary 15.1. If a belongs to e modulo m, then $e \mid \varphi(m)$.

Theorem 15.2. If a belongs to e modulo m, then

$$a^{k_1} \equiv a^{k_2} \qquad \text{mod } m$$

if and only if

$$k_1 \equiv k_2 \qquad \text{mod } e.$$

Suppose $k_1 > k_2$ and $a^{k_1} \equiv a^{k_2} \bmod m$. Then by Theorem 5.4,

$$a^{k_1-k_2} \equiv 1 \qquad \bmod m.$$

By Theorem 15.1, $e \mid k_1 - k_2$.

Conversely if $e \mid k_1 - k_2$, let $k_1 - k_2 = he$. Then

$$a^{k_1-k_2} = (a^e)^h \equiv 1 \qquad \bmod m.$$

Theorem 15.3. If $e \mid \varphi(p)$ where p is a prime, there are exactly $\varphi(e)$ numbers which belong to e modulo p.

The proof is by induction. Write the divisors of $\varphi(p) = p - 1$ in order of magnitude

$$d_1 < d_2 < \cdots < d_s,$$

where $d_1 = 1$ and $d_s = p - 1$. Evidently 1 is the only number which belongs to the exponent 1, and $\varphi(1) = 1$. Hence the theorem is true for the first divisor of the sequence.

Assume the theorem for every divisor in the set

(15.1) $$d_1 < d_2 < \cdots < d_{i-1}.$$

The congruence

$$x^{d_i} \equiv 1 \qquad \bmod p$$

has exactly d_i solutions by Theorem 13.5. Each of these solutions belongs either to d_i or to some divisor of d_i less than d_i by Theorem 15.1. Denote by $\psi(d_i)$ the number of integers which belong to d_i. Then $\psi(d_i)$ is equal to d_i diminished by the number of integers which belong to the divisors of d_i less than d_i. But the divisors of d_i less than d_i are divisors of $p - 1$ and occur in (15.1), and we assumed that the number of integers belonging to a number d of this set was $\varphi(d)$. Hence

$$\psi(d_i) = d_i - \Sigma\varphi(d_j),$$

the summation extending over all the divisors of d_i less than d_i. But by Theorem 10.3,

$$d_i = \varphi(d_i) + \Sigma\varphi(d_j).$$

so that $\psi(d_i) = \varphi(d_i)$.

Corollary 15.3. If p is a prime, there exists at least one primitive root modulo p.

EXERCISES

1. Show that there exists a primitive root modulo 2, and one modulo 4, but none modulo 8.

2. How many primitive roots are there modulo 5? modulo 7? Find them.

3. Find a primitive root modulo 9.

4. If a and b are reciprocals modulo m, show that they belong to the same exponent modulo m.

5. Show that, if p and q are distinct odd primes, there exists no primitive root modulo pq.

HINT: $[\varphi(p), \varphi(q)] < \varphi(pq)$.

16. Indices. The theory of logarithms in arithmetic has its counterpart in number theory in the theory of indices. If b is a primitive root modulo p, and if

(16.1) $$b^x \equiv n \qquad \mathrm{mod}\ p,$$

then $x = \mathrm{ind}_b n$. In other words,

$$n \equiv b^{\mathrm{ind}_b n} \qquad \mathrm{mod}\ p.$$

The subscript b will often be omitted, it being understood that the same b is used throughout.

Theorem 16.1. If b is a primitive root modulo p, and if $n \not\equiv 0$ modulo p, then $\mathrm{ind}_b n$ exists.

The powers
$$b, b^2, \cdots, b^{p-1} \equiv 1$$
are distinct modulo p, for by Theorem 15.2 a relation

$$b^i \equiv b^j \qquad \mathrm{mod}\ p, \qquad\qquad p > i > j > 0,$$

would imply

$$i \equiv j \qquad \mathrm{mod}\ p - 1,$$

which is impossible. None of these powers is $\equiv 0$, since the last is $\equiv 1$. They are, then, the integers $1, 2, \cdots, p - 1$ in some order, and n is congruent to one of them.

Theorem 16.2. If neither r, s, nor t is $\equiv 0$ modulo p, and if $rs \equiv t$ modulo p, then

$$\mathrm{ind}\ r + \mathrm{ind}\ s \equiv \mathrm{ind}\ t \qquad \mathrm{mod}\ p - 1,$$

and conversely.

By Theorem 16.1 each of r, s, t has an index. Let

$$r \equiv b^{\mathrm{ind}\ r}, \qquad s \equiv b^{\mathrm{ind}\ s}, \qquad t \equiv b^{\mathrm{ind}\ t} \qquad \mathrm{mod}\ p,$$

so that

$$b^{\mathrm{ind}\ r} b^{\mathrm{ind}\ s} = b^{\mathrm{ind}\ r\ +\ \mathrm{ind}\ s} \equiv b^{\mathrm{ind}\ t} \qquad \mathrm{mod}\ p.$$

By Theorem 15.2,

$$\mathrm{ind}\ r + \mathrm{ind}\ s \equiv \mathrm{ind}\ t \qquad \mathrm{mod}\ p - 1.$$

The steps are reversible; therefore, the converse holds.

Theorem 16.3. *If* $a \not\equiv 0$ *modulo* p *and if* $a^s \equiv c$ *modulo* p, *then*

$$s \text{ ind } a \equiv \text{ind } c \qquad \bmod p - 1,$$

and conversely.

For

$$a \equiv b^{\text{ind } a}, \ a^s \equiv b^{s \text{ ind } a} \equiv c \equiv b^{\text{ind } c} \qquad \bmod p.$$

By Theorem 15.2,

$$s \text{ ind } a \equiv \text{ind } c \qquad \bmod p - 1.$$

Since the steps are reversible, the converse holds.

The following tables of indices are taken from Tschebyscheff, *Theorie der Congruenzen*, Berlin, 1889, Appendix, p. 6.

Modulus..	3	5	7	11	13	17	19	23	29		19	23	29
Base......	2	2	3	2	6	10	10	10	10				
1	0	0	0	0	0	0	0	0	0	17	8	17	7
2	1	1	2	1	5	10	17	8	11	18	9	4	9
3	....	3	1	8	8	11	5	20	27	19	.....	5	15
4	....	2	4	2	10	4	16	16	22	20	.....	9	12
5	....	....	5	4	9	7	2	15	18	21	.....	19	19
6	....	....	3	9	1	5	4	6	10	22	.....	11	6
7	....	....	....	7	7	9	12	21	20	23	.....	.....	24
8	....	....	....	3	3	14	15	2	5	24	.....	.....	4
9	....	....	....	6	4	6	10	18	26	25	.....	.....	8
10	....	....	....	5	2	1	1	1	1	26	.....	.....	13
11	....	....	....	....	11	13	6	3	23	27	.....	.....	25
12	....	....	....	....	6	15	3	14	21	28	.....	.....	14
13	....	....	....	....	....	12	13	12	2	.....	.....	.....	.....
14	....	....	....	....	....	3	11	7	3	.....	.....	.....	.....
15	....	....	....	....	....	2	7	13	17	.....	.....	.....	.....
16	....	....	....	....	....	8	14	10	16	.....	.....	.....	.....

EXERCISES

1. Solve $x^9 \equiv 11 \bmod 17$.
2. Solve $4x^6 \equiv 13 \bmod 17$.
3. Solve $3x^5 \equiv 7 \bmod 11$.
4. Solve $x^6 \equiv 7 \bmod 19$.
5. If a belongs to e modulo p, and $a \not\equiv 1 \bmod p$, then

$$1 + a + a^2 + \cdots + a^{e-1} = 0 \qquad \bmod p.$$

6. Find a primitive root modulo 31.
7. What are the last three digits of 7^{9999}?

17. Quadratic residues.   An examination of the congruences

$$x^2 \equiv 1, \quad x^2 \equiv 2, \quad x^2 \equiv 3, \quad x^2 \equiv 4 \qquad \mod 5$$

shows that the first has the solutions 1 and 4, the last the solutions 2 and 3, while the second and third have no solutions.

If the congruence $x^2 \equiv a \mod m$ where a is prime to m has a solution, a is called a *quadratic residue* modulo m.   If the congruence has no solution, a is called a *quadratic non-residue*.   If a is not prime to m, a is neither a residue nor a non-residue.

Theorem 17.1.   If p is a positive odd prime and $p \nmid a$, the number a is a quadratic residue or non-residue modulo p according as ind a is even or odd.

Let b be a primitive root modulo p.   Then the congruence $x^2 \equiv a \mod p$ is equivalent to the congruence

$$2 \operatorname{ind} x \equiv \operatorname{ind} a \qquad \mod p - 1$$

by Theorem 16.3.   Since $p - 1$ is even, this congruence will have solutions (Theorem 6.2) if and only if ind a is even.

Theorem 17.2.   A product is a quadratic non-residue modulo p if and only if one factor is a residue and the other a non-residue.

For

$$\operatorname{ind} ac \equiv \operatorname{ind} a + \operatorname{ind} c$$

modulo $p - 1$ and hence modulo 2.   But ind ac will be odd if and only if one of the two numbers ind a and ind c is odd and the other even.

There is an analogy between the positive numbers of the real field and the quadratic residues modulo p.   Both the definition and the above theorem exhibit this analogy.

Theorem 17.3.   In the set of numbers $1, 2, \cdots, p - 1$ exactly half are quadratic residues modulo p.

These numbers form a complete set of residues modulo $p - 1$, so the index of every number prime to p is congruent to one of them.   But exactly half of them are even, so the theorem follows from Theorem 17.1.

Theorem 17.4.   (Euler.)   The number a is a quadratic residue or non-residue modulo p according as it satisfies the first or second of the congruences

$$a^{(p-1)/2} \equiv 1, \quad a^{(p-1)/2} \equiv -1 \qquad \mod p.$$

By Theorem 17.3 there are exactly $(p - 1)/2$ quadratic residues in the set $1, 2, \cdots, p - 1$.   Let a be one of them.   Then there is a c such that $c^2 \equiv a \bmod p$. But $c^{p-1} \equiv 1 \bmod p$ by Corollary 11.1, so a satisfies the congruence

$$(17.1) \qquad\qquad a^{(p-1)/2} \equiv 1 \qquad \bmod p.$$

Since (17.1) has just $(p-1)/2$ solutions (Theorem 13.5), the totality of quadratic residues modulo p coincides with the totality of solutions of (17.1).

From the fact that the congruence

$$x^{p-1} - 1 \equiv (x^{(p-1)/2} + 1)(x^{(p-1)/2} - 1) \equiv 0 \qquad \bmod p$$

is satisfied by all the numbers $1, 2, \cdots, p-1$ (Corollary 11.1), it follows that the $(p-1)/2$ quadratic non-residues must coincide with the solutions of the congruence

$$x^{(p-1)/2} \equiv -1 \qquad \bmod p.$$

EXERCISES

1. Find the numbers which are quadratic residues modulo 7; also modulo 11.

2. Show that -1 is a quadratic residue of primes of the form $4k + 1$ and is a non-residue of primes of the form $4k + 3$.

3. If $x^2 \equiv 1 \bmod n$ has exactly k solutions, and if $(c, n) = 1$, then $x^2 \equiv c$ has no solution or exactly k solutions.

4. If c is a quadratic residue modulo n, and if $x^2 \equiv c \bmod n$ has k roots, there are exactly $\varphi(n)/k$ quadratic residues of n.

18. The Legendre symbol. The last theorem suggests the definition of a function, called the *Legendre symbol*, as follows. Let p be an odd prime. The function $\left(\dfrac{a}{p}\right)$, or (a/p), shall have the value 1 if a is a quadratic residue modulo p, and the value -1 if a is a quadratic non-residue modulo p.

Theorem 18.1. $a^{(p-1)/2} \equiv (a/p) \bmod p$.

This is a restatement of Theorem 17.4.

Theorem 18.2. If $a \equiv b \bmod p$, then $(a/p) = (b/p)$.

For $a \equiv x^2 \bmod p$ and $a \equiv b \bmod p$ imply $b \equiv x^2 \bmod p$, and conversely.

Theorem 18.3. $(a^2/p) = 1$.

This is obvious.

Theorem 18.4. $(ab/p) = (a/p)(b/p)$.

This is a restatement of Theorem 17.2.

Theorem 18.5. $(1/p) = 1$, $(-1/p) = (-1)^{(p-1)/2}$.

This follows directly from Theorem 18.1.

EXERCISES

1. Show that $(3/7)\,(2/7) = (6/7)$.

2. If p is an odd prime, show that a quadratic residue of p is a quadratic residue of p^n.

HINT: Use induction on n.

19. The quadratic reciprocity law.

Theorem 19.1.   If q is prime to the odd prime p, and if k is the number of least positive residues modulo p in the set

(19.1) $$q,\ 2q,\ 3q,\ \cdots,\ \tfrac{1}{2}(p-1)q$$

which exceed $\tfrac{1}{2}p$, then $(q/p) = (-1)^k$.

None of the numbers (19.1) is $\equiv 0 \bmod p$, and no two of them are congruent to each other, for $aq \equiv bq \bmod p$ would imply $a \equiv b \bmod p$.

Let

(19.2) $r_1, r_2, \cdots, r_h, s_1, s_2, \cdots, s_k,$ $h + k = \tfrac{1}{2}(p-1)$

be the set of least positive residues of (19.1) mod p where the r_i are $< \tfrac{1}{2}p$ and the s_i are $> \tfrac{1}{2}p$.   Each number of

(19.3) $r_1, r_2, \cdots, r_h, p - s_1, p - s_2, \cdots, p - s_k$

lies between 0 and $\tfrac{1}{2}p$, and we shall see that they are all incongruent modulo p.   The relations

$$p - s_i \not\equiv p - s_j, \quad r_i \not\equiv r_j, \qquad\qquad (i \neq j)$$

follow from the fact that the numbers of (19.1) are incongruent to each other.   The only remaining possibility is a relation

$$p - s_j \equiv r_i \qquad \bmod p.$$

This would imply

$$r_i + s_j \equiv 0 \qquad \bmod p.$$

But r_i and s_j are congruent to numbers of the set (19.1), say to $a_i q$ and $b_j q$, respectively, where a_i and b_j are $\leq \tfrac{1}{2}(p-1)$.   Therefore we should have

$$r_i + s_j \equiv (a_i + b_j)q \equiv 0 \qquad \bmod p.$$

But this is not possible.

Since the numbers of (19.3) are between 0 and $\tfrac{1}{2}p$, are incongruent each to each, and are $\frac{1}{2}(p-1)$ in number, they must be in some order the numbers $1, 2, \cdots, \frac{1}{2}(p-1)$. Hence

$$\prod_{i=1}^{k} (p - s_i) \prod_{j=1}^{h} r_j \equiv \lfloor \tfrac{1}{2}(p-1) \rfloor \quad \text{mod } p.$$

But $p - s_i \equiv -s_i \bmod p$, so

$$(-1)^k \prod_{i=1}^{k} s_i \prod_{j=1}^{h} r_j \equiv \lfloor \tfrac{1}{2}(p-1) \rfloor \quad \text{mod } p.$$

Since (19.2) are residues of (19.1), we may substitute the product of (19.1) for the product of (19.2), viz.,

$$(-1)^k \lfloor \tfrac{1}{2}(p-1) \rfloor q^{(p-1)/2} \equiv \lfloor \tfrac{1}{2}(p-1) \rfloor \quad \text{mod } p.$$

Since each number $2, 3, \cdots, \frac{1}{2}(p-1)$ is prime to p,

$$(-1)^k q^{(p-1)/2} \equiv 1 \quad \text{mod } p,$$

or by Theorem 18.1,

$$\left(\frac{q}{p}\right) = (-1)^k.$$

The notation $[a]$ is here used to denote the greatest integer in a. Thus

$$[7\tfrac{2}{5}] = 7, \quad [\pi] = 3, \quad [5] = 5.$$

In the division transformation

$$a = qd + r \qquad\qquad 0 \leqq r < d,$$

where a and q are positive, evidently $q = [a/d]$.

In reducing (19.1) modulo p we obtain the relations

$$(19.4) \qquad iq = \left[\frac{iq}{p}\right] p + \epsilon_i, \quad 0 \leqq \epsilon_i < p, (i = 1, 2, \cdots, \tfrac{1}{2}(p-1)),$$

where ϵ_i is one of the numbers (19.2). Define

$$A = \sum_{i=1}^{h} r_i, \quad B = \sum_{i=1}^{k} s_i,$$

$$M = \left[\frac{q}{p}\right] + \left[\frac{2q}{p}\right] + \cdots + \left[\frac{\tfrac{1}{2}(p-1)q}{p}\right] = \sum_{i=1}^{\frac{1}{2}(p-1)} \left[\frac{iq}{p}\right].$$

Theorem 19.2. If p and q are distinct odd primes, $(q/p) = (-1)^M$.

Theorem 19.3. If p is an odd prime, $(2/p) = (-1)^{(p^2-1)/8}$.

We shall make the proofs together. Let q be prime to the odd prime p. The sum of the numbers of (19.4) is

$$\sum_{i=1}^{\frac{1}{2}(p-1)} iq = \sum_{i=1}^{\frac{1}{2}(p-1)} \left[\frac{iq}{p}\right] p + \sum_{i=1}^{\frac{1}{2}(p-1)} \epsilon_i.$$

But

$$1 + 2 + \cdots + n = \frac{n(n+1)}{2},$$

so

$$\sum_{i=1}^{\frac{1}{2}(p-1)} i = \frac{1}{8}(p^2 - 1).$$

Since the numbers ϵ_i are the numbers of (19.2), we have

(19.5) $\frac{1}{8}(p^2 - 1)q = Mp + A + B.$

Now add the numbers (19.3). Since they are the numbers $1, 2, \cdots,$ $\frac{1}{2}(p - 1)$ in some order, we have

$$\sum_{i=1}^{k} (p - s_i) + \sum_{i=1}^{h} r_i = \sum_{i=1}^{\frac{1}{2}(p-1)} i.$$

That is,

$$kp - B + A = (p^2 - 1)/8.$$

Subtracting this equation transposed from (19.5) gives

(19.6) $\frac{1}{8}(p^2 - 1)(q - 1) = (M - k)p + 2B.$

We now suppose that q is odd. Then $q - 1$ is even and

$$(M - k)p \equiv 0 \qquad \mod 2.$$

As p is odd, $M \equiv k \mod 2$, and the equation

$$\left(\frac{q}{p}\right) = (-1)^M$$

follows from Theorem 19.1. This proves Theorem 19.2.
    Secondly, suppose $q = 2$. Then

$$M = \left[\frac{2}{p}\right] + \left[\frac{4}{p}\right] + \cdots + \left[\frac{p-1}{p}\right] = 0,$$

so that (19.6) gives

$$\frac{1}{8}(p^2 - 1) \equiv -kp \qquad \mod 2.$$

Hence k is odd or even according as $(p^2 - 1)/8$ is odd or even, and

$$\left(\frac{2}{p}\right) = (-1)^{(p^2-1)/8},$$

thus proving Theorem 19.3.

We define M as before, and similarly define

$$N = \left[\frac{p}{q}\right] + \left[\frac{2p}{q}\right] + \cdots + \left[\frac{\frac{1}{2}(q-1)p}{q}\right].$$

Theorem 19.4. (*Eisenstein.*) *If p and q are distinct odd primes,*

$$M + N = \frac{p-1}{2}\frac{q-1}{2}.$$

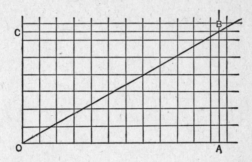

The proof is geometric. Using rectangular cartesian coördinates, draw the lines $x = p/2$, $y = q/2$ intersecting at B, and the line l whose equation is $y = qx/p$. Points both of whose coördinates are integers are called *lattice points*. No lattice point lies on l inside the rectangle $OABC$, for q is prime to p.

The number $[iq/p]$ is the greatest integer in an ordinate of the point $(i, iq/p)$ and is therefore the number of lattice points on the line $x = i$ below l. Hence M is the number of lattice points in $OABC$ below l. Similarly N is the number of lattice points in $OABC$ above l. But the total number of lattice points in $OABC$ is $\frac{1}{2}(p-1)\frac{1}{2}(q-1)$, so

$$M + N = \frac{p-1}{2}\frac{q-1}{2}.$$

Theorem 19.5. The quadratic reciprocity law. (*Legendre-Gauss.*) *If p and q are distinct odd primes,*

$$\left(\frac{p}{q}\right)\left(\frac{q}{p}\right) = (-1)^{(p-1)/2 \cdot (q-1)/2}.$$

For by Theorem 19.2,

$$\left(\frac{p}{q}\right) = (-1)^M, \quad \left(\frac{q}{p}\right) = (-1)^N,$$

so by Theorem 19.4

$$\left(\frac{p}{q}\right)\left(\frac{q}{p}\right) = (-1)^{M+N} = (-1)^{(p-1)/2 \cdot (q-1)/2}$$

EXERCISES

1. Determine if $x^2 \equiv -15 \bmod 23$ has solutions.

$$\left(\frac{-15}{23}\right) = \left(\frac{-1}{23}\right)\left(\frac{3}{23}\right)\left(\frac{5}{23}\right).$$

$$\left(\frac{-1}{23}\right) = (-1)^{(23-1)/2} = -1.$$

$$\left(\frac{3}{23}\right) = \left(\frac{23}{3}\right)(-1)^{11} = -\left(\frac{23}{3}\right) = -\left(\frac{2}{3}\right) = (-1)(-1)^{(9-1)/8} = 1.$$

$$\left(\frac{5}{23}\right) = \left(\frac{23}{5}\right)(-1)^{11 \cdot 2} = \left(\frac{23}{5}\right) = \left(\frac{3}{5}\right) = \left(\frac{5}{3}\right) = \left(\frac{2}{3}\right) = -1.$$

Hence

$$\left(\frac{-15}{23}\right) = (-1)(+1)(-1) = +1,$$

so that $x^2 \equiv -15 \bmod 23$ does have a solution. In fact, 10 is a solution.

2. Evaluate $\left(\dfrac{365}{1847}\right)$.

3. Show that 2 is a quadratic residue or non-residue of every prime of the form $4k + 1$ according as k is even or odd.

4. Show that -1 is a quadratic residue of every prime of the form $4k + 1$, and a non-residue of every prime of the form $4k - 1$.

5. Find all odd prime moduli of which 7 is a quadratic residue.

20. Quadratic congruences.

Theorem 20.1. *If p is an odd prime and $a \not\equiv 0 \bmod p$, the congruence*

$$ax^2 + bx + c \equiv 0 \qquad \bmod p$$

is equivalent to the chain

$$u^2 \equiv b^2 - 4ac, \quad 2ax \equiv -b + u \qquad \bmod p.$$

Let x_1 be a number such that

$$ax_1^2 + bx_1 + c \equiv 0 \qquad \mathrm{mod}\ p.$$

Then

$$4a^2x_1^2 + 4abx_1 + 4ac \equiv 0 \qquad \mathrm{mod}\ p,$$

$$(2ax_1 + b)^2 \equiv b^2 - 4ac \qquad \mathrm{mod}\ p.$$

Hence $u_1^2 \equiv b^2 - 4ac$, where $u_1 \equiv 2ax_1 + b$.

Conversely let $2ax_1 \equiv -b + u_1$, where $u_1^2 \equiv b^2 - 4ac \ \mathrm{mod}\ p$. Then

$$(2ax_1 + b)^2 \equiv 4a^2x_1^2 + 4abx_1 + b^2$$

$$\equiv u_1^2 \equiv b^2 - 4ac \qquad \mathrm{mod}\ p,$$

$$4a^2x_1^2 + 4abx_1 + 4ac \equiv 0 \qquad \mathrm{mod}\ p.$$

Since $4a$ is prime to p,

$$ax_1^2 + bx_1 + c \equiv 0 \qquad \mathrm{mod}\ p$$

so that every solution of the chain gives a solution of the given congruence.

Corollary 20.1.   If p is an odd prime and $a \not\equiv 0 \ mod\ p$, the congruence

$$ax^2 + bx + c \equiv 0 \qquad \mathrm{mod}\ p$$

has a solution if and only if its discriminant $D \equiv b^2 - 4ac \equiv 0$ or is a quadratic residue modulo p.

EXERCISES

1. Solve $5x^2 - 8x - 3 \equiv 0 \ \mathrm{mod}\ 23$.
2. Solve $3x^2 + x - 4 \equiv 0 \ \mathrm{mod}\ 10$.
3. Solve $7x^4 - 3x^2 + 11 \equiv 0 \ \mathrm{mod}\ 19$.
4. Show that an integer of the form $N^2 + 1$ cannot have a prime factor of the form $4k - 1$.

HINT: Consider $x^2 \equiv -1 \ \mathrm{mod}\ 4k - 1$.

5. Prove that the number of primes of the form $4k + 1$ is infinite (cf. Ex. 1, § 3).

HINT: Set $N = 2 \cdot 5 \cdot 13 \cdot 17 \cdot 29 \cdots$, and consider $N^2 + 1$.

Suggested Readings

CARMICHAEL, R. D.   *The Theory of Numbers.*   Wiley, 1914.

WRIGHT, H. N.   *First Course in the Theory of Numbers.*   Wiley, 1939.

REID, L. W.   *The Elements of the Theory of Algebraic Numbers.*   Chapters I–IV. Macmillan, 1910.

USPENSKY, J. V., and HEASLET, M. A.   *Elementary Number Theory.*   McGraw-Hill, 1939.

DICKSON, L. E. *Introduction to the Theory of Numbers.* University of Chicago Press, 1929.

DICKSON, L. E. *Modern Elementary Theory of Numbers.* University of Chicago Press, 1939.

HARDY, G. H., and WRIGHT, A. A. *Introduction to the Theory of Numbers.* Oxford, 1938.

MATHEWS, G. B. *Theory of Numbers.* Deighton, Bell and Co., Cambridge, 1892.

STIELTJES, T. J. *Essai sur la théorie des nombres.* Gauthier-Villars, Paris, 1895.

CAHEN, E. *Théorie des nombres,* Vol. 1. Gauthier-Villars, Paris, 1914.

LANDAU, E. *Vorlesungen über Zahlentheorie,* Vol. 1. Hirzel, Leipzig, 1927.

CHAPTER II

FINITE GROUPS

21. Definitions. A *mathematical system* consists of elements which we may denote by a, b, c, $\cdots$, an equals relation, and certain operations. The equals relation serves to separate the elements into classes, two elements being equal if and only if they belong to the same class.

An *equals relation* $a = b$ is characterized by the following four properties:

(a) Either $a = b$ or $a \neq b$. (The relation is *determinative*.)
(b) $a = a$. (The relation is *reflexive*.)
(c) If $a = b$, then $b = a$. (The relation is *symmetric*.)
(d) If $a = b$ and $b = c$, then $a = c$. (The relation is *transitive*.)

It is evident from the inclusion of Property (b) that equality as thus defined is an extension of an earlier equals relation which we call identity, or is this identity itself. Ultimately all mathematics rests upon undefined relations.

An *operation* relates to every ordered pair of elements a, b a third element c. If we use the symbol $\times$ as the symbol of the operation, we write

$$a \times b = c,$$

or merely $ab = c$. The operation is *well defined* (relative to the equals relation) if, when a or b or both are replaced by elements equal to them, respectively, c is replaced by an element equal to it.

It is probably correct to say that a *group* is the simplest mathematical system of consequence. It is composed of elements, an equals relation, and one operation (which we shall call abstract multiplication and denote by the symbol $\times$) subject to the following four postulates:

1. *The system is closed under the operation* $\times$, *which is well defined.*
2. *The operation is associative. That is,*

$$(a \times b) \times c = a \times (b \times c).$$

47

3. *There exists an identity element i such that*

$$a \times i = i \times a = a$$

for every element a of the group.

4. *Every element a has an inverse a^{-1} such that*

$$a^{-1}a = aa^{-1} = i.$$

If the group should happen to satisfy Postulate 5 as well, it is called a *commutative* or *abelian* group.

5. *The operation is commutative.   That is,*

$$a \times b = b \times a.$$

A group consisting of but a finite number of elements is called a *finite group*.

The postulates defining a group may be proved consistent by exhibiting one representation of a group. The known representations are, in fact, many and diverse, as the following examples indicate.

EXERCISES

1. Show that these systems form groups.
   (a) All integers, the operation being addition.
   (b) All rational numbers with 0 omitted, the operation being multiplication.
   (c) The numbers 1, -1, i, $-i$, ($i^2 = -1$), the operation being multiplication.
2. Show that the euclidean transformations

$$x' = x \cos \theta + y \sin \theta,$$

$$y' = -x \sin \theta + y \cos \theta,$$

the operation being composition of transformations, form a group which is not finite.

3. Show that the integers $\not\equiv 0$ mod 5 form a group relative to multiplication mod 5.

4. Show that the functions

$$r, \; 1/r, \; 1 - r, \; 1/(1 - r), \; (r - 1)/r, \; r/(r - 1)$$

form a group, the operation being the substitution of the second factor for r in the first.

5. Show that the permutations on the three letters a, b, c form a group, the product of two permutations being the permutation which gives directly the arrangement produced by applying the two permutations successively.

6. Show that under matric (row by column) multiplication, the matrices

$$\begin{bmatrix} 1 & 0 \\ 0 & 1 \end{bmatrix}, \quad \begin{bmatrix} -1 & 0 \\ 0 & -1 \end{bmatrix}, \quad \begin{bmatrix} 1 & 0 \\ 0 & -1 \end{bmatrix}, \quad \begin{bmatrix} -1 & 0 \\ 0 & 1 \end{bmatrix}$$

form a group.

22. Elementary properties.

Theorem 22.1. The product of k elements of a group is independent of the manner in which the elements are associated.

Suppose that the theorem is true for $k - 1$ or fewer elements. Let

$$a = (a_1 a_2 \cdots a_s)(a_{s+1} a_{s+2} \cdots a_k),$$

$$b = (a_1 a_2 \cdots a_t)(a_{t+1} a_{t+2} \cdots a_k)$$

where $0 < t < s < k$. Then by assumption

$$a = [(a_1 a_2 \cdots a_t)(a_{t+1} \cdots a_s)](a_{s+1} \cdots a_k).$$

By the associative law

$$a = (a_1 a_2 \cdots a_t)[(a_{t+1} \cdots a_s)(a_{s+1} \cdots a_k)]$$

which by assumption is equal to

$$(a_1 a_2 \cdots a_t)(a_{t+1} \cdots a_k) = b.$$

Thus the proof is complete by induction.

By a^n we mean $a \times a \times a \cdots$ to n factors.

Corollary 22.1. The power a^n where n is a positive integer is well defined.

Theorem 22.2. The identity is unique.

Suppose that i and j are both identity elements. Since i is an identity,

$$i \times j = j.$$

Since j is an identity,

$$i \times j = i.$$

Hence $i = j$.

Theorem 22.3. If $ab = ac$, then $b = c$.

For

$$a^{-1}(ab) = a^{-1}(ac),$$

$$(a^{-1}a)b = (a^{-1}a)c,$$

$$b = c.$$

Corollary 22.31.   The inverse is unique.

For if b is an inverse of a,

$$ab = i = aa^{-1},$$

$$b = a^{-1}.$$

Corollary 22.32.   The equation $ax = b$ has a unique solution.

For if

$$ax = b = aa^{-1}b,$$

then

$$x = a^{-1}b.$$

Theorem 22.4.   The inverse of the inverse of a is a.

By the definition of inverse,

$$a^{-1}(a^{-1})^{-1} = i.$$

Then from the uniqueness of the product,

$$a[a^{-1}(a^{-1})^{-1}] = ai = a.$$

From the associative law this equals

$$(a \times a^{-1})\,(a^{-1})^{-1} = i\,(a^{-1})^{-1} = (a^{-1})^{-1}.$$

Theorem 22.5.   The inverse of a product is the product of the inverses taken in reverse order.

Set

$$p = (ab \cdots lm)\,(m^{-1}\,l^{-1} \cdots b^{-1}\,a^{-1}).$$

By Theorem 22.1,

$$p = (ab \cdots l)\,(mm^{-1})\,(l^{-1} \cdots b^{-1}\,a^{-1})$$

$$= (ab \cdots l)\,(l^{-1} \cdots b^{-1}\,a^{-1}).$$

Continuing, we finally have $p = i$.   Then by Corollary **22.31**.

$$(m^{-1}\,l^{-1} \cdots b^{-1}a^{-1}) = (ab \cdots lm)^{-1}.$$

We now define a^{-m} to mean $(a^m)^{-1}$.

Corollary 22.5. $a^{-m} = (a^{-1})^m = (a^m)^{-1}$.

We define $a^0 = i$ for every element a.   Now a^m is well defined for every rational integer m.

Theorem 22.6.   If m and n are rational integers, $a^m \times a^n = a^{m+n}$.

For a^m equals i multiplied by m factors a if $m > 0$, equals i multiplied by $-m$ factors a^{-1} if $m < 0$, and equals just i if $m = 0$. The theorem follows easily in each of the nine possible cases.

Theorem 22.7. If m and n are rational integers, $(a^m)^n = a^{mn}$.

If $n > 0$, the result follows from Theorem 22.1. If $n = 0$, it is obvious. If $n < 0$, let $n = -p$. Then

$$(a^m)^{-p} = [(a^m)^p]^{-1} = [a^{mp}]^{-1} = a^{-mp} = a^{mn}.$$

Theorem 22.8. If a and b are commutative, $a^n \times b^n = (ab)^n$.

If $n > 0$,

$$(a \times b)^n = a \times b \times a \times b \times \cdots \times a \times b$$

$$= a \times a \times \cdots \times a \times b \times b \times \cdots \times b = a^n \times b^n$$

by Theorem 22.1 and the commutative law. If $n < 0$, write $a^n = (a^{-1})^{-n}$ and proceed as before. If $n = 0$, the theorem reduces to $i \times i = i$.

EXERCISES

1. Show that a reduced residue system modulo m forms an abelian group of order $\varphi(m)$ under multiplication mod m.

2. Show that the five fifth roots of unity form an abelian group under multiplication.

3. Prove that not every abelian group can be represented by a reduced residue system, the operation being multiplication mod m.

HINT: The group of Ex. 2 cannot.

4. Prove directly from the associative law that

$$(a \times b) \times (c \times d) = [a \times (b \times c)] \times d.$$

5. Postulates 3 and 4 of § 21 can be replaced by the apparently weaker postulates:

3′. There exists a right identity i, such that $a \times i = a$ for every a.

4′. Every element a has a right inverse a^{-1}, such that $a \times a^{-1} = i$.

HINT: Let $a^{-1} \times a = b$, and prove that $b = i$. Then let $i \times a = c$, and prove that $c = a$.

23. Finite groups.

A *finite group* is a group consisting of only a finite number of elements. The number of elements is called the *order* of the finite group.

Theorem 23.1. If a is an element of a finite group, there is a positive integer r such that $a^r = i$. Hence $a^{-1} = a^{r-1}$.

The elements of the sequence

$$i, a, a^2, \cdots, a^g$$

cannot all be different if g is the order of the group. Suppose that

$$a^s = a^t, \qquad\qquad s > t.$$

Then by Corollary 22.5

$$i = a^s(a^t)^{-1} = a^s a^{-t},$$

and by Theorem 22.6 this equals a^{s-t}, where $s - t$ is a positive integer.

The least positive integer r such that $a^r = i$ is called the *period* of a. The use of the relation $a^{-1} = a^{r-1}$ makes the use of negative exponents unnecessary in finite group theory.

A *subgroup* of a group $\mathfrak{G}$* is a set of elements of $\mathfrak{G}$ which by them-selves constitute a group. Evidently i is a subgroup of every group. So is the entire group. A subgroup of $\mathfrak{G}$ different from $\mathfrak{G}$ and from the identity is called a *proper subgroup* of $\mathfrak{G}$.

If $\mathfrak{G}_1$ and $\mathfrak{G}_2$ are subgroups of $\mathfrak{G}$, the elements common to $\mathfrak{G}_1$ and $\mathfrak{G}_2$ form a group called the *intersection* of $\mathfrak{G}_1$ and $\mathfrak{G}_2$, written $\mathfrak{G}_1 \wedge \mathfrak{G}_2$.

Theorem 23.2.   The order of a subgroup of a group $\mathfrak{G}$ is a divisor of the order of $\mathfrak{G}$.

For, suppose the subgroup $\mathfrak{H}$ of $\mathfrak{G}$ to be of order h, and to consist of the elements $a_1, a_2, \cdots, a_h$. Let $\mathfrak{G}$ be of order g. If $h = g$, the theorem is true. If $g > h$, $\mathfrak{G}$ has an element b_2 not in $\mathfrak{H}$. Then the h elements

$$b_2a_1, b_2a_2, \cdots, b_2a_h$$

are all in $\mathfrak{G}$, and by Theorem 22.3 they are all different. Furthermore, they are different from the elements of $\mathfrak{H}$, for $b_2a_i = a_j$ would imply $b_2 = a_j a_i^{-1}$, i.e., that b_2 was in $\mathfrak{H}$, contrary to its selection. Hence if $g > h$, $g \geqq 2h$. If $g = 2h$, the theorem holds. If $g > 2h$, $\mathfrak{G}$ has an element b_3 not in $\mathfrak{H}$ and not in $b_2\mathfrak{H}$. Then the h elements

$$b_3a_1, b_3a_2, \cdots, b_3a_h$$

are distinct among themselves and distinct from the elements of $\mathfrak{H}$. They are also distinct from the elements of $b_2\mathfrak{H}$. For, if $b_3a_i = b_2a_j$, we should have $b_3 = b_2a_ja_i^{-1}$. But this would mean that b_3 was in $b_2\mathfrak{H}$, contrary to its selection. Thus $g \geqq 3h$. By this process we can

---

* $\mathfrak{G}$ is German G. See page 297 for the script, which the student should learn to write.

show that, if $g > (k - 1)h$, then $g \geqq kh$. Since the group $\mathfrak{G}$ is of finite order g, a stage must finally be reached where $g = kh$.

A set of elements of a group $\mathfrak{G}$ are said to be *independent* if no element of the set can be expressed as a product of the remaining elements, allowing any number of repetitions. A set of independent elements of $\mathfrak{G}$ which have the property that every element of $\mathfrak{G}$ can be represented in terms of them is called a set of *independent generators* of $\mathfrak{G}$.

Theorem 23.3. *Every finite group possesses a set of independent generators.*

Take the set of all elements of $\mathfrak{G}$. Remove i, since it is a power of every other element. If the next element (in any ordering) can be expressed in terms of the remaining elements, remove it. Continue until the elements which are left are independent.

A set of generators is ordinarily not unique.

A group generated by a single element is called *cyclic*. A cyclic group has as its elements the powers of a single generator. Every element of a group generates a cyclic subgroup whose order is equal to the period of the element.

EXERCISES

1. Every group of prime order is cyclic.
2. The period of every element of a group is a divisor of the order of the group.
3. Every cyclic group is abelian.
4. Find a set of generators of the four-group:

	1	a_1	a_2	a_3
1	1	a_1	a_2	a_3
a_1	a_1	1	a_3	a_2
a_2	a_2	a_3	1	a_1
a_3	a_3	a_2	a_1	1

5. Construct the multiplication table of the cyclic group of order 4.
6. A group of order 8, known as the octic group, has elements

$$u^i v^j \ (i = 0, 1, 2, 3; \ j = 0, 1), \ u^4 = 1, \ v^2 = 1, \ vu = u^3 v.$$

Construct its multiplication table.

7. The alternating group of order 12 has elements

$$p^i q^j r^k \qquad (i = 0, 1, 2; \ j = 0, 1; \ k = 0, 1),$$

where $p^3 = q^2 = r^2 = 1$, $qp = pqr$, $rp = pq$, $rq = qr$. Construct its multiplication table.

8. Prove that every subgroup of a cyclic group is cyclic.

24. Automorphisms. Consider two mathematical systems $A = (a_i)$, $B = (b_i)$. Let O_A be an operation well defined for A, and O_B for B. Let there be a correspondence $a_i \to b_i$ by means of which every element a_i of A determines a unique element b_i of B, such that every element b_i of B is the correspondent of at least one a_i of A. If it is true that

$$a_i \to b_i, \quad a_j \to b_j \text{ imply } O_A(a_i, a_j) \to O_B(b_i, b_j),$$

this correspondence is called a *homomorphism*, or *mapping* of A onto B. If a homomorphism of A onto B exists, we write $A \sim B$.

The concept of homomorphism can be visualized by the diagram below.

$$\begin{cases} a_i & \to & b_i \\ a_j & \to & b_j \end{cases}$$
$$\downarrow \qquad \quad \downarrow$$
$$O_A(a_i, a_j) \to O_B(b_i, b_j).$$

We start with the two elements a_i and a_j of A. By means of the correspondence

$$a_i \to b_i, \quad a_j \to b_j,$$

we obtain b_i and b_j, and then, by means of the operation O_B, we obtain the element $O_B(b_i, b_j)$ of B. Again starting with a_i and a_j, by means of the operation O_A we obtain the element $O_A(a_i, a_j)$ of A. By the correspondence $\to$, this leads to a number b' of B. If $b' = O_B(b_i, b_j)$, the correspondence is a homomorphism relative to the two corresponding operations O_A and O_B.

If every element of B is the correspondent of one and only one element of A, the correspondence is called *biunique* (or *one-to-one reciprocal*), and is written

$$a_i \leftrightarrow b_i.$$

If now

$$a_i \leftrightarrow b_i, \quad a_j \leftrightarrow b_j \text{ imply } O_A(a_i, a_j) \leftrightarrow O_B(b_i, b_j),$$

the homomorphism is called an *isomorphism*, and we write $A \cong B$. Two isomorphic mathematical systems are abstractly identical.

A homomorphism of a system onto itself, or part of itself, is called an *endomorphism*.

An isomorphism of a system with itself is called an *automorphism*.

Let us consider an automorphism of A,

(24.1) $$a_i \leftrightarrow a_i',$$

the a_i' being the elements of A in some order. We write $a_i a_j$ for $O_A(a_i, a_j)$. Since the correspondence is an automorphism, $(a_i a_j)' = a_i' a_j'$. If

(24.2) $$a_i \leftrightarrow a_i''$$

is a second automorphism, we denote $(a_i')''$ by $a_i'\,''$. Then

$$(a_i a_j)'\,'' = [(a_i a_j)']'' = [a_i' a_j']'' = a_i'\,'' a_j'\,'',$$

so the correspondence

$$a_i \leftrightarrow a_i'\,''$$

is an automorphism of A, called the *product* of the automorphisms (24.1) and (24.2).

Theorem 24.1. *The automorphisms of a mathematical system form a group.*

We have proved that the product of two automorphisms is an automorphism.

The correspondence $a_i \leftrightarrow a_i$, called the *identity automorphism*, is the identity element of the automorphism group.

Since the correspondence $a_i \leftrightarrow a_i'$ is biunique, it can be written $a_i' \leftrightarrow a_i$, thus determining the automorphism inverse to $a_i \leftrightarrow a_i'$.

To prove the associative law, rearrange the correspondences

$$R:\ a_i \leftrightarrow a_i';\quad S:\ a_i \leftrightarrow a_i'';\quad T:\ a_i \leftrightarrow a_i'''$$

in the form

$$R:\ a_i \leftrightarrow a_i';\quad S:\ a_i' \leftrightarrow a_i'\,'';\quad T:\ a_i'\,'' \leftrightarrow a_i'\,''\,''''$$

which can be done, since the a_i' and the $a_i'\,''$ are merely the a_i in another order. Now the $a_i'\,''\,''''$ corresponding to a_i under the automorphism TSR is uniquely determined whether we obtain it as $(a_i'\,'')'''$ from the automorphism $T(SR)$ or as $(a_i')''\,''''$ from the automorphism $(TS)R$.

Let $\mathfrak{G} = (a_1, a_2, \cdots)$ be a group, and suppose that t is any one of its elements. Set

$$a_1' = t^{-1} a_1 t,\quad a_2' = t^{-1} a_2 t,\ \cdots.$$

We call a_i' the *transform* of a_i by t. The correspondence $a_i \leftrightarrow a_i'$ is biunique, for $a_i = t a_i' t^{-1}$ is uniquely determined by a_i' and t. The correspondence is an automorphism of $\mathfrak{G}$, for

$$a_i' a_j' = t^{-1} a_i t t^{-1} a_j t = t^{-1} a_i a_j t = (a_i a_j)'.$$

An automorphism $a_i \leftrightarrow t^{-1}a_i t = a_i'$ is called an *inner automorphism*. It is the identity automorphism if and only if t is commutative with every element of $\mathfrak{G}$. All automorphisms which are not inner are called *outer automorphisms*.

Theorem 24.2. *The inner automorphisms of a group $\mathfrak{G}$ form a subgroup of the group of all automorphisms.*

Let

$$T: a_i \leftrightarrow t^{-1}a_i t, \qquad S: a_i \leftrightarrow s^{-1}a_i s$$

be two automorphisms. Their product is

$$TS: a_i \leftrightarrow t^{-1}(s^{-1}a_i s)t = (st)^{-1}a_i(st),$$

which is again an inner automorphism. If t is the identity element of $\mathfrak{G}$, T is the identity automorphism. Let T^{-1} be defined by

$$T^{-1}: a_i \leftrightarrow t a_i t^{-1} = (t^{-1})^{-1}a_i t^{-1}.$$

Then TT^{-1} is the identity automorphism, so that the inverse T^{-1} of T is inner.

EXERCISES

1. Let A be the integers 0, 1, 2, and let O_A be addition modulo 3. Let B be the cube roots of unity 1, ω, ω^2, and let O_B be multiplication. Show that the correspondence

$$0 \leftrightarrow 1, \quad 1 \leftrightarrow \omega, \quad 2 \leftrightarrow \omega^2$$

is an isomorphism if $O_A \leftrightarrow O_B$.

2. Consider the cyclic group of order 5 with the elements 1, a, a^2, a^3, a^4, $a^5 = 1$. Show that there are just four automorphisms, none of which except the identity is inner. Find the multiplication table of this automorphism group.

3. Find the total automorphism group of the octic group, also the group of its inner automorphisms.

HINT: A correspondence $u \leftrightarrow u'$, $v \leftrightarrow v'$ is an automorphism if and only if it preserves the generating relations $u^4 = 1$, $v^2 = 1$, $vu = u^3 v$.

4. Let A be the set of positive integers, and let O_A be addition. Show that the correspondence $a_i \leftrightarrow a_i' = m a_i$, where m is a fixed positive integer, is an endomorphism. Compare this statement with Theorem 1.4.

5. Show that for every positive integer n there exists a cyclic group of order n, and that any two such groups are isomorphic.

25. Conjugate subgroups.

Theorem 25.1. *Under every automorphism of $\mathfrak{G}$, the elements of a subgroup $\mathfrak{G}_1$ of $\mathfrak{G}$ correspond isomorphically to the elements of a subgroup $\mathfrak{G}_1'$ of $\mathfrak{G}$.*

The proof follows from the definition of automorphism. Let $a_i \leftrightarrow a_i'$. Since $a_1, \cdots, a_g$ form a group $\mathfrak{G}_1$, $\mathfrak{G}_1$ contains every product $a_i a_j$, the identity a_1, and every inverse a_i^{-1}. Then the set $a_1', \cdots, a_g'$, contains every product $a_i' a_j' = (a_i a_j)'$. If a_1 is the identity of $\mathfrak{G}_1$, $a_i a_1 = a_1 a_i = a_i$ for every a_i in $\mathfrak{G}_1$. Hence

$$a_i' a_1' = a_1' a_i' = a_i'$$

for every a_i' in $\mathfrak{G}_1'$, so a_1' is the (unique) identity of $\mathfrak{G}_1'$. Similarly if $a_i a_i^{-1} = a_i^{-1} a_i = a_1$, then $a_i'(a_i^{-1})' = (a_i^{-1})' a_i' = a_1'$, so that $(a_i^{-1})' = (a_i')^{-1}$. Then $\mathfrak{G}_1'$ is a subgroup of $\mathfrak{G}$ isomorphic with $\mathfrak{G}_1$ by the correspondence $a_i \leftrightarrow a_i'$.

Let $\mathfrak{G}_1$ be a subgroup of $\mathfrak{G}$, the latter of order g. Consider the g inner automorphisms $a_i \leftrightarrow a_i' = t^{-1} a_i t$, where t ranges over each of the elements of $\mathfrak{G}$. Under each of these automorphisms, $\mathfrak{G}_1$ is carried into a subgroup $\mathfrak{G}_1'$, so that, under all inner automorphisms, $\mathfrak{G}_1$ determines k distinct subgroups of $\mathfrak{G}$,

$$\mathfrak{G}_1, \ \mathfrak{G}_1', \ \mathfrak{G}_1'', \ \cdots, \ \mathfrak{G}_1^{(k-1)},$$

all isomorphic with one another. The original subgroup $\mathfrak{G}_1$ is in the set.

The set of subgroups determined from $\mathfrak{G}_1$ by all the inner automorphisms of $\mathfrak{G}$ constitute a set of *conjugate subgroups*. If in particular all the subgroups conjugate to $\mathfrak{G}_1$ coincide with $\mathfrak{G}_1$, then $\mathfrak{G}_1$ is called an *invariant subgroup* of $\mathfrak{G}$. This concept is very important.

Theorem 25.2. The same set of conjugate subgroups is obtained no matter which of them is used (in place of $\mathfrak{G}_1$) to determine the set.

Let $\mathfrak{G}_1$ determine the conjugate set

$$\mathfrak{G}_1, \ \mathfrak{G}_1', \ \mathfrak{G}_1'', \ \cdots.$$

Then there exist elements $t_1, t_2, \cdots$ of $\mathfrak{G}$ such that

$$\mathfrak{G}_1' = t_1^{-1} \mathfrak{G}_1 t_1,$$
$$\mathfrak{G}_1'' = t_2^{-1} \mathfrak{G}_1 t_2,$$
$$\mathfrak{G}_1''' = t_3^{-1} \mathfrak{G}_1 t_3,$$
$$\cdots \cdots \cdots .$$

Then

$$\mathfrak{G}_1 = t_1 \mathfrak{G}_1' t_1^{-1},$$
$$\mathfrak{G}_1'' = t_2^{-1} t_1 \mathfrak{G}_1' t_1^{-1} t_2 = (t_1^{-1} t_2)^{-1} \mathfrak{G}_1' (t_1^{-1} t_2),$$
$$\mathfrak{G}_1''' = t_3^{-1} t_1 \mathfrak{G}_1' t_1^{-1} t_3 = (t_1^{-1} t_3) \mathfrak{G}_1' (t_1^{-1} t_3),$$
$$\cdots \cdots \cdots \cdots \cdots \cdots$$

so that every subgroup of the conjugate set determined by $\mathfrak{G}_1$ is in the conjugate set determined by $\mathfrak{G}_1'$. A similar argument shows that every subgroup of the conjugate set determined by $\mathfrak{G}_1'$ is in the conjugate set determined by $\mathfrak{G}_1$, so that the sets coincide. Any subgroup of the set could have been taken for $\mathfrak{G}_1'$.

Theorem 25.3. The elements of $\mathfrak{G}$ which transform a set S of elements of $\mathfrak{G}$ into itself form a subgroup of $\mathfrak{G}$.

Let t_1 and t_2 be elements of $\mathfrak{G}$ such that

$$t_1^{-1}St_1 = S, \qquad t_2^{-1}St_2 = S.$$

Then

$$(t_1t_2)^{-1}S(t_1t_2) = t_2^{-1}t_1^{-1}St_1t_2 = t_2^{-1}St_2 = S,$$

so the set of t's is closed. Obviously the identity transforms S into itself. If $t^{-1}St = S$, then $S = tSt^{-1}$, so that the inverse of t transforms S into itself.

The set of elements which transform each element of $\mathfrak{G}$ into itself consists of all elements commutative with every element of $\mathfrak{G}$. This set is a group called the *central* of $\mathfrak{G}$.

The subgroup of elements of $\mathfrak{G}$ which transform an invariant subgroup of $\mathfrak{G}$ into itself is obviously $\mathfrak{G}$ itself. Note that $\mathfrak{G}$ and the identity are invariant subgroups of $\mathfrak{G}$.

Let S be any set of elements of $\mathfrak{G}$. Under the group of inner automorphisms of $\mathfrak{G}$, the set S will be carried into a certain number, say k, of distinct sets

$$S_1, S_2, \cdots, S_k$$

where $S_1 = S$. If in particular S is a subgroup of $\mathfrak{G}$, these sets are the conjugates of S.

Theorem 25.4. The number of elements of $\mathfrak{G}$ which transform S into S_i is equal to the number of elements which transform S into itself.

Suppose that the elements transforming S into itself are denoted by $t_1, t_2, \cdots, t_h$. Let $g^{-1}Sg = S_i$. Then $(t_ig)^{-1}S(t_ig) = g^{-1}t_i^{-1}St_ig = g^{-1}Sg = S_i$. Moreover, the t_ig are all distinct, for $t_ig = t_jg$ would imply $t_i = t_j$ (Theorem 22.3), contrary to assumption. Hence there are at least as many elements transforming S into S_i as there are transforming S into itself.

Now suppose that the elements transforming S into S_i are denoted by $g_1, g_2, \cdots, g_r$. Then $g_1^{-1}, g_2^{-1}, \cdots, g_r^{-1}$ transform S_i into S. Hence

$$(g_1g_j^{-1})^{-1}S(g_1g_j^{-1}) = g_jg_1^{-1}Sg_1g_j^{-1}$$

$$= g_jS_ig_j^{-1} = S.$$

Moreover the $g_1 g_j^{-1}$ are all distinct by Theorem 22.3. Hence there are at least as many elements transforming S into itself as there are transforming S into S_i. This proves the theorem.

Corollary 25.4. The number of subgroups in a conjugate set is a divisor of the order of the given group.

For every element of $\mathfrak{G}$ transforms S into itself or into just one of the $k - 1$ conjugates of S different from S. Thus the elements of $\mathfrak{G}$ can be distributed into k sets, each set containing the same number g/k of elements.

EXERCISES

1. Arrange all the subgroups of the octic group (see Ex. 6, § 23) into conjugate sets.
2. The alternating group of order 12 (see Ex. 7, § 23) has the cyclic group of order 3 as a subgroup. Find its conjugates.
3. Find the subgroup of the alternating group of order 12 which transforms $S = (1, p, p^2)$ into itself.
4. Find the central of the octic group and of the alternating group of order 12.
5. Show that the group of inner automorphisms of the alternating group of order 12 is the group itself.

26. Quotient groups. Denote by $\mathfrak{G}$ the set of all rational integers, and by $\mathfrak{H}$ the set of all multiples of 5. We say that

$$a \equiv b \qquad \text{mod } 5$$

if there exists a number h in $\mathfrak{H}$ such that $a = b + h$. If equality is congruence modulo $\mathfrak{H}$ (i.e., modulo 5), the rational integers form a group of order 5 with respect to addition, the group being representable by a complete set of residues modulo 5.

The same concept can be extended to groups in general, but it is customary to denote the group operation by $\times$ instead of by $+$. Let $\mathfrak{G}$ be a group, and let $\mathfrak{H}$ be a subset of $\mathfrak{G}$. We shall call two elements a_i and a_j of $\mathfrak{G}$ *right congruent modulo* $\mathfrak{H}$ if $a_i = a_j h_1$ for some element h_1 of $\mathfrak{H}$—in symbols,

$$a_i \equiv a_j \qquad \text{mod } \mathfrak{H}.$$

Theorem 26.1. Congruence modulo $\mathfrak{H}$ is an equals relation if and only if $\mathfrak{H}$ is a group.

Given a_i and a_j of $\mathfrak{G}$; either $a_j^{-1} a_i$ lies in $\mathfrak{H}$ or it does not, so the relation is determinative.

For any element a_i of $\mathfrak{G}$, $a_i \equiv a_i$ if and only if there is an element h_1 in $\mathfrak{H}$ such that $a_i = a_i h_1$—that is, if and only if h_1 is the identity of $\mathfrak{G}$.

Let $a_i = a_j h_1$. If (and only if) h_1 has an inverse, can we write

$$a_j = a_i h_2,$$

for this implies that $h_2 h_1 = i$, $h_2 = h_1^{-1}$. Now every h_1 of $\mathfrak{H}$ is involved in some relation $a_i = a_j h_1$, for we may define a_i to be $a_j h_1$, which is in $\mathfrak{G}$ since h_1 is in $\mathfrak{G}$. Hence congruence modulo $\mathfrak{H}$ is symmetric if and only if every element of $\mathfrak{H}$ has an inverse.

Let $a_i = a_j h_1$ and $a_j = a_k h_2$. Then $a_i = a_k h_2 h_1$. This is of the form $a_i = a_k h$ if and only if $h_2 h_1 = h$. Thus congruence modulo $\mathfrak{H}$ is transitive if and only if $\mathfrak{H}$ is closed under multiplication.

Since $\mathfrak{G}$ is associative and $\mathfrak{H}$ is a subset of $\mathfrak{G}$, $\mathfrak{H}$ is associative.

Note how each of the group properties of $\mathfrak{H}$ is related to one of the postulates for an equals relation modulo $\mathfrak{H}$.

A similar theory can be developed for the relation $a_i = h a_j$, called *left congruence* modulo $\mathfrak{H}$.

Let $a_1, a_2, \cdots, a_k$ be numbers of $\mathfrak{G}$ which are distinct modulo $\mathfrak{H}$ and such that every number of $\mathfrak{G}$ is congruent to one of them. There is no loss in generality in assuming that a_1 is the identity of $\mathfrak{G}$. Let $\mathfrak{H}_i$ be the class of all elements of $\mathfrak{G}$ which are congruent to a_i modulo $\mathfrak{H}$. Then the elements of $\mathfrak{G}$ can be separated into k sets,

$$\mathfrak{H}_1, \mathfrak{H}_2, \cdots, \mathfrak{H}_k, \qquad\qquad \mathfrak{H}_1 = \mathfrak{H},$$

and in the notation of sets we can write

$$\mathfrak{G} = \mathfrak{H}_1 + \mathfrak{H}_2 + \cdots + \mathfrak{H}_k.$$

The sets $\mathfrak{H}_1, \cdots, \mathfrak{H}_k$ are called the *cosets* of $\mathfrak{G}$ relative to $\mathfrak{H}$.

As a matter of fact, these cosets are the same sets which were obtained in the proof of Theorem 23.2. If a_i is any element of $\mathfrak{H}_i$, then all the elements of $\mathfrak{H}_i$ are obtained from $a_i h$ by letting h range over the elements of $\mathfrak{H}$. Each set is completely determined by one of its elements and $\mathfrak{H}$.

Theorem 26.2. The elements of $\mathfrak{G}$ modulo a subgroup $\mathfrak{H}$ form a group if and only if $\mathfrak{H}$ is an invariant subgroup of $\mathfrak{G}$.

We must show that "if equals be multiplied by equals, the products are equal" or, in other words, that the product is well defined. Let

$$a_i \equiv a_j, \quad a_k \equiv a_l, \qquad \mathrm{mod}\ \mathfrak{H}.$$

Then

$$a_i = a_j h_1, \qquad a_k = a_l h_2,$$

$$a_i a_k = a_j h_1 a_l h_2.$$

In order that this equal $a_j a_l h$ for some element h of $\mathfrak{H}$, it is necessary and sufficient that

$$h_1 a_l h_2 = a_l h,$$

or that

$$a_l^{-1} h_1 a_l = h h_2^{-1}.$$

Since h_1 ranges over $\mathfrak{H}$ as a_i and a_j range over $\mathfrak{G}$, and since a_l is any element of $\mathfrak{G}$, this means that $\mathfrak{H}$ must be an invariant subgroup of $\mathfrak{G}$. And this condition is obviously sufficient.

The other group properties follow easily. Since congruence modulo $\mathfrak{H}$ is reflexive, the equation

$$(a_i a_k) a_m = a_i (a_k a_m)$$

implies the congruence

$$(a_i a_k) a_m \equiv a_i (a_k a_m) \qquad \text{mod } \mathfrak{H}.$$

Hence the associative law holds. Also, if a_1 is the identity of $\mathfrak{G}$,

$$a a_1 = a, \qquad a a^{-1} = a_1$$

imply that

$$a a_1 \equiv a, \qquad a a^{-1} \equiv a_1, \qquad \text{mod } \mathfrak{H},$$

so that the identity exists modulo $\mathfrak{H}$, and every element a has an inverse modulo $\mathfrak{H}$.

This group is called the *quotient group* $\mathfrak{G}/\mathfrak{H}$. It is usually not isomorphic with a subgroup of $\mathfrak{G}$, but is nevertheless uniquely determined by $\mathfrak{G}$ and the invariant subgroup $\mathfrak{H}$. Its order is the number of cosets of $\mathfrak{G}$ relative to $\mathfrak{H}$, namely, g/h.

Theorem 26.3. The same quotient group is obtained from right congruence as from left congruence.

For, if $\mathfrak{H}$ is invariant, for every a_j in $\mathfrak{G}$ and every h_1 in $\mathfrak{H}$ there is an h_2 in $\mathfrak{H}$ such that $a_j h_1 = h_2 a_j$. Hence

$$a_i \equiv a_j \qquad \text{mod } \mathfrak{H} \quad \textit{(left)}$$

implies

$$a_i \equiv a_j \qquad \text{mod } \mathfrak{H} \quad \textit{(right)},$$

and conversely.

Theorem 26.4. If $\mathfrak{G}$ is cyclic and $\mathfrak{H}$ is a subgroup of $\mathfrak{G}$, then $\mathfrak{G}/\mathfrak{H}$ is cyclic.

Since $\mathfrak{G}$ is cyclic, it is abelian, and $\mathfrak{H}$ is an invariant subgroup of $\mathfrak{G}$. Then $\mathfrak{H}$ is cyclic (Ex. 8, § 23). Let

$$\mathfrak{G} = (1, a, a^2, \cdots, a^{g-1}), \quad \mathfrak{H} = (1, a^i, a^{2i}, \cdots, a^{(h-1)i}), \qquad hi = g.$$

Set

$$l = qi + r, \qquad\qquad 0 \leqq r < i.$$

Then every element of $\mathfrak{G}$ is expressible in the form

$$a^l = a^r a^{qi}, \qquad\qquad 0 \leqq r < i, l = 0, \cdots, g - 1.$$

That is, every element of $\mathfrak{G}$ is congruent modulo $\mathfrak{H}$ to one and only one of the elements

$$1, a, a^2, \cdots, a^{i-1}.$$

Thus $\mathfrak{G}/\mathfrak{H}$ is isomorphic with the cyclic group

$$1, a, a^2, \cdots, a^{i-1}, \qquad\qquad g = ih.$$

Another way of looking at the concept of quotient group, which after all is not essentially different, is to consider the cosets $\mathfrak{H}_1, \mathfrak{H}_2, \cdots, \mathfrak{H}_k$ as the elements of $\mathfrak{G}/\mathfrak{H}$, the product coset $\mathfrak{H}_i\mathfrak{H}_j$ being the coset containing h_ih_j, where h_i is any element of $\mathfrak{H}_i$ and h_j is any element of $\mathfrak{H}_j$. If $\mathfrak{H}$ is invariant in $\mathfrak{G}$, this product coset is unique.

EXERCISES

1. What are the invariant subgroups of the octic group? Find the quotient groups. (See Ex. 1, § 25.)

2. Show that $(1, q, r, qr)$ is an invariant subgroup of the alternating group of order 12. Find the quotient group.

3. If $\mathfrak{H}$ is any subgroup of $\mathfrak{G}$, we can write

$$\mathfrak{G} = \mathfrak{H} + b_2\mathfrak{H} + b_3\mathfrak{H} + \cdots.$$

Prove that

$$\mathfrak{G} = \mathfrak{H} + \mathfrak{H}b_2^{-1} + \mathfrak{H}b_3^{-1} + \cdots.$$

4. If a group $\mathfrak{G}$ of order n has a subgroup $\mathfrak{H}$ of order $n/2$, show that $\mathfrak{H}$ is invariant in $\mathfrak{G}$.

27. The Jordan-Hölder Theorem.

Theorem 27.1. The intersection $\mathfrak{D} = \mathfrak{H} \wedge \mathfrak{K}$ of two invariant subgroups $\mathfrak{H}$ and $\mathfrak{K}$ of $\mathfrak{G}$ is an invariant subgroup of $\mathfrak{G}$.

Clearly $\mathfrak{D}$ is a subgroup, as we saw in § 23. Moreover, it is invariant. For, if g_1 is any element of $\mathfrak{G}$, and if d_i is any element of $\mathfrak{D}$, then $g_1^{-1}d_ig_1$ is in $\mathfrak{H}$ (since $\mathfrak{H}$ is invariant) and is also in $\mathfrak{K}$ (since $\mathfrak{K}$ is invariant). Hence it is in $\mathfrak{D}$.

The following notation will be found convenient. If $\mathfrak{H}$ is a subgroup of $\mathfrak{G}$, we write $\mathfrak{H} \subseteq \mathfrak{G}$, or $\mathfrak{G} \supseteq \mathfrak{H}$. If $\mathfrak{H}$ is a proper subgroup of $\mathfrak{G}$, we write $\mathfrak{H} \subset \mathfrak{G}$, or $\mathfrak{G} \supset \mathfrak{H}$. If g is an element of $\mathfrak{G}$, we write $g \in \mathfrak{G}$.

By the *product* $\mathfrak{H}\mathfrak{K}$ of two subgroups $\mathfrak{H}$ and $\mathfrak{K}$ of $\mathfrak{G}$, we mean all products h_ik_j where h_i ranges over $\mathfrak{H}$ and k_j ranges over $\mathfrak{K}$.

Theorem 27.2. *If $\mathfrak{H}$ and $\mathfrak{K}$ are invariant subgroups of $\mathfrak{G}$, their product $\mathfrak{H}\mathfrak{K} = \mathfrak{K}\mathfrak{H}$ is an invariant subgroup of $\mathfrak{G}$.*

First we show that set $\mathfrak{H}\mathfrak{K}$ equals set $\mathfrak{K}\mathfrak{H}$. Since $\mathfrak{H}$ is invariant,

$$h_i k_j = k_j h_l, \qquad\qquad h_l \in \mathfrak{H},$$

for every h_i in $\mathfrak{H}$ and every k_j in $\mathfrak{K}$, so that $\mathfrak{H}\mathfrak{K} \subseteq \mathfrak{K}\mathfrak{H}$. Similarly $\mathfrak{K}\mathfrak{H} \subseteq \mathfrak{H}\mathfrak{K}$.

Second, the elements of $\mathfrak{H}\mathfrak{K}$ form a group. For

$$h_i k_j h_l k_m = h_i h_p k_q k_m \in \mathfrak{H}\mathfrak{K},$$

since every element $k_j h_l$ of $\mathfrak{K}\mathfrak{H}$ is equal to some element $h_p k_q$ of $\mathfrak{H}\mathfrak{K}$. The identity of $\mathfrak{H}\mathfrak{K}$ is the product of the identity of $\mathfrak{H}$ and the identity of $\mathfrak{K}$. Since

$$h_i k_j k_j^{-1} h_i^{-1} = i,$$

$k_j^{-1} h_i^{-1} = (h_i k_j)^{-1}$, which is in $\mathfrak{K}\mathfrak{H} = \mathfrak{H}\mathfrak{K}$. The associative law holds for $\mathfrak{H}\mathfrak{K}$, since it holds for $\mathfrak{G}$.

Third, $\mathfrak{H}\mathfrak{K}$ is invariant. For, if g_1 is any element of $\mathfrak{G}$,

$$g_1^{-1} h_i k_j g_1 = g_1^{-1} h_i g_1 g_1^{-1} k_j g_1 = h_p k_q \in \mathfrak{H}\mathfrak{K},$$

since both $\mathfrak{H}$ and $\mathfrak{K}$ are invariant in $\mathfrak{G}$.

Theorem 27.3. *If $\mathfrak{G}/\mathfrak{H} \supset \mathfrak{K}$, where $\mathfrak{H}$ is of order h, and $\mathfrak{K}$ is of order k, then $\mathfrak{G}$ contains a subgroup $\mathfrak{L}$ of order kh, $\mathfrak{L} \supset \mathfrak{H}$. If $\mathfrak{K}$ is invariant in $\mathfrak{G}/\mathfrak{H}$, then $\mathfrak{L}$ is invariant in $\mathfrak{G}$.*

The elements of $\mathfrak{G}/\mathfrak{H}$ are the elements of $\mathfrak{G}$ taken modulo $\mathfrak{H}$. Let $\mathfrak{L}$ consist of all elements of $\mathfrak{G}$ which are congruent modulo $\mathfrak{H}$ to the elements of $\mathfrak{K}$. Obviously $\mathfrak{L} \supset \mathfrak{H}$, since the elements of $\mathfrak{H}$ are all congruent to the identity of $\mathfrak{K}$. Hence $\mathfrak{L}$ contains the identity of $\mathfrak{G}$. Let l_1 and l_2 be two elements of $\mathfrak{L}$, and let $l_1 l_2 = g_3$. Since $\mathfrak{K}$ is the group consisting of all elements of $\mathfrak{L}$ modulo $\mathfrak{H}$, g_3 is congruent modulo $\mathfrak{H}$ to an element of $\mathfrak{K}$, and hence is in $\mathfrak{L}$. Since $\mathfrak{K}$ is a group, every element l_1 has an inverse l_2. That is, for every l_1, there is an element l_2 such that

$$l_1 l_2 \equiv i \qquad \mathrm{mod}\ \mathfrak{H}.$$

That is, there is an element h_1 in $\mathfrak{H}$ such that $l_1 l_2 = h_1$. Thus $l_1 l_2 h_1^{-1} = i$, so that l_1 has the inverse $l_2 h_1^{-1}$ in $\mathfrak{L}$.

Since the elements of $\mathfrak{L}$ are the elements in k cosets of $\mathfrak{G}$ relative to $\mathfrak{H}$, they are kh in number.

Now if $\mathfrak{K}$ is invariant in $\mathfrak{G}/\mathfrak{H}$, for every element g_1 in $\mathfrak{G}$ and every element l_1 in $\mathfrak{L}$ there is an element l_2 in $\mathfrak{L}$ such that

$$g_1 l_1 \equiv l_2 g_1 \qquad \text{mod } \mathfrak{H},$$

or

$$g_1 l_1 = l_2 g_1 h_2.$$

But $g_1 h_2 = h_1 g_1$, since $\mathfrak{H}$ is invariant in $\mathfrak{G}$, so that

$$g_1 l_1 = l_2 h_1 g_1 = l_3 g_1,$$

and $\mathfrak{L}$ is invariant in $\mathfrak{G}$.

An invariant subgroup is *maximal* if it is not properly contained in another proper invariant subgroup of $\mathfrak{G}$.

A group is called *simple* if it has no invariant subgroup other than itself and the identity.

Corollary 27.3. $\mathfrak{G}/\mathfrak{H}$ *is simple if and only if* $\mathfrak{H}$ *is maximal.*

If $\mathfrak{G}/\mathfrak{H}$ is not simple, it contains an invariant subgroup $\mathfrak{K}$, and then by the theorem there is an invariant subgroup $\mathfrak{L}$, $\mathfrak{G} \supset \mathfrak{L} \supset \mathfrak{H}$, so that $\mathfrak{H}$ is not maximal.

Now suppose $\mathfrak{H}$ not maximal. Then there is an invariant subgroup $\mathfrak{L}$, $\mathfrak{G} \supset \mathfrak{L} \supset \mathfrak{H}$, whose elements modulo $\mathfrak{H}$ form a subset of the elements of $\mathfrak{G}$ modulo $\mathfrak{H}$. Since $\mathfrak{H}$ is invariant in $\mathfrak{G}$, it is invariant in $\mathfrak{L}$. Then $\mathfrak{G}/\mathfrak{H} \supset \mathfrak{L}/\mathfrak{H}$. Since

$$g_1 l_1 = l_2 g_1,$$

it follows that

$$g_1 l_1 \equiv l_2 g_1 \qquad \text{mod } \mathfrak{H}$$

so that $\mathfrak{L}/\mathfrak{H}$ is invariant in $\mathfrak{G}/\mathfrak{H}$. Thus $\mathfrak{G}/\mathfrak{H}$ is not simple.

Theorem 27.4. *If* $\mathfrak{H}$ *and* $\mathfrak{K}$ *are maximal invariant subgroups of* $\mathfrak{G}$, $\mathfrak{H} \neq \mathfrak{K}$, *and if* $\mathfrak{D} = \mathfrak{H} \wedge \mathfrak{K}$, *then*

$$\frac{\mathfrak{G}}{\mathfrak{H}} \cong \frac{\mathfrak{K}}{\mathfrak{D}}, \qquad\qquad \frac{\mathfrak{G}}{\mathfrak{K}} \cong \frac{\mathfrak{H}}{\mathfrak{D}}.$$

If $\mathfrak{H}$ and $\mathfrak{K}$ are both maximal, $\mathfrak{H}\mathfrak{K} = \mathfrak{G}$, for otherwise $\mathfrak{H}\mathfrak{K}$ would be an invariant subgroup of $\mathfrak{G}$ (Theorem 27.2) containing both $\mathfrak{H}$ and $\mathfrak{K}$ properly so that the latter would not be maximal.

The elements of $\mathfrak{G}/\mathfrak{H}$ are the elements $k_i h_j$ of $\mathfrak{G}$ modulo $\mathfrak{H}$. Since $h_j \in \mathfrak{H}$, these are congruent to the elements k_i of $\mathfrak{K}$ taken modulo $\mathfrak{H}$. But a relation $k_i = k_j h_1$ implies that h_1 is in $\mathfrak{K}$ as well as in $\mathfrak{H}$. Hence only the numbers h_1 of $\mathfrak{D}$ are actually used. Thus the elements of $\mathfrak{G}/\mathfrak{H}$ are the elements of $\mathfrak{K}$ taken modulo $\mathfrak{D}$. Hence $\mathfrak{G}/\mathfrak{H} \cong \mathfrak{K}/\mathfrak{D}$.

The relation $\mathfrak{G}/\mathfrak{K} \cong \mathfrak{H}/\mathfrak{D}$ is similarly proved.

If $\mathfrak{H}_1$ is a maximal invariant subgroup of $\mathfrak{G}$, and $\mathfrak{H}_2$ is a maximal invariant subgroup of $\mathfrak{H}_1$ (but not necessarily even an invariant subgroup of $\mathfrak{G}$), $\mathfrak{H}_3$ a maximal invariant subgroup of $\mathfrak{H}_2$, etc., the groups

$$\mathfrak{G}, \mathfrak{H}_1, \mathfrak{H}_2, \cdots, I,$$

where I is the identity, constitute a *series of composition* of $\mathfrak{G}$.

The quotient groups

$$\frac{\mathfrak{G}}{\mathfrak{H}_1}, \frac{\mathfrak{H}_1}{\mathfrak{H}_2}, \frac{\mathfrak{H}_2}{\mathfrak{H}_3}, \cdots,$$

are called the *prime factor groups* of $\mathfrak{G}$. Their orders are the *factors of composition* of $\mathfrak{G}$. The factors of composition of a group are very important in the Galois theory of equations.

Theorem 27.5. (*Jordan-Hölder.*) *For two series of composition of $\mathfrak{G}$ the prime factor groups are isomorphic* (*and hence the factors of composition are the same*) *except possibly for order.*

The theorem is evidently true for simple groups, and in particular for groups whose orders are prime. The proof is by induction on the number of prime factors of the order g of $\mathfrak{G}$. If g has n prime factors, we assume the theorem for all groups whose orders are a product of less than n prime factors.

Suppose that we have for $\mathfrak{G}$ two series of composition

$$\mathfrak{G}, \mathfrak{H}_1, \mathfrak{H}_2, \cdots, \mathfrak{H}_r = I; \quad \mathfrak{G}, \mathfrak{K}_1, \mathfrak{K}_2, \cdots, \mathfrak{K}_s = I.$$

If $\mathfrak{H}_1 = \mathfrak{K}_1$, the theorem holds by the assumption of induction, for the order h_1 of $\mathfrak{H}_1$ contains at least one fewer prime factors than g. Accordingly we assume that $\mathfrak{H}_1$ and $\mathfrak{K}_1$ are distinct maximal invariant subgroups of $\mathfrak{G}$. Let $\mathfrak{D}_1$ be their intersection. Then, by Theorem 27.4,

$$\frac{\mathfrak{G}}{\mathfrak{H}_1} \cong \frac{\mathfrak{K}_1}{\mathfrak{D}_1}, \quad \frac{\mathfrak{G}}{\mathfrak{K}_1} \cong \frac{\mathfrak{H}_1}{\mathfrak{D}_1}.$$

Since $\mathfrak{G}/\mathfrak{H}_1$ and $\mathfrak{G}/\mathfrak{K}_1$ (and therefore $\mathfrak{K}_1/\mathfrak{D}_1$ and $\mathfrak{H}_1/\mathfrak{D}_1$) are simple (Corollary 27.3), $\mathfrak{D}_1$ is a maximal invariant subgroup of both $\mathfrak{H}_1$ and $\mathfrak{K}_1$. Now form the series of composition

$$\mathfrak{G}, \mathfrak{H}_1, \mathfrak{D}_1, \mathfrak{D}_2, \cdots, \mathfrak{D}_t = I; \quad \mathfrak{G}, \mathfrak{K}_1, \mathfrak{D}_1, \mathfrak{D}_2, \cdots, \mathfrak{D}_t = I.$$

The corresponding prime factor groups $\mathfrak{G}/\mathfrak{H}_1$, $\mathfrak{H}_1/\mathfrak{D}_1$, $\mathfrak{D}_1/\mathfrak{D}_2$, $\cdots$,

$\mathfrak{G}/\mathfrak{K}_1$, $\mathfrak{K}_1/\mathfrak{D}_1$, $\mathfrak{D}_1/\mathfrak{D}_2$, $\cdots$, are isomorphic except for a permutation of the first two groups.   But

$$\frac{\mathfrak{G}}{\mathfrak{H}_1}, \frac{\mathfrak{H}_1}{\mathfrak{D}_1}, \frac{\mathfrak{D}_1}{\mathfrak{D}_2}, \cdots \cong \frac{\mathfrak{G}}{\mathfrak{H}_1}, \frac{\mathfrak{H}_1}{\mathfrak{H}_2}, \frac{\mathfrak{H}_2}{\mathfrak{H}_3}, \cdots,$$

$$\frac{\mathfrak{G}}{\mathfrak{K}_1}, \frac{\mathfrak{K}_1}{\mathfrak{D}_1}, \frac{\mathfrak{D}_1}{\mathfrak{D}_2}, \cdots \cong \frac{\mathfrak{G}}{\mathfrak{K}_1}, \frac{\mathfrak{K}_1}{\mathfrak{K}_2}, \frac{\mathfrak{K}_2}{\mathfrak{K}_3}, \cdots$$

except possibly for order by the assumption of induction.   Hence the theorem is proved.

EXERCISES

1. Find two different composition series, and corresponding sets of prime factor groups, for the cyclic group of order 6.

2. Find the various composition series and prime factor groups of the octic group.

3. Find one composition series for the alternating group of order 12, and the corresponding prime factor groups.

28. The direct product.   Let $\mathfrak{H}$ and $\mathfrak{K}$ be two groups of orders h and k, respectively.   Consider the system of elements (h_i, k_j), where h_i ranges over $\mathfrak{H}$ and k_j ranges over $\mathfrak{K}$.   We shall say that

$$(h_i, k_j) = (h_l, k_m)$$

if and only if $h_i = h_l$ and $k_j = k_m$.   It is easily seen that this is a legitimate equals relation.

We define the product as follows:

$$(h_i, k_j)(h_l, k_m) = (h_i h_l, k_j k_m).$$

Theorem 28.1.   The elements (h_i, k_j) constitute a group $\mathfrak{G}$ of order hk containing subgroups $\mathfrak{H}'$ and $\mathfrak{K}'$ isomorphic with $\mathfrak{H}$ and $\mathfrak{K}$, respectively. Every element of $\mathfrak{G}$ is uniquely expressible as a product of an element of $\mathfrak{H}'$ by an element of $\mathfrak{K}'$, and this product is commutative.

Multiplication is obviously associative, since it is associative in $\mathfrak{H}$ and in $\mathfrak{K}$.

Closure is evident.

If h_1 is the identity of $\mathfrak{H}$, and k_1 is the identity of $\mathfrak{K}$, then (h_1, k_1) is the identity of $\mathfrak{G}$.   Also (h_i^{-1}, k_j^{-1}) is the inverse of (h_i, k_j).

The elements (h_i, k_1) of $\mathfrak{G}$ constitute a subgroup of $\mathfrak{G}$ isomorphic with $\mathfrak{H}$, for

$$(h_i, k_1)(h_l, k_1) = (h_i h_l, k_1).$$

Denote this subgroup by $\mathfrak{H}'$. Similarly the elements (h_1, k_j) constitute a subgroup $\mathfrak{K}'$ of $\mathfrak{G}$ isomorphic with $\mathfrak{K}$.

Since

$$(h_i, k_1)(h_1, k_j) = (h_1, k_j)(h_i, k_1) = (h_i, k_j),$$

the last statement in the theorem is proved.

We shall say that $\mathfrak{G}$ is the *direct product* of the two groups $\mathfrak{H}$ and $\mathfrak{K}$, or of its two subgroups $\mathfrak{H}'$ and $\mathfrak{K}'$, written $\mathfrak{G} = \mathfrak{H} \times \mathfrak{K}$. In the sense of isomorphism $\mathfrak{H}$ does not differ from $\mathfrak{H}'$ nor $\mathfrak{K}$ from $\mathfrak{K}'$.

Theorem 28.2. If $\mathfrak{G} = \mathfrak{H}\mathfrak{K}$, if $\mathfrak{H} \wedge \mathfrak{K}$ is the identity, and if every element of $\mathfrak{H}$ is commutative with every element of $\mathfrak{K}$, then $\mathfrak{G} \cong \mathfrak{H} \times \mathfrak{K}$.

Since $\mathfrak{G} = \mathfrak{H}\mathfrak{K}$, every element of $\mathfrak{G}$ can be written $g_1 = h_1 k_1$ where h_1 is in $\mathfrak{H}$ and k_1 is in $\mathfrak{K}$. If $\mathfrak{H}$ and $\mathfrak{K}$ have only the identity i in common, then $h_1 k_1 = h_2 k_2$ implies that

$$h_2^{-1} h_1 = k_2 k_1^{-1} = i,$$

so that $h_2 = h_1$ and $k_2 = k_1$. Thus g_1 is uniquely expressible as the product of an element of $\mathfrak{H}$ by one of $\mathfrak{K}$. Then the correspondence

$$g_1 = h_1 k_1 \leftrightarrow (h_1, k_1)$$

is biunique. Suppose also that

$$g_2 = h_2 k_2 \leftrightarrow (h_2, k_2).$$

Then, since $k_1 h_2 = h_2 k_1$,

$$g_1 g_2 = h_1 k_1 h_2 k_2 = h_1 h_2 k_1 k_2 \leftrightarrow (h_1 h_2, k_1 k_2),$$

so that $\mathfrak{G} \cong \mathfrak{H} \times \mathfrak{K}$.

Theorem 28.3. If $\mathfrak{G} = \mathfrak{H} \times \mathfrak{K}$, then $\mathfrak{H}$ and $\mathfrak{K}$ are invariant subgroups of $\mathfrak{G}$ and $\mathfrak{G}/\mathfrak{H} \cong \mathfrak{K}$, $\mathfrak{G}/\mathfrak{K} \cong \mathfrak{H}$.

Let $g = h_i k_j = k_j h_i$ be any element of $\mathfrak{G}$, and let h be any element of $\mathfrak{H}$. Then

$$g^{-1} hg = (h_i k_j)^{-1} h(h_i k_j) = k_j^{-1} h_i^{-1} h h_i k_j = k_j^{-1} h_l k_j.$$

But, since $h_l k_j = k_j h_l$, this gives just h_l. Similarly $\mathfrak{K}$ is an invariant subgroup of $\mathfrak{G}$.

The elements of $\mathfrak{G}/\mathfrak{H}$ are the elements $g = k_j h_i$ taken modulo $\mathfrak{H}$— that is, they are isomorphic with the elements of $\mathfrak{K}$, so that $\mathfrak{G}/\mathfrak{H} \cong \mathfrak{K}$. Similarly $\mathfrak{G}/\mathfrak{K} \cong \mathfrak{H}$.

EXERCISES

1. Prove that the four-group is the direct product of two cyclic groups of order 2.

2. Find the direct product of the four-group and the cyclic group of order 3.

3. The elements of a reduced set of residues modulo 15 form an abelian group with respect to multiplication. Prove that it is the direct product of the group of reduced residues modulo 3 by the group of reduced residues modulo 5.

HINT: The correspondence is given in the proof of Theorem 10.1.

4. State and prove the general theorem exemplified in Ex. 3.

5. Find the direct product of the cyclic group of order 3 with itself.

6. Show that the direct product of commutative groups is commutative.

29. Permutation groups. Let x_1, x_2, x_3, x_4 be four distinct letters. By the symbol

$$p = \begin{pmatrix} 1 & 2 & 3 & 4 \\ 2 & 1 & 4 & 3 \end{pmatrix}$$

we mean the operation of replacing x_1 by x_2, x_2 by x_1, x_3 by x_4, x_4 by x_3. Such an operation is called a *permutation*. Obviously an interchange of the columns of p does not affect it. Thus the effect of p upon

$$f(x_1, x_2, x_3, x_4) = (x_1 - x_2)x_3$$

is to change it into $(x_2 - x_1)x_4$. The effect upon $f = (x_1 - x_2)$ is to change it into $-f$. The permutation p leaves the function

$$(x_1 - x_2)(x_3 - x_4)$$

unaltered.

The result obtained by applying to $f(x_1, x_2, \cdots, x_n)$ two permutations successively can obviously be accomplished by applying a single permutation. This single permutation is called the *product* of the first two permutations.

Thus

$$\begin{pmatrix} 1 & 2 & 3 & 4 \\ 2 & 1 & 4 & 3 \end{pmatrix} \begin{pmatrix} 1 & 2 & 3 & 4 \\ 2 & 3 & 4 & 1 \end{pmatrix} = \begin{pmatrix} 1 & 2 & 3 & 4 \\ 2 & 1 & 4 & 3 \end{pmatrix} \begin{pmatrix} 2 & 1 & 4 & 3 \\ 3 & 2 & 1 & 4 \end{pmatrix}$$

$$= \begin{pmatrix} 1 & 2 & 3 & 4 \\ 3 & 2 & 1 & 4 \end{pmatrix}.$$

This process for forming the product is of general application. Rearrange the columns of the second permutation until its first row is the same as the second row of the first permutation. The product is the permutation whose first row is the first row of the first factor and whose second row is the second row of the second factor.

Since there are but $n!$ distinct arrangements of n letters, it is evident that the set of all permutations on n letters satisfies the first postulate for a group. Since

$$\begin{pmatrix} 1 & 2 & \cdots & n \\ a_1 & a_2 & \cdots & a_n \end{pmatrix} \begin{pmatrix} a_1 & a_2 & \cdots & a_n \\ b_1 & b_2 & \cdots & b_n \end{pmatrix} \begin{pmatrix} b_1 & b_2 & \cdots & b_n \\ c_1 & c_2 & \cdots & c_n \end{pmatrix} = \begin{pmatrix} 1 & 2 & \cdots & n \\ c_1 & c_2 & \cdots & c_n \end{pmatrix}$$

whether the first two or the last two factors are first multiplied, the associative law holds. The identity

$$\begin{pmatrix} 1 & 2 & \cdots & n \\ 1 & 2 & \cdots & n \end{pmatrix}$$

is in the set. The inverse of

$$\begin{pmatrix} a_1 & a_2 & \cdots & a_n \\ b_1 & b_2 & \cdots & b_n \end{pmatrix} \quad \text{is} \quad \begin{pmatrix} b_1 & b_2 & \cdots & b_n \\ a_1 & a_2 & \cdots & a_n \end{pmatrix}.$$

Hence we have proved

Theorem 29.1.   The set of all permutations on n letters form a group of order $n!$.

This group is called the *symmetric group* on n letters, or of order $n!$. Of course the symmetric group of order $n!$ may contain subgroups. For instance, the set

$$\begin{pmatrix} 1 & 2 & 3 \\ 1 & 2 & 3 \end{pmatrix}, \quad \begin{pmatrix} 1 & 2 & 3 \\ 2 & 3 & 1 \end{pmatrix}, \quad \begin{pmatrix} 1 & 2 & 3 \\ 3 & 1 & 2 \end{pmatrix}$$

constitutes a group on three letters of order 3. A permutation group of order n on n letters is *regular*.

The great profusion of substitution groups is indicated by the following theorem of Cayley.

Theorem 29.2.   Every finite group can be represented by a regular substitution group.

Let $\mathfrak{G}$ be any finite group with elements $(a_1, a_2, \cdots, a_n)$. Let a_i be any one of these elements.   Then

$$a_1 a_i, \ a_2 a_i, \ \cdots, \ a_n a_i$$

are all distinct (Theorem 22.3), and hence are the elements $a_1, a_2, \cdots, a_n$ in some order, say

$$a_{i_1}, a_{i_2}, \cdots, a_{i_n}.$$

We shall make the permutation

$$p_i = \begin{pmatrix} 1 & 2 & \cdots & n \\ i_1 & i_2 & \cdots & i_n \end{pmatrix}$$

correspond to the element a_i of $\mathfrak{G}$. The theorem will be proved by showing that this correspondence is an isomorphism.

Let a_j be any element of $\mathfrak{G}$. If $(a_1 a_j, a_2 a_j, \cdots, a_n a_j) = (a_{j_1}, a_{j_2}, \cdots, a_{j_n})$, then corresponding to a_j we have the permutation

$$p_j = \begin{pmatrix} 1 & 2 & \cdots & n \\ j_1 & j_2 & \cdots & j_n \end{pmatrix},$$

which may be written

$$p_j = \begin{pmatrix} i_1 & i_2 & \cdots & i_n \\ k_1 & k_2 & \cdots & k_n \end{pmatrix}$$

by that rearrangement of its columns which puts the order $(1, 2, \cdots, n)$ into the order $(i_1, i_2, \cdots, i_n)$. Hence, if

$$(a_1 a_j, a_2 a_j, \cdots, a_n a_j) = (a_{j_1}, a_{j_2}, \cdots, a_{j_n}),$$

then, by a mere rearrangement,

$$(a_{i_1} a_j, a_{i_2} a_j, \cdots, a_{i_n} a_j) = (a_{k_1}, a_{k_2}, \cdots, a_{k_n}).$$

But this first set is equal to

$$(\overline{a_1 a_i} a_j, \overline{a_2 a_i} a_j, \cdots, \overline{a_n a_i} a_j) = (a_1 \overline{a_i a_j}, a_2 \overline{a_i a_j}, \cdots, a_n \overline{a_i a_j}).$$

Hence $a_i a_j$ corresponds to the permutation

$$\begin{pmatrix} 1 & 2 & \cdots & n \\ k_1 & k_2 & \cdots & k_n \end{pmatrix}.$$

But, by the rule for forming the product of permutations, this is $p_i p_j$.

EXERCISES

1. Represent the cyclic group of order 3 as a regular permutation group.
2. Represent the four-group as a regular permutation group.
3. Show that p_i is the permutation which carries the first column of the multiplication table into the ith.
4. Represent the octic group as a regular permutation group.

5. Represent the alternating group of order 12 as a regular permutation group.

30. Cycles. A permutation which replaces x_{i_1} by x_{i_2}, x_{i_2} by x_{i_3}, $\cdots$ and finally x_{i_k} by x_{i_1}, leaving all other letters unchanged, is called a *cyclic permutation* or *cycle*. Thus

$$\begin{pmatrix} 1 & 2 & 3 & 4 & 5 & 6 \\ 1 & 4 & 2 & 5 & 3 & 6 \end{pmatrix}$$

is a cycle. A much more condensed notation for the above cycle is (2 4 5 3), where it is understood that x_2 is to be replaced by x_4, x_4 by x_5, x_5 by x_3, and x_3 by x_2, while x_1 and x_6 are to remain unchanged.

Theorem 30.1. Every permutation can be written as a product of cycles, no two of which have a letter in common.

Let

$$p = \begin{pmatrix} 1 & 2 & \cdots & n \\ i_1 & i_2 & \cdots & i_n \end{pmatrix}.$$

If $i_1 \neq 1$, find i_1 in the first row of p and let the element under i_1 be j_1. We cannot have $j_1 = i_1$, for i_1 cannot occur twice in the second row of p. If $j_1 = 1$, the cycle $(1, i_1)$ is closed. If $j_1 \neq 1$, find it in the first row of p, and let the element beneath it be k_1. Then k_1 is different from both i_1 and j_1. If $k_1 = 1$, the cycle $(1, i_1, j_1)$ is closed. If $k_1 \neq 1$, continue the process. After at most n steps, the cycle must close.

If the first cycle does not involve all the letters of p which are actually changed, take i_2 as any other letter in the first row of p, and obtain a second cycle. Continue until the letters of p are exhausted. We have, finally, p expressed as a product of cycles involving distinct letters.

Thus the elements of the four-group in this notation are

$$1, \quad (1\ 2)\ (3\ 4), \quad (1\ 3)\ (2\ 4), \quad (1\ 4)\ (2\ 3).$$

A cycle of two letters is called a *transposition*. Thus (1 2) and (5 4) are transpositions.

Theorem 30.2. Every cycle can be written as a product of transpositions in infinitely many ways.

Thus

$$(i_1\ i_2\ i_3\ \cdots\ i_n) = (i_1\ i_2)(i_1\ i_3)\ \cdots\ (i_1\ i_n).$$

Since $(i_p\ i_q)(i_p\ i_q) = 1$, as many pairs of equal transpositions may be multiplied in as one may desire.

Corollary 30.2.   Every permutation can be written as a product of transpositions in infinitely many ways.

Theorem 30.3.   The number of transpositions into which a given permutation can be factored is definitely even or odd.

Consider the function

$$f = \prod_{i < j \,=\, 1}^{n} (x_i - x_j)$$

$$= (x_1 - x_2)(x_1 - x_3)(x_1 - x_4) \cdots (x_1 - x_{n-1})(x_1 - x_n)$$

$$(x_2 - x_3)(x_2 - x_4) \cdots (x_2 - x_{n-1})(x_2 - x_n)$$

$$(x_3 - x_4) \cdots (x_3 - x_{n-1})(x_3 - x_n)$$

$$\cdots \cdots \cdots \cdots \cdots$$

$$(x_{n-2} - x_{n-1})(x_{n-2} - x_n)$$

$$(x_{n-1} - x_n).$$

This may be written

$$f = (x_k - x_l) \prod_{i \neq k,l} (x_i - x_k)(x_i - x_l)F,$$

where F involves neither x_k nor x_l. The transposition $(k\ l)$ has no effect upon F, changes $(x_i - x_k)(x_i - x_l)$ into itself, and changes the sign of $x_k - x_l$. Hence $(k\ l)$ changes f into $-f$.

Let p be any permutation. If p can be factored into an even number of transpositions, the effect of p upon f is to leave it unchanged. If p can be factored into an odd number of transpositions, the effect of p upon f is to change it into $-f$. These possibilities are mutually exclusive.

A permutation is called *even* or *odd* according as it can be factored into an even or odd number of transpositions.

EXERCISES

1. Show that, if a group contains odd permutations, exactly half of its permutations are odd.

2. Show that the even permutations of a group constitute a subgroup.

3. Write each element of the cyclic group of order 3 as a product of transpositions.   Do the same for the four-group.

4. Show that the period of a permutation is the l.c.m. of the periods of its component cycles if no two cycles have a letter in common.

5. Write each element of the octic group as a product of cycles.   Do the same for the alternating group of order 12.

31. Abelian groups.   Let $\mathfrak{G}$ be an abelian group with elements a_1, $a_2, \cdots, a_g$, the period of a_i being α_i.

Theorem 31.1. Every element of $\mathfrak{G}$ is represented the same number of times in the form

$$a_1^{\beta_1} a_2^{\beta_2} \cdots a_g^{\beta_g} \qquad (\beta_i = 0, 1, \cdots, \alpha_i - 1).$$

It is obvious that each of the above products is in $\mathfrak{G}$, and that every element of $\mathfrak{G}$ is represented at least once.

Suppose that the identity i is represented k times. If we multiply each of these representations by any element a, we get k representations for a, all different; for, if two were equal, we could multiply by a^{-1} and see that we had started with identical representations of i. Hence, if a has just l distinct representations, $l \geqq k$.

Multiply each of the l representations for a by one representation for a^{-1}. This gives l representations for i. As before, these are distinct. Thus $k \geqq l$. Hence $k = l$.

Corollary 31.1. $\alpha_1 \alpha_2 \cdots \alpha_g = kg$.

Theorem 31.2. If $\mathfrak{G}$ is abelian of order g, and if p is a prime dividing g, then there exists at least one element of period p.

If $p \mid g$, then $p \mid \alpha_1 \alpha_2 \cdots \alpha_g$ by Corollary 31.1, and hence divides one of the α's, say α_1. Let $\alpha_1 = ph$. Then a_1^h is of period p.

Theorem 31.3. If $g = rs$ where $(r, s) = 1$, then $\mathfrak{G} = \mathfrak{H} \times \mathfrak{K}$ where $\mathfrak{H}$ is of order r and consists of all elements of $\mathfrak{G}$ whose periods divide r, and $\mathfrak{K}$ is of order s and consists of all elements of $\mathfrak{G}$ whose periods divide s.

Let $\mathfrak{H}$ denote the set of all elements $b_1, b_2, \cdots, b_h$ of $\mathfrak{G}$ whose periods divide r, and $\mathfrak{K}$ the set of all elements $c_1, c_2, \cdots, c_k$, whose periods divide s. Then $\mathfrak{H} \wedge \mathfrak{K} = i$, since $(r, s) = 1$.

Step I. $\mathfrak{H}$ and $\mathfrak{K}$ are groups. The period of $b_i b_j$ is a divisor of the l.c.m. of the periods of b_i and b_j. Since r is a common multiple of these periods, it is a multiple of their l.c.m., and so $b_i b_j$ is in $\mathfrak{H}$. The identity is in $\mathfrak{H}$. The period of b_i^{-1} is the period of b_i. Thus $\mathfrak{H}$ is a group. Similarly $\mathfrak{K}$ is a group.

Step II. $(h, s) = (k, r) = 1$. Let p be a prime dividing the order h of $\mathfrak{H}$. By Theorem 31.2, there is an element b_1 in $\mathfrak{H}$ of period p so that $p \mid r$. But $(r, s) = 1$, so that $p \nmid s$. That is, h has no prime factor in common with s, so that $(h, s) = 1$. Similarly $(k, r) = 1$, where k is the order of $\mathfrak{K}$.

Step III. Every element a of $\mathfrak{G}$ is of the form $b_i c_j$. Since $(r, s) = 1$, there are integers x and y such that

$$rx + sy = 1.$$

Then

$$a = a^{rx+sy} = a^{rx} a^{sy}.$$

Now a^{sy} is of period dividing r, since

$$(a^{sy})^r = a^{gy} = 1,$$

and so $a^{sy} \in \mathfrak{H}$. Similarly $a^{rx} \in \mathfrak{K}$. Thus $\mathfrak{G} = \mathfrak{H}\mathfrak{K}$.

Step IV. The b_i and c_j of Step III are unique. For, if

$$a = b_i c_j = b_l c_m,$$

then

$$b_i b_l^{-1} = c_m c_j^{-1}$$

is in both $\mathfrak{H}$ and $\mathfrak{K}$, and so it is i. Then $b_i = b_l$ and $c_m = c_j$.

Step V. $r = h$, $s = k$. Since $g = rs = hk$, $r \mid hk$. Since $(r, k) = 1$ (Step II), $r \mid h$ (Theorem 4.1). Similarly $h \mid r$, so that $r = h$. Then $s = k$.

Now $\mathfrak{G}$ is commutative, and $\mathfrak{G} = \mathfrak{H}\mathfrak{K}$, and $\mathfrak{H} \wedge \mathfrak{K} = i$; therefore, by Theorem 28.2, $\mathfrak{G} = \mathfrak{H} \times \mathfrak{K}$.

Corollary 31.3. *If the abelian group $\mathfrak{G}$ is of order*

$$g = p_1^{\alpha_1} p_2^{\alpha_2} \cdots p_r^{\alpha_r},$$

then

$$\mathfrak{G} = \mathfrak{H}_1 \times \mathfrak{H}_2 \times \cdots \times \mathfrak{H}_r,$$

where $\mathfrak{H}_i$ is of order $p_i^{\alpha_i}$, and consists of all elements of $\mathfrak{G}$ whose periods are powers of p_i.

Theorem 31.4. *Every abelian group $\mathfrak{G}$ is the direct product of cyclic groups.*

We need consider only a group $\mathfrak{H}$ whose order is a power of the prime p. Let p^α be the highest period of any element of $\mathfrak{H}$. We shall make a proof by induction on α.

Let $\alpha = 1$. Every element of $\mathfrak{H}$ except i is of period p. Let a_1 be such an element. Either $\mathfrak{H}$ is cyclic or there is an element a_2 not in the cyclic subgroup $\mathfrak{A}_1$ generated by a_1. The p^2 elements

$$a_1^{i_1} a_2^{i_2} \qquad (i_1, i_2 = 0, 1, \cdots, p - 1)$$

are all distinct, for if they were not, there would be a relation

$$a_2^r = a_1^s, \qquad\qquad (r, p) = 1.$$

If t is the reciprocal of r modulo p, we should have

$$a_2 = a_1^{st},$$

whereas a_2 is not in $\mathfrak{A}_1$. If the p^2 elements $a_1^{i_1} a_2^{i_2}$ do not exhaust $\mathfrak{H}$, let

a_3 be another element not of this form. We can show similarly that

$$a_1^{i_1}a_2^{i_2}a_3^{i_3} \qquad (i_1, i_2, i_3 = 0, 1, \cdots, p-1)$$

are all distinct. Eventually (see Theorem 28.2) we have $\mathfrak{H}$ represented as a direct product of cyclic groups.

We now assume the theorem for every abelian group $\mathfrak{K}$ the highest period of any of whose elements is $p^{\alpha-1}$. Such a group is $\mathfrak{K}$, which consists of the pth powers of the elements of $\mathfrak{H}$. Let

$$\mathfrak{K} = \mathfrak{K}_1 \times \mathfrak{K}_2 \times \cdots \times \mathfrak{K}_r,$$

where $\mathfrak{K}_i$ is a cyclic group of order m_i. Let k_i be a generator of $\mathfrak{K}_i$, and let

$$k_i = h_i^p, \qquad\qquad h_i \in \mathfrak{H}.$$

The period of h_i is $n_i = pm_i$.

Suppose that a relation

$$h_1^{i_1}h_2^{i_2} \cdots h_r^{i_r} = h_1^{j_1}h_2^{j_2} \cdots h_r^{j_r}$$

existed with some $i_t \neq j_t$. We should have

$$h_1^{x_1}h_2^{x_2} \cdots h_r^{x_r} = i$$

with some x_t between 0 and n_t. If $p \mid x_t$ for every t, say $x_t = py_t$, we should have

$$k_1^{y_1}k_2^{y_2} \cdots k_r^{y_r} = i$$

with some y_t between 0 and m_t, which is not possible. Hence some x_t, say x_1, is prime to p. Then

$$(h_1^{x_1}h_2^{x_2} \cdots h_r^{x_r})^p = k_1^{x_1}k_2^{x_2} \cdots k_r^{x_r} = i,$$

which also is not possible. Hence $i_t = j_t$ for every t, and (see Theorem 28.2)

$$\mathfrak{H} \supseteq \mathfrak{H}_1 \times \mathfrak{H}_2 \times \cdots \times \mathfrak{H}_r = \mathfrak{M},$$

where $\mathfrak{H}_i$ is cyclic of order n_i.

If $\mathfrak{H} \supset \mathfrak{M}$, there is an element b in $\mathfrak{H}$ not in $\mathfrak{M}$. But $b^p = c$ is in $\mathfrak{K}$, and so is c^{-1}. Let

$$c^{-1} = k_1^{l_1}k_2^{l_2} \cdots k_r^{l_r} = (h_1^{l_1}h_2^{l_2} \cdots h_r^{l_r})^p = d^p$$

where $d \in \mathfrak{M}$. Now

$$(bd)^p = b^p d^p = cc^{-1} = i.$$

Since b is not in $\mathfrak{M}$ and d is in $\mathfrak{M}$, $bd \neq i$, so bd is of period p. Also no power of bd less than the pth is in $\mathfrak{M}$, for then bd would be in $\mathfrak{M}$ and hence b also. Then bd generates a cyclic subgroup $\mathfrak{H}_{r+1}$ of $\mathfrak{H}$ such that

$$\mathfrak{H} \supseteq \mathfrak{H}_1 \times \mathfrak{H}_2 \times \cdots \times \mathfrak{H}_r \times \mathfrak{H}_{r+1} = \mathfrak{M}_1.$$

We continue this process until no more elements lie outside our $\mathfrak{M}_s$, and

$$\mathfrak{H} = \mathfrak{H}_1 \times \mathfrak{H}_2 \times \cdots \times \mathfrak{H}_r \times \cdots \times \mathfrak{H}_{r+s},$$

where each $\mathfrak{H}_i$ is cyclic.

EXERCISES

1. Prove that a cyclic group of order n has $\varphi(n)$ generators.

2. If $d \mid n$, where n is the order of a cyclic group, show that there are exactly $\varphi(d)$ elements of period d.

3. Prove Theorem 10.3 by group theory.

4. The least positive residues modulo 15 form a cyclic group under addition. Express it as a direct product of groups of orders 5 and 3.

5. Show that the number pairs (a, b), a taken modulo m and b taken modulo n, form a group isomorphic with the direct product of the cyclic groups of orders m and n, the group operation being addition, defined as follows:

$$(a, b) + (c, d) = (a + c, b + d).$$

6. Show that the direct product of two cyclic groups of relatively prime orders is cyclic.

7. Carry through the proof of Theorem 31.4 with the group given in Ex. 5 of § 28.

32. The basis. Elements $a_1, a_2, \cdots, a_r$ are called a *basis* for the abelian group $\mathfrak{G}$ if their periods $n_1, n_2, \cdots, n_r$ are powers of prime numbers and if every element of the group is uniquely expressible in the form

$$a = a_1^{\alpha_1} a_2^{\alpha_2} \cdots a_r^{\alpha_r}, \quad (\alpha_i = 0, 1, 2, \cdots, n_i - 1).$$

The fundamental theorem of abelian group theory is

Theorem 32.1.   Every abelian group has a basis.

This theorem is actually a corollary of Theorem 31.4, the a_i being generators of the cyclic groups composing $\mathfrak{G}$.

The numbers $n_1, n_2, \cdots, n_r$ are called the *invariants* of the abelian group.

Theorem 32.2.   The invariants are uniquely determined for the group and are independent of the basis chosen.

If the order g of $\mathfrak{G}$ is written as a product of prime powers, $\mathfrak{G}$ is a direct product of groups of these prime power orders (Corollary 31.3). Thus the theorem will be proved in general if we can prove it when g is a power of a prime p.

Let $a_1, a_2, \cdots, a_r$ and $b_1, b_2, \cdots, b_s$ be bases for the same group, and let $m_1, m_2, \cdots, m_r$ and $n_1, n_2, \cdots, n_s$ be their corresponding periods.

Assume the basis elements so ordered that $n_1 \geqq n_2 \geqq \cdots \geqq n_s$, and $m_1 \geqq m_2 \geqq \cdots \geqq m_r$. All these m's and n's divide g; therefore, they are powers of p. Let n_i be the first of the n's which differs from the corresponding m_i, if there be such a one, so that

$$n_1 = m_1, \quad n_2 = m_2, \cdots, n_{i-1} = m_{i-1}, \quad n_i \neq m_i.$$

It is a matter of notation to assume $n_i > m_i$.

The m_ith powers of all elements of $\mathfrak{G}$ form a group having as basis the m_ith powers of any basis of $\mathfrak{G}$. From its manner of formation, this group is independent of the basis. On the one hand, the elements

$$a_1^{m_i}, a_2^{m_i}, \cdots, a_r^{m_i}$$

form a basis. Now a_1 is of period m_1, and every m is a power of p. If $m_i \mid m_1$, then $a_1^{m_i}$ is of period m_1/m_i, while if $m_1 \mid m_i$, $a_1^{m_i}$ is of period 1. Hence the order of the subgroup is

$$\frac{m_1}{m_i} \frac{m_2}{m_i} \cdots \frac{m_i}{m_i}.$$

Similarly the order of the same subgroup with basis $b_1^{m_i}, b_2^{m_i}, \cdots, b_s^{m_i}$ is at least

$$\frac{n_1}{m_i} \frac{n_2}{m_i} \cdots \frac{n_i}{m_i},$$

which exceeds the previous value since $n_i > m_i$. Thus there is no such i that $n_i \neq m_i$.

Theorem 32.3. Two groups with the same invariants are isomorphic.

If two groups $\mathfrak{G}_1$ and $\mathfrak{G}_2$ have the same invariants $n_1, n_2, \cdots, n_r$, we can write

$$\mathfrak{G}_1 = \mathfrak{A}_1 \times \mathfrak{A}_2 \times \cdots \times \mathfrak{A}_r, \quad \mathfrak{G}_2 = \mathfrak{B}_1 \times \mathfrak{B}_2 \times \cdots \times \mathfrak{B}_r,$$

where $\mathfrak{A}_i$ and $\mathfrak{B}_i$ are both cyclic groups of the same order n_i, so that by Ex. 5, § 24, $\mathfrak{A}_i \cong \mathfrak{B}_i$. Since the direct product is unique, $\mathfrak{G}_1 \cong \mathfrak{G}_2$.

Since the direct product of abelian groups is independent of the order of the components, the order in which the invariants are written is immaterial.

Since an abelian group is completely determined by its invariants, the group is customarily named by giving its invariants. Thus $(2, 2)$ is the four-group, while (2^2) is the cyclic group of order 4. The cyclic group of order 36 is denoted by $(2^2, 3^2)$, while the other abelian groups of order 36 are $(2^2, 3, 3)$, $(2, 2, 3^2)$, and $(2, 2, 3, 3)$.

EXERCISES

1. List the abelian groups of order 108.

2. Let $n_1, n_2, \cdots, n_r$ be powers of primes. Show that the abelian group $(n_1, n_2, \cdots, n_r)$ exists. HINT: Cf. Ex. 5, § 24, and Ex. 6, § 28.

3. Prove Ex. 2 by considering the sets of integers $(x_1, x_2, \cdots, x_r)$, where x_i ranges over all residues modulo n_i, the group operation being addition. Cf. Ex. 5, § 31.

4. Show that the factors of composition of an abelian group are primes.

SUGGESTED READINGS

MATHEWSON, L. C. *Elementary Theory of Finite Groups.* Houghton Mifflin, 1930.

CARMICHAEL, R. D. *Introduction to the Theory of Groups of Finite Order.* Ginn, 1937.

MILLER, G. A., BLICHFELDT, H. F., and DICKSON, L. E. *Theory and Applications of Finite Groups*, Parts I and II. Wiley, 1916.

NETTO, E., trans. by COLE, F. N. *The Theory of Substitutions and Its Applications to Algebra*, Part I. Wahr, Ann Arbor, 1892.

BURNSIDE, W. *Theory of Groups of Finite Order.* Cambridge University Press, 1911.

SPEISER, A. *Theorie der Gruppen von endlicher Ordnung.* Springer, Berlin, 1937.

VAN DER WAERDEN, B. L. *Moderne Algebra*, Vol. I, Chapter II. Springer, Berlin, 1937.

ZASSENHAUS, H. *Lehrbuch der Gruppentheorie.* Teubner, Leipzig, 1937.

CHAPTER III

ALGEBRAIC FIELDS

33. Abstract fields. A field is a mathematical system of greater complexity than a group, but one which is of great importance.

A *field* $\mathfrak{F}$ is a mathematical system composed of elements $a, b, \cdots$, an equals relation, and two well-defined operations, *addition* ($+$) and *multiplication* ($\times$), relative to which $\mathfrak{F}$ is closed, defined by the postulates:

A. The elements constitute an abelian group relative to the operation $+$, the identity element being denoted by z, and the inverse of a by ^-a.

M. The elements with z omitted constitute an abelian group relative to the operation $\times$, the identity element being denoted by i and the inverse of a by a^{-1}.

D. Multiplication is distributive with respect to addition. That is,

$$a \times (b + c) = a \times b + a \times c$$

for every a, b, c in $\mathfrak{F}$.

The five postulates for an abelian group (see § 21) which define the addition group of $\mathfrak{F}$ will be denoted by A_1, A_2, A_3, A_4, A_5. The postulates defining the multiplication group will be denoted by $M_1, \cdots, M_5$. Thus, counting D, a field is actually defined by eleven postulates.

The behavior of z relative to multiplication is not given by M, but we shall find that it is implicitly defined by A and D.

Theorem 33.1. A product is equal to z if and only if at least one of the factors is equal to z.

By A_3, $b = b + z$ for every b. Hence by D,

$$ab + z = ab = a(b + z) = ab + az$$

for every a. Then, applying Theorem 22.3 to the additive group, we have $az = z$ for every a.

If $a \neq z$ and $b \neq z$, then ab is in the multiplicative group and hence is $\neq z$. Thus if $ab = z$, at least one of a and b must be outside the multiplicative group and hence be z.

79

The theorems of § 22 may now be interpreted as theorems on fields. Thus if $a + a + \cdots + a$ to n summands be written na, and if $a \times a \times \cdots \times a$ to n factors be written a^n, we have

Theorem 33.2. The expressions na and a^n, where n is a positive integer, are well defined.

By Corollary 22.1, na is well defined, and a^n for $a \neq z$ is well defined. But $z^n = z$ for all manners of grouping, by Theorem 33.1.

Theorem 33.3.   The identities z and i are unique.

This follows from Theorem 22.2.

Theorem 33.4.   If $a + b = a + c$, then $b = c$.   If $ab = ac$ and $a \neq z$, then $b = c$.

The first part of this theorem follows from Theorem 22.3, and also the second part if $b \neq z$ and $c \neq z$.   If $b = z$, then $ab = z$ (Theorem 33.1); and if $ac = z$, $a \neq z$, then $c = z$ (also by Theorem 33.1), so that in this case also $b = c$.

Theorem 33.5.   The inverse ^-a is unique.   If $a \neq z$, the inverse a^{-1} is unique.

This comes from Corollary 22.31.

Theorem 33.6.   The equation $a + x = b$ has a unique solution. If $a \neq z$, the equation $ax = b$ has a unique solution.

The first statement, and the second statement with $b \neq z$, follow from Corollary 22.32.   If $b = z$ and $a \neq z$, then x has the unique value z by Theorem 33.1.

Theorem 33.7. $^-(^-a) = a$.   If $a \neq z$, $(a^{-1})^{-1} = a$.

These come from Theorem 22.4.

Theorem 33.8. $^-(a + b) = {}^-a + {}^-b$.   If $a \neq z$ and $b \neq z$, $(a \times b)^{-1} = a^{-1} \times b^{-1}$.

This comes from Theorem 22.5 and the commutative laws.

As in § 22, if m is a positive integer we define $(^-m)a$ to mean $^-(ma)$, and write it ^-ma. We define $0 \times a$ to mean z. Where $a \neq z$ we define a^{-m} to mean $(a^m)^{-1}$ and a^0 to mean i. Then by Corollary 22.5 we have

Theorem 33.9. $^-(ma) = m(^-a) = {}^-ma$.   If $a \neq z$, $(a^m)^{-1} = (a^{-1})^m = a^{-m}$.

Theorem 33.10. *If m and n are rational integers,*

$$ma + na = (m + n)a, \quad a^m \times a^n = a^{m+n}.$$

The first equation, and the second equation for $a \neq z$, follow from Theorem 22.6. If $a = z$, the second equation follows from Theorem 33.1.

Theorem 33.11. *If m and n are rational integers,*

$$n(ma) = (nm)a, \quad (a^m)^n = a^{mn}.$$

The first equation, and the second equation for $a \neq z$, follow from Theorem 22.7. If $a = z$, the second equation follows from Theorem 33.1.

Theorem 33.12. *If n is a rational integer,*

$$na + nb = n(a + b), \quad a^n \times b^n = (a \times b)^n.$$

These follow from Theorems 22.8 and 33.1.

Theorem 33.13. *If m and n are rational integers,*

$$ma \times nb = mn(a \times b).$$

If m and n are positive,

$$ma \times nb = (a + a + \cdots + a) \times (b + b + \cdots + b)$$
$$= a \times (b + b + \cdots + b) + \cdots$$
$$+ a \times (b + b + \cdots + b)$$
$$= a \times b + a \times b + \cdots + a \times b + \cdots$$
$$+ a \times b + a \times b + \cdots + a \times b = mn(a \times b)$$

by D.

If $m < 0$, $ma = (^-m)(^-a)$, where ^-m is positive, and the proof is as before with ^-a's instead of a's. Similarly for n negative, or for both m and n negative. If $m = 0$, $ma = z$ by definition, so that both sides of the stated equation reduce to z by Theorem 33.1.

EXERCISES

1. Show that the rational numbers form a field.
2. Show that, if p is a prime, the rational integers modulo p form a field.
3. Show that the set of all numbers $a + b\sqrt{2}$ where a and b are rational form a field.
4. Which of the following are fields?
   (a) The real numbers.
   (b) The complex numbers.

(c) The rational integers modulo 12.

(d) The rational integers.

(e) The numbers $a + b\sqrt{2}$ where a and b are rational integers.

34. Quadratic fields. The present development of algebraic fields is mainly from the intuitive point of view to give the reader a background for a more abstract approach to come later (§ 78).

Let

(34.1) $$px^2 + qx + r = 0, \qquad p \neq 0,$$

be a quadratic equation with rational coefficients which does not have a rational root. Let ρ be one of its irrational roots. Denote by $Ra(\rho)$ the set of numbers $a + b\rho$ where a and b range over the rational field Ra.

Theorem 34.1. There exists a rational integer m without a repeated prime factor such that $Ra(\rho) = Ra(\sqrt{m})$.

We can assume that p, q, r in (34.1) are rational integers. This does not alter ρ. Let $m_1 = q^2 - 4pr$. Then

$$\rho = \frac{-q \pm \sqrt{m_1}}{2p}, \qquad \sqrt{m_1} = \pm\,(2p\rho + q).$$

The first equation shows that every number of the form $a + b\rho$ is of the form $c + d\sqrt{m_1}$. The second equation shows that every number of the form $a_1 + b_1\sqrt{m_1}$ is of the form $c_1 + d_1\rho$. Then $Ra(\rho) = Ra(\sqrt{m_1})$.

Now set $m_1 = l^2 m$, where m has no square factor. Then

$$a + b\sqrt{m_1} = a + bl\sqrt{m}.$$

As before, $Ra(\sqrt{m_1}) = Ra(\sqrt{m})$.

Theorem 34.2. The set $Ra(\rho)$ is a field.

That these numbers form an abelian group relative to addition is evident. Since the set $Ra(\rho)$ is contained in the complex field, the distributive law holds, and also the associative and commutative laws of multiplication. It is evident that 1 is the identity element of multiplication and is in $Ra(\rho)$. We need to prove: (a) that the product of two numbers of $Ra(\rho)$ is in $Ra(\rho)$; and (b) that every number except 0 in $Ra(\rho)$ has its reciprocal in $Ra(\rho)$.

Proof of (a):

$$(a_1 + b_1\sqrt{m})(a_2 + b_2\sqrt{m}) = (a_1a_2 + b_1b_2m) + (a_1b_2 + a_2b_1)\sqrt{m}.$$

Proof of (b):

$$\frac{1}{a + b\sqrt{m}} = \frac{a - b\sqrt{m}}{a^2 - b^2m}.$$

If $a^2 - b^2m = 0$, then either $b = 0$, $a = 0$ and $a + b\sqrt{m} = 0$, or else $b \neq 0$, $\sqrt{m} = \pm a/b$, and $\sqrt{m}$ is rational. Then ρ is rational, contrary to assumption.

Theorem 34.3. All quadratic fields are of the type $Ra(\sqrt{m})$, where m is an integer with distinct prime factors. If $m_1 \neq m_2$, then $Ra(\sqrt{m_1}) \neq Ra(\sqrt{m_2})$. *

That $Ra(\sqrt{m})$ is a field follows from Theorem 34.2. That there are no other quadratic fields follows from Theorem 34.1. To show that they are distinct, assume that

$$\sqrt{m_1} = a + b\sqrt{m_2}.$$

Then

$$m_1 = a^2 + b^2m_2 + 2ab\sqrt{m_2}.$$

If $ab \neq 0$, then $\sqrt{m_2}$ is rational, contrary to assumption. If $b = 0$, $\sqrt{m_1}$ is rational. Hence $a = 0$. Then

$$m_1 = b^2m_2.$$

Let $b = r/s$, where r and s are relatively prime integers. Then

$$s^2m_1 = r^2m_2.$$

Since r^2 is prime to s^2, $r^2 \mid m_1$. Since m_1 has no repeated prime factor, $r = \pm 1$, $r^2 = 1$. Similarly $s^2 = 1$, $m_1 = m_2$.

EXERCISES

1. If (34.1) is $3x^2 + 2x + 1 = 0$, find m.
2. If $\rho_1 = a + b\rho$, where ρ and ρ_1 are quadratic irrationalities, show that $Ra(\rho_1) = Ra(\rho)$.
3. Is it possible for one quadratic field to be properly contained in another? Prove.
4. Prove that the intersection of two distinct quadratic fields is the rational field.

35. Automorphisms of quadratic fields. Let $\alpha = a + b\sqrt{m}$ be any number of $Ra(\sqrt{m})$. Then α satisfies the equation

$$(35.1) \qquad (x - a)^2 - b^2m = x^2 - 2ax + a^2 - b^2m = 0.$$

That is,

Theorem 35.1. Every number of $Ra(\sqrt{m})$ satisfies a quadratic equation with rational coefficients.

* This justifies the statement, commonly given without proof in elementary algebra, that dissimilar quadratic surds cannot equal each other.

The equation (35.1) is called the *principal equation* of $\alpha = a + b\sqrt{m}$. Its constant term

$$N(a + b\sqrt{m}) = a^2 - b^2 m$$

is called the *norm* of $a + b\sqrt{m}$, and the negative of the coefficient of x,

$$T(a + b\sqrt{m}) = 2a,$$

is called the *trace* of $a + b\sqrt{m}$.

Two fields are said to be *isomorphic* if there exists a biunique correspondence between their elements which is an isomorphism with respect to both addition and multiplication. An isomorphism of a field with itself is called an *automorphism*.

Theorem 35.2. The rational field Ra has no automorphism except the identity.

Let $a \leftrightarrow a'$ be an automorphism of the rational field. Since $a \cdot 1 = a$ for every a, it follows that $a' \cdot 1' = a'$ for every a'. Hence $1' = 1$, since the identity is unique (Theorem 33.3.).

Let a be any integer. Then

$$a' = 1' + 1' + \cdots + 1' = 1 + 1 + \cdots + 1 = a,$$

and so, if $a' \leftrightarrow a$ is an automorphism, $a' = a$.

Let $aa^{-1} = 1$. Then $a'(a^{-1})' = 1' = 1$. By Theorem 33.5, $(a')^{-1} = (a^{-1})'$. Similarly $0' = 0$, $(-a)' = -a'$, so that $a \leftrightarrow a'$ implies $a = a'$ for every rational integer a.

Finally, let p/q be any number of Ra. If $p/q \leftrightarrow (p/q)'$ is an automorphism, then

$$(p/q)' = p'(1/q)' = p'/q' = p/q.$$

Theorem 35.3. The correspondence

$$a + b\sqrt{m} \leftrightarrow a - b\sqrt{m}$$

is the only automorphism of $Ra(\sqrt{m})$ other than the identity.

Since

$$(a + b\sqrt{m}) + (c + d\sqrt{m}) = (a + c) + (b + d)\sqrt{m},$$
$$(a - b\sqrt{m}) + (c - d\sqrt{m}) = (a + c) - (b + d)\sqrt{m},$$

the correspondence is an automorphism relative to addition. Since

$$(a + b\sqrt{m}) \times (c + d\sqrt{m}) = ac + bdm + (ad + bc)\sqrt{m},$$
$$(a - b\sqrt{m}) \times (c - d\sqrt{m}) = ac + bdm - (ad + bc)\sqrt{m},$$

the correspondence is an automorphism relative to multiplication.

If $\alpha \leftrightarrow \alpha'$ is an automorphism, it follows from (35.1) that

$$\alpha'^2 - 2'a'\alpha' + a'^2 - b'^2m' = 0.$$

By Theorem 35.2 this means

$$\alpha'^2 - 2a\alpha' + a^2 - b^2m = 0.$$

Hence the only possible automorphism other than the identity is a correspondence between the two roots of (35.1)—that is,

$$a + b\sqrt{m} \leftrightarrow a - b\sqrt{m}.$$

The number $\bar{\alpha} = a - b\sqrt{m}$ is called the *conjugate* of $\alpha = a + b\sqrt{m}$. Note that α is also the conjugate of $\bar{\alpha}$, so that $\bar{\bar{\alpha}} = \alpha$. A number of Ra is its own conjugate. The product of two conjugate numbers is the norm of each, and the sum of two conjugate numbers is the trace of each.

Corollary 35.3. The conjugate of the sum (product) of two numbers of $Ra(\sqrt{m})$ is equal to the sum (product) of the conjugates.

This is merely the statement that $\alpha \leftrightarrow \bar{\alpha}$ is an isomorphism.

Theorem 35.4. The norm of the product of two numbers of $Ra(\sqrt{m})$ is equal to the product of their norms. The trace of a sum is equal to the sum of their traces.

For if $\alpha = \beta\gamma$, then, by Corollary 35.3,

$$N(\alpha) = \alpha\bar{\alpha} = \beta\gamma\overline{\beta\gamma} = \beta\gamma\bar{\beta}\bar{\gamma} = \beta\bar{\beta}\gamma\bar{\gamma} = N(\beta)N(\gamma).$$

Similarly, if $\alpha = \beta + \gamma$, $T(\alpha) = T(\beta) + T(\gamma)$.

Theorem 35.5. $N(\alpha) = 0$ if and only if $\alpha = 0$.

This follows as in the proof of Theorem 34.2, Step (b).

EXERCISES

1. If α is a root of $x^2 + px + q = 0$, the other root is $\theta(\alpha) = -p - \alpha$. Show that $\theta(\alpha)$ generates the cyclic group of order 2, the operation being substitution for α.

2. Let $a + b\sqrt{m} \leftrightarrow a - b\sqrt{m} = a' + b'\sqrt{m}$. The automorphism is then expressed as a transformation

$$a' = a, \qquad b' = -b,$$

of matrix

$$A = \begin{bmatrix} 1 & 0 \\ 0 & -1 \end{bmatrix}$$

on the coördinates of the numbers. Show that A generates the cyclic group of order 2, the operation being matric multiplication.

3. Show that (35.1) is reducible when and only when α is in Ra, and in that case it is a perfect square.

4. If $\mathfrak{F}$ is any field containing the rational field Ra as a subfield, prove that every automorphism of $\mathfrak{F}$ leaves every number of Ra unchanged.

36. Cubic fields. A polynomial $f(x)$ with coefficients in a field $\mathfrak{F}$ is said to be *reducible* in $\mathfrak{F}$ if it can be written as a product of two polynomials, each with coefficients in $\mathfrak{F}$ and of degree $\geqq 1$. If it cannot be so written, it is called *irreducible* in $\mathfrak{F}$.

Theorem 36.1. If $x^3 + ax^2 + bx + c = 0$ is irreducible in the rational field Ra, each of its roots ρ defines a field $Ra(\rho)$.

Such a field is called a *cubic field.*

Since the coefficient of x^2 can be made 0 by a linear substitution, there is no loss of generality in assuming that the cubic has been reduced to the form

$$(36.1) \qquad f(x) = x^3 + px + q = 0.$$

Let ρ be a root of (36.1). The numbers

$$(36.2) \qquad \alpha = a_0 + a_1\rho + a_2\rho^2,$$

where a_0, a_1, a_2 range over Ra, constitute a field, as we shall show.

That the set (36.2) form a group under addition is evident. Since

$$(36.3) \qquad \rho^3 = -p\rho - q,$$

the set is closed under multiplication. The only property of fields which is not immediate is the existence of the reciprocal.

Define

$$g(x) = a_0 + a_1x + a_2x^2$$

so that $g(\rho) = \alpha$. We shall suppose that $\alpha \neq 0$ so that $g(x)$ is not zero. Since $f(x)$ is irreducible and $g(x)$ is of degree < 3, they are relatively prime. By the Euclid algorithm * we can determine polynomials $A(x)$ and $B(x)$ with rational coefficients such that

$$f(x) \cdot A(x) + g(x) \cdot B(x) = 1.$$

Since $f(\rho) = 0$,

$$g(\rho) \cdot B(\rho) = \alpha \cdot B(\rho) = 1.$$

That is, $B(\rho)$ is the reciprocal of α.

---

* See, for instance, H. B. Fine, *A College Algebra*, Ginn, 1901, p. 208; or L. Weisner, *Introduction to the Theory of Equations*, Macmillan, 1938, p. 30.

Theorem 36.2.   Every number of $Ra(\rho)$ satisfies a cubic equation with rational coefficients.

Let $\alpha = a_0 + a_1\rho + a_2\rho^2$.   Then, using (36.3),

$$\rho\alpha = -qa_2 + (a_0 - pa_2)\rho + a_1\rho^2,$$

$$\rho^2\alpha = -qa_1 + (-pa_1 - qa_2)\rho + (a_0 - pa_2)\rho^2.$$

The system of equations

$$a_0 - \alpha \qquad\qquad + a_1\rho \qquad\qquad + a_2\rho^2 = 0,$$

$$-qa_2 + (a_0 - pa_2 - \alpha)\rho \qquad\qquad + a_1\rho^2 = 0,$$

$$-qa_1 + (-pa_1 - qa_2)\rho + (a_0 - pa_2 - \alpha)\rho^2 = 0$$

obviously has the solution $(1, \rho, \rho^2) \neq (0, 0, 0)$, which can happen only when the determinant

$$(36.4) \qquad \begin{vmatrix} a_0 - \alpha & a_1 & a_2 \\ -qa_2 & a_0 - pa_2 - \alpha & a_1 \\ -qa_1 & -pa_1 - qa_2 & a_0 - pa_2 - \alpha \end{vmatrix} = 0.$$

This equation of degree 3 in α is called the *principal equation* of α. Its constant term (obtained by setting $\alpha = 0$ in the left member of (36.4)) is called the *norm* $N(\alpha)$ of α, and the coefficient of α^2 is called the *trace*,

$$T(\alpha) = 3a_0 - 2pa_2.$$

Let ρ, ρ', ρ'' be the three roots of (36.1). They are distinct, since otherwise (36.1) would be reducible. Define

$$\alpha = a_0 + a_1\rho + a_2\rho^2,$$

$$\alpha' = a_0 + a_1\rho' + a_2\rho'^2,$$

$$\alpha'' = a_0 + a_1\rho'' + a_2\rho''^2$$

as a *set of conjugates*. It is evident that they are the three roots of (36.4), since the only identity used in deriving (36.4) was (36.3), which is also satisfied by ρ' and ρ''. Hence conjugate numbers have the same trace and the same norm.

Theorem 36.3.   The fields $Ra(\rho)$, $Ra(\rho')$, $Ra(\rho'')$ are isomorphic. These are the only fields isomorphic with $Ra(\rho)$.

It is evident that the correspondences

$$\alpha \leftrightarrow \alpha', \quad \alpha \leftrightarrow \alpha''$$

are isomorphisms under addition. If also $\beta \leftrightarrow \beta'$, then $\alpha\beta$ is formed by multiplying the polynomial α by the polynomial β and replacing ρ^3 by $-p\rho - q$ until a polynomial of degree < 3 in ρ is obtained. Since also $\rho'^3 = -p\rho' - q$, the product $\alpha'\beta'$ may be obtained by using this relation on the product of the polynomials α' and β', or by replacing ρ by ρ' in the reduced product $\alpha\beta$. That is,

$$(\alpha\beta)' = \alpha'\beta',$$

so that the correspondence is an isomorphism relative to multiplication.

If $\mathfrak{F}$ is a cubic field isomorphic with $Ra(\rho)$, it contains a number $\bar{\rho}$ corresponding to ρ and every number of $\mathfrak{F}$ is a polynomial in $\bar{\rho}$. Then $\bar{\rho}$ is a root of (36.1) and is either ρ, ρ', or ρ''. Hence $\mathfrak{F} = Ra(\rho)$, $Ra(\rho')$, or $Ra(\rho'')$.

An essential point of difference now appears between the quadratic and cubic fields. Although every isomorphism of a quadratic field is an automorphism, the same is not true of cubic fields. Usually the three fields $Ra(\rho)$, $Ra(\rho')$, $Ra(\rho'')$ are distinct fields, having only the rational field Ra in common. There are certain cubic fields, however, which coincide with their conjugate fields. Such fields are called *normal*. Normal cubic fields are also called *cyclic*, for a reason to appear later.

EXERCISES

1. Show that (36.4) reduces to a perfect cube when α is in Ra.

2. Show that every cubic field is defined by an equation $x^3 + px + q = 0$, where p and q are rational integers, $q > 0$, such that there exists no rational integer $k \neq \pm 1$ such that $k^2 \mid p$, $k^3 \mid q$.

3. Find the reciprocal of $1 + \rho^2$ in the field defined by $x^3 - 3x + 1 = 0$.

4. (a) Find the principal equation of α in the field of Ex. 3. (b) Find by the method of proof of Theorem 36.2 the principal equation of $2 + \rho - \rho^2$ in this field, and check by (a).

37. Cyclic cubic fields. If ρ is one root of

$$(37.1) \qquad f(x) = x^3 + px + q = 0,$$

then by division

$$f(x) = (x - \rho)(x^2 + \rho x + p + \rho^2) = 0,$$

so that ρ' and ρ'' are the zeros of the second factor of $f(x)$. The field $Ra(\rho)$ is normal if and only if this factor is the product of two numbers of $Ra(\rho)$—that is, if and only if the discriminant

$$\rho^2 - 4(p + \rho^2) = -4p - 3\rho^2$$

is the square of a number $a_0 + a_1\rho + a_2\rho^2$ of $Ra(\rho)$. If we set

$$-4p - 3\rho^2 = (a_0 + a_1\rho + a_2\rho^2)^2,$$

expand, and make use of (36.3), we have a quadratic polynomial in ρ, with rational coefficients, equal to 0. Since ρ satisfies no quadratic equation with rational coefficients, each coefficient must be 0. That is,

$$a_1^2 + 2a_0a_2 - a_2^2p + 3 = 0,$$
(37.2)
$$2a_0a_1 - a_2^2q - 2a_1a_2p = 0,$$
$$a_0^2 - 2a_1a_2q + 4p = 0.$$

Since $(p, q, 1)$ is a solution $\neq (0, 0, 0)$ of this system, it must be true that

$$\begin{vmatrix} -a_2^2 & 0 & a_1^2 + 2a_0a_2 + 3 \\ -2a_1a_2 & -a_2^2 & 2a_0a_1 \\ 4 & -2a_1a_2 & a_0^2 \end{vmatrix} = 0,$$

or

$$a_2^2(2a_1^2 + a_0a_2 + 2)(2a_1^2 + a_0a_2 + 6) = 0.$$

Thus there are three cases to be considered according as the first, second, or third factor vanishes.

Case I: $a_2 = 0$. Then the first equation of (37.2) reduces to $a_1^2 + 3 = 0$, so that a_1 is not rational. Thus this case does not occur.

Case II: $2a_1^2 + a_0a_2 + 2 = 0$. Then equations (37.2) reduce to

$$a_2^2 p = -3a_1^2 - 1, \quad a_2^3q = 2a_1^3 - 2a_1,$$

so that

$$a_2^3(x^3 + px + q) = a_2^3x^3 - (3a_1^2 + 1)a_2x + 2a_1^3 - 2a_1$$
$$= (a_2x + 2a_1)(a_2x - a_1 + 1)(a_2x - a_1 - 1).$$

Since $f(x)$ is irreducible, this case is excluded.

Case III: $2a_1^2 + a_0a_2 + 6 = 0$. From the first equation of (37.2),

$$a_2^2p = 3 + a_1^2 + 2a_0a_2 = -3(a_1^2 + 3);$$

and, from the second equation of (37.2),

$$a_2^3 q = a_2(2a_0a_1 - 2a_1a_2p) = 2a_1(a_1^2 + 3).$$

Let $r = a_1/a_2$ and $s = 1/a_2$. Then

$$p = -3\left(\frac{a_1^2}{a_2^2} + \frac{3}{a_2^2}\right) = -3(r^2 + 3s^2),$$

$$q = 2r(r^2 + 3s^2).$$

Thus (37.1) becomes

$$(37.3) \qquad x^3 - 3(r^2 + 3s^2)x + 2r(r^2 + 3s^2) = 0,$$

and we have

Theorem 37.1. *Every normal cubic field is defined by a root of an equation (37.3) where r and s are rational parameters, $s \neq 0$. Conversely, (37.3) defines a normal cubic field if it is irreducible.*

Clearly $a_2 = 1/s$, $a_1 = a_2 r = r/s$, and from the equation defining Case III,

$$a_0 a_2 = - 6 - 2a_1^2.$$

Hence

$$a_0 = s\left(-6 - \frac{2r^2}{s^2}\right) = - \frac{2(r^2 + 3s^2)}{s}.$$

Since ρ' and ρ'' are the numbers

$$\tfrac{1}{2}[-\rho \pm (a_0 + a_1\rho + a_2\rho^2)],$$

we have

$$\rho' = - \frac{1}{s}(r^2 + 3s^2) + \frac{r - s}{2s}\rho + \frac{1}{2s}\rho^2,$$

$$(37.4)$$

$$\rho'' = \frac{1}{s}(r^2 + 3s^2) - \frac{r + s}{2s}\rho - \frac{1}{2s}\rho^2.$$

Theorem 37.2. *The automorphisms of the normal cubic field defined by a root of (37.3) are*

$$\rho \leftrightarrow \rho, \quad \rho \leftrightarrow \rho', \quad \rho \leftrightarrow \rho'',$$

where ρ' and ρ'' are given by (37.4).

By an argument similar to that used in the proof of Theorem 24.1, it can be shown that the automorphisms of any field form a group. Since there is only one group of order 3, we have

Theorem 37.3. *The automorphisms of a normal cubic field give a representation of the cyclic group of order 3.*

This is why a normal cubic field is called a cyclic cubic field.

If we call $\rho' = \theta_1(\rho)$ and $\rho'' = \theta_2(\rho)$, the three roots of (37.3) are $\rho, \theta_1(\rho), \theta_2(\rho)$. But, since ρ was *any* root, $\theta_1[\theta_1(\rho)], \theta_2[\theta_1(\rho)]$, etc., are all roots of (37.5), and hence are $\rho, \theta_1(\rho), \theta_2(\rho)$ in some order.

EXERCISES

1. Show that the fields defined by

(a) $x^3 - 3x + 1 = 0$,   (b) $x^3 - 7x + 7 = 0$

are cyclic. Find values of r and s which put each of these equations into the form (37.3).

2. Find the functions θ_1 and θ_2 for each field of Ex. 1. Verify that they represent the cyclic group of order 3.

3. Obtain a matric representation for the automorphism group of Ex. 1a; of Ex. 1b. HINT: See Ex. 2, § 35.

4. Find the discriminant $\Delta = -4p^3 - 27q^2$ of (37.3).

5. Prove that a cubic field is normal if and only if its discriminant is the square of a rational number.

38. Algebraic stem fields.

In the remainder of this chapter we shall use $\mathfrak{F}$ to denote a field which is a subfield of the complex field. The quadratic and cubic fields already discussed are of this type, and there are many more. From the Fundamental Theorem of Algebra (§ 87) it follows that a polynomial equation $p(x) = 0$ of degree n with coefficients in $\mathfrak{F}$ has exactly n complex roots, which ordinarily will not be in $\mathfrak{F}$. Such a root ρ is said to be *algebraic* relative to $\mathfrak{F}$, and if $\mathfrak{F}$ is the rational field, ρ is called an *algebraic number*. Later (§ 78) we shall have a more abstract approach to algebraic fields which does not depend upon the Fundamental Theorem.

Let $p(x)$ be a polynomial of degree n with coefficients in a field $\mathfrak{F}$, irreducible in $\mathfrak{F}$. Let ρ be a root of the equation $p(x) = 0$.

Theorem 38.1.   If $g(\rho) = 0$, then $p(x) \mid g(x)$.

Since $p(x)$ is irreducible, the g.c.d. of $p(x)$ and $g(x)$ is either $p(x)$ or 1. It cannot be 1, for if it were, there would exist polynomials $h(x)$ and $k(x)$ such that

$$1 = h(x) \cdot p(x) + k(x) \cdot g(x),$$

whence, upon substituting ρ for x,

$$1 = h(\rho) \cdot p(\rho) + k(\rho) \cdot g(\rho) = 0.$$

Corollary 38.11.   The irreducible equation $p(x) = 0$ satisfied by ρ is unique.

Corollary 38.12.   The number ρ satisfies no equation of degree $< n$.

The roots of $p(x) = 0$ are called the *conjugates* of ρ and may be written

$$\rho, \rho', \rho'', \cdots, \rho^{(n-1)}.$$

Corollary 38.13.   Each one of a system of conjugates determines the whole system uniquely.

Theorem 38.2.   The set of all rational functions of ρ with coefficients in $\mathfrak{F}$ form a field $\mathfrak{F}(\rho)$, called the stem field of $p(x) = 0$.

The sum, difference, product, and quotient of two rational functions is a rational function, with the usual restriction as to division by 0. The postulates A, M, and D of § 33 all hold.

Theorem 38.3.   The elements of $\mathfrak{F}(\rho)$ are uniquely expressible in the form

$$\alpha = a_0 + a_1\rho + a_2\rho^2 + \cdots + a_{n-1}\rho^{n-1}$$

where the a's are in $\mathfrak{F}$.

Every rational function of ρ can be written as the quotient of two polynomials,

$$f(\rho) = \frac{\alpha(\rho)}{\beta(\rho)}, \qquad\qquad \beta(\rho) \neq 0.$$

Since $p(x)$ is irreducible, the g.c.d. of $p(x)$ and $\beta(x)$ is either 1 or $p(x)$, and in the latter instance we should have $\beta(\rho) = 0$. Hence polynomials $h(x)$ and $k(x)$ exist such that

$$h(x) \cdot p(x) + k(x) \cdot \beta(x) = 1,$$

and therefore $k(\rho) \cdot \beta(\rho) = 1$. That is,

$$f(\rho) = \alpha(\rho) \cdot k(\rho),$$

which is a polynomial in ρ.

If we write

$$p(x) = p_0 + p_1 x + p_2 x^2 + \cdots + p_{n-1}x^{n-1} + x^n,$$

then

(38.1) $$\rho^n = - p_0 - p_1\rho - p_2\rho^2 - \cdots - p_{n-1}\rho^{n-1}.$$

Hence every polynomial in ρ can be written as a polynomial of degree $< n$.

Let

$$\alpha = a_0 + a_1\rho + a_2\rho^2 + \cdots + a_{n-1}\rho^{n-1}$$

$$= b_0 + b_1\rho + b_2\rho^2 + \cdots + b_{n-1}\rho^{n-1}.$$

Then

$$(a_0 - b_0) + (a_1 - b_1)\rho + (a_2 - b_2)\rho^2 + \cdots + (a_{n-1} - b_{n-1})\rho^{n-1} = 0.$$

But, by Corollary 38.12, ρ satisfies no equation of degree $< n$; therefore

$$a_0 = b_0, \quad a_1 = b_1, \quad \cdots, a_{n-1} = b_{n-1},$$

and the representation is unique.

The process of passing from the field $\mathfrak{F}$ to the field $\mathfrak{F}(\rho)$ is called the *adjunction* of ρ to $\mathfrak{F}$. If ρ lies in $\mathfrak{F}$, $\mathfrak{F}(\rho) = \mathfrak{F}$.

The conjugates of ρ determine fields

$$\mathfrak{F}(\rho), \ \mathfrak{F}(\rho'), \ \mathfrak{F}(\rho''), \ \cdots, \ \mathfrak{F}(\rho^{(n-1)}),$$

called a *set of conjugate fields*. They may all be distinct, or they may all be equal, or (as we shall see) they may fall into sets of equal fields. In any case they are all isomorphic. If

$$\mathfrak{F}(\rho) = \mathfrak{F}(\rho') = \cdots = \mathfrak{F}(\rho^{(n-1)}),$$

the field $\mathfrak{F}(\rho)$ is called *normal*.

EXERCISES

1. In the field defined by $x^3 - 5x + 7 = 0$, express $\dfrac{1 - 7\rho + 2\rho^2}{1 + \rho - \rho^2}$ as a polynomial in ρ. Also $\dfrac{14\rho^2 + 12\rho - 35}{2\rho^2 + \rho}$, and $\dfrac{9 - 8\rho - 4\rho^2}{1 - 2\rho - \rho^2}$. Use undetermined coefficients.

2. Find the conjugates of $\rho = \sqrt[3]{2}$.

3. Find a value of c for which the field defined by $x^3 - 9x + c = 0$ is normal.

39. Conjugates.

A set of numbers $u_0, u_1, \cdots, u_{n-1}$ of $\mathfrak{F}(\rho)$ such that every number α of $\mathfrak{F}(\rho)$ is uniquely expressible in the form

$$\alpha = a_0 u_0 + a_1 u_1 + \cdots + a_{n-1} u_{n-1}$$

where the a's are in $\mathfrak{F}$ are said to form a *basis* for $\mathfrak{F}(\rho)$. By Theorem 38.3 one such basis is $1, \rho, \rho^2, \cdots, \rho^{n-1}$. The numbers

$$\alpha = a_0 + a_1\rho + a_2\rho^2 + \cdots + a_{n-1}\rho^{n-1},$$
$$\alpha' = a_0 + a_1\rho' + a_2\rho'^2 + \cdots + a_{n-1}\rho'^{n-1},$$
$$\alpha'' = a_0 + a_1\rho'' + a_2\rho''^2 + \cdots + a_{n-1}\rho''^{n-1},$$
$$\cdot \quad \cdot \quad \cdot \quad \cdot \quad \cdot \quad \cdot \quad \cdot \quad \cdot \quad \cdot \quad \cdot$$

are called the *conjugates of* α. Note that in general they lie in different fields.

Theorem 39.1. Every number α of $\mathfrak{F}(\rho)$ satisfies an equation $f(x) = 0$ of degree n with coefficients in $\mathfrak{F}$, whose n roots are the n conjugates of α.

Form the equation

$$f(x) = (x - \alpha)(x - \alpha')(x - \alpha'') \cdots (x - \alpha^{(n-1)})$$
$$= x^n + f_{n-1}x^{n-1} + \cdots + f_1 x + f_0 = 0.$$

Each f_i is an elementary symmetric function of the α's and hence is unchanged by every permutation of the α's. It is then unchanged by every permutation of the ρ's, and is therefore a symmetric function in the ρ's. By the fundamental theorem on symmetric functions,[*] each f_i is a polynomial in the elementary symmetric functions, and is therefore a polynomial in the coefficients of $p(x) = 0$. That is, it is a number of $\mathfrak{F}$. This equation $f(x) = 0$ is called the *principal equation* of α.

Theorem 39.2. The n conjugates $\alpha, \alpha', \cdots, \alpha^{(n-1)}$ are either all distinct or else they fall into h systems, each system containing k equal numbers. In the first case $f(x)$ is irreducible; in the second case $f(x)$ is the kth power of an irreducible polynomial of degree h.

Suppose $f(x)$ to be factored into its irreducible factors,

$$f(x) = f_1(x) \cdot f_2(x) \cdots,$$

and let $f_1(x)$ be a factor which vanishes for $x = \alpha$. But α is a polynomial in ρ, say $a(\rho)$. Then $f_1[a(x)]$ vanishes for $x = \rho$ and therefore for

$$x = \rho, \rho', \rho'', \cdots, \rho^{(n-1)}.$$

Then $f_1(x)$ vanishes for

$$x = \alpha, \alpha', \alpha'', \cdots, \alpha^{(n-1)}.$$

If these are all distinct, $f_1(x)$ is of degree n so that $f(x)$ is irreducible.

Let $\alpha, \alpha', \alpha'', \cdots, \alpha^{(h-1)}$ be a maximal set of distinct α's. They are roots of $f_1(x) = 0$, and they are simple roots, for if $f_1(x) = 0$ had a repeated root it would be reducible. Hence $f_1(x)$ is of degree h.

If $h < n$, some other factor, say $f_2(x)$, has some α for a root. Then $f_1(x) \mid f_2(x)$ by Theorem 38.1, and, since $f_2(x)$ is also irreducible, $f_2(x) = f_1(x)$, except possibly for a constant factor. If $2h < n$, we have another factor $f_3(x)$ also equal to $f_1(x)$. If we choose each f so that the coefficient of x^h is 1, we have eventually

$$f(x) = [f_1(x)]^k, \qquad\qquad hk = n.$$

Then each α is repeated just k times in its set of conjugates.

---

[*] See, for instance, L. E. Dickson, *New First Course in the Theory of Equations*, Wiley, 1939, p. 177.

EXERCISES

1. Prove the first statement of Theorem 39.1 in the same way that Theorem 36.2 was proved.

2. In the quartic field defined by $x^4 + 3x^2 + 9 = 0$, show that the principal equation of every number of the form $a_0 + 6a_3\rho + a_3\rho^3$ is a perfect square.

3. Let ρ be a root of $x^3 + 3x + 2 = 0$. By the method of symmetric functions, find the principal equation in Ra of $\alpha = 1 + \rho^2$. Check with (36.4).

40. Adjunction. A number of $\mathfrak{F}(\rho)$ whose principal equation is irreducible is called a *primitive number* of $\mathfrak{F}(\rho)$. The principal equation of a number a of $\mathfrak{F}$ is $(x - a)^n = 0$. The principal equation of ρ is $p(x) = 0$.

Theorem 40.1. If η is a primitive number of $\mathfrak{F}(\rho)$, then $\mathfrak{F}(\rho) = \mathfrak{F}(\eta)$.

Since η is in $\mathfrak{F}(\rho)$, every number of $\mathfrak{F}(\eta)$ is in $\mathfrak{F}(\rho)$. We need only show that ρ is in $\mathfrak{F}(\eta)$ to complete the proof.

Let

$$f(x) = (x - \eta)(x - \eta') \cdots (x - \eta^{(n-1)}) = 0$$

be the principal equation of η, and define

$$\varphi(x) = f(x) \left[\frac{\rho}{x - \eta} + \frac{\rho'}{x - \eta'} + \cdots + \frac{\rho^{(n-1)}}{x - \eta^{(n-1)}} \right].$$

This is a polynomial in x of degree $n - 1$, and every coefficient is symmetric in the ρ's. Hence by symmetric function theory the coefficients of $\varphi(x)$ are in $\mathfrak{F}$. Now

$$\varphi(\eta) = \rho(\eta - \eta')(\eta - \eta'') \cdots (\eta - \eta^{(n-1)}).$$

By the usual method of differentiation,

$$f'(x) = \sum_{i=0}^{n-1} (x - \eta) \cdots (x - \eta^{(i-1)})(x - \eta^{(i+1)}) \cdots (x - \eta^{(n-1)}),$$

$$f'(\eta) = (\eta - \eta')(\eta - \eta'') \cdots (\eta - \eta^{(n-1)}).$$

Hence

$$\rho = \frac{\varphi(\eta)}{f'(\eta)},$$

so that ρ is in $\mathfrak{F}(\eta)$. Since $f(x) = 0$ is irreducible, it has no multiple root, and $f'(\eta) \neq 0$.

The two equations $p(x) = 0$ and $f(x) = 0$ where $f(x)$ is irreducible are closely related. All the roots of the first are the same polynomial function of the roots of the second, and all the roots of the second are the same polynomial function of the roots of the first. Two such equations are said to be related by a *birational Tschirnhaus transformation*.

Theorem 40.2. Every imprimitive number of $\mathfrak{F}(\rho)$ defines a subfield of $\mathfrak{F}(\rho)$.

Let η be an imprimitive number of $\mathfrak{F}(\rho)$. Its principal equation is

$$f(x) = [f_1(x)]^k, \qquad k > 1,$$

where $f_1(x)$ is irreducible of degree h, so that η defines an algebraic field of degree h. Since η is in $\mathfrak{F}(\rho)$, $\mathfrak{F}(\eta) \subset \mathfrak{F}(\rho)$.

Theorem 40.3. If ρ_1 and ρ_2 are two algebraic numbers over $\mathfrak{F}$, the adjunction of ρ_2 to $\mathfrak{F}(\rho_1)$ gives the same field $\mathfrak{F}(\rho_1, \rho_2)$ as the adjunction of ρ_1 to $\mathfrak{F}(\rho_2)$. There exists a single algebraic number ρ such that $\mathfrak{F}(\rho_1, \rho_2)$ is equal to $\mathfrak{F}(\rho)$.

That the order of adjunction is immaterial can be seen by considering $\mathfrak{F}(\rho_1, \rho_2)$ in its original sense, the set of all numbers which are obtainable rationally from ρ_1 and ρ_2 with coefficients in $\mathfrak{F}$.

If ρ_1 is in $\mathfrak{F}(\rho_2)$ or if ρ_2 is in $\mathfrak{F}(\rho_1)$, the ρ is obvious.

Let ρ_1 be a root of an irreducible equation $p_1(x) = 0$ of degree n_1 and ρ_2 a root of an irreducible equation $p_2(x) = 0$ of degree n_2. Let

$$\rho_1, \rho_1', \cdots, \rho_1^{(n_1-1)}; \; \rho_2, \rho_2', \cdots, \rho_2^{(n_2-1)}$$

be the conjugates of ρ_1 and ρ_2, respectively. Set $\rho = a_1\rho_1 + a_2\rho_2$, where a_1 and a_2 are for the moment undetermined. Define

$$\rho' = a_1\rho_1' + a_2\rho_2,$$
$$\cdots \cdots \cdots \cdots \cdots \cdots$$
$$\rho^{(n_1-1)} = a_1\rho_1^{(n_1-1)} + a_2\rho_2,$$
$$\rho^{(n_1)} = a_1\rho_1 + a_2\rho_2',$$
$$\rho^{(n_1+1)} = a_1\rho_1' + a_2\rho_2',$$
$$\cdots \cdots \cdots \cdots \cdots \cdots$$
$$\rho^{(n_1n_2-1)} = a_1\rho_1^{(n_1-1)} + a_2\rho_2^{(n_2-1)}.$$

No two ρ's are identically equal in a_1, a_2, for this would imply that either $p_1(x)$ or $p_2(x)$ had a multiple factor and hence was reducible. Hence we have only to avoid a finite number of values of the ratio a_1/a_2 in order to choose values in $\mathfrak{F}$ for a_1 and a_2 such that the n_1n_2 ρ's are all different.

Now form

$$f(x) = (x - \rho)(x - \rho') \cdots (x - \rho^{(n_1n_2-1)}),$$

which has no multiple factor. Its coefficients are symmetric in the roots of $p_1(x) = 0$ and also in the roots of $p_2(x) = 0$, and so they are numbers of $\mathfrak{F}$. Let η be any number of $\mathfrak{F}(\rho_1, \rho_2)$, and define its $n_1 n_2$ conjugates similarly to those of ρ. Then form

$$\varphi(x) = f(x) \left[\frac{\eta}{x - \rho} + \frac{\eta'}{x - \rho'} + \cdots + \frac{\eta^{(n_1 n_2 - 1)}}{x - \rho^{(n_1 n_2 - 1)}} \right].$$

As in the proof of Theorem 40.1, we can show that

$$\eta = \frac{\varphi(\rho)}{f'(\rho)}.$$

Since $f(x) = 0$ has no multiple root, $f'(\rho) \neq 0$.

It does not follow that $f(x)$ is irreducible, but the irreducible function having ρ as a zero is either $f(x)$ or one of its factors.

Let $\mathfrak{F}(\rho_2)$ have the $\mathfrak{F}$-basis $u_0, u_1, \cdots, u_{n-1}$. If these basis numbers are linearly independent with respect to $\mathfrak{F}(\rho_1)$, the field $\mathfrak{F}(\rho_1, \rho_2)$ is called the *direct product* $\mathfrak{F}(\rho_1) \times \mathfrak{F}(\rho_2)$ of the fields $\mathfrak{F}(\rho_1)$ and $\mathfrak{F}(\rho_2)$. Evidently it consists of all numbers

$$a_0 u_0 + a_1 u_1 + \cdots + a_{n-1} u_{n-1}$$

where the a's range over $\mathfrak{F}(\rho_1)$. Or we may take a basis for $\mathfrak{F}(\rho_1)$, and let the coefficients range over $\mathfrak{F}(\rho_2)$. By Theorem 40.3, the same field is obtained by either method.

EXERCISES

1. In the field defined by $x^3 - x + 2 = 0$, the number $\eta = 1 + \rho + \rho^2$ is primitive. Express ρ as a polynomial in η, and thus show that $\mathfrak{F}(\rho) = \mathfrak{F}(\eta)$. Derive the principal equation of η.

2. Prove Theorem 40.1 by the method of Ex. 1.

3. Show that ρ^2 is an imprimitive number of the field defined by $x^4 + 3x^2 + 9 = 0$, and find the quadratic field which it defines.

4. Find an equation of degree 6 which defines the field $Ra(\sqrt{3}, \sqrt[3]{2})$.

5. Show that, if ρ is algebraic relative to the algebraic field $\mathfrak{F}$, then ρ is an algebraic number.

Hint: Let ρ satisfy the irreducible equation $f(x) = 0$ with coefficients in $\mathfrak{F}$. Show that the product of $f(x)$ and its conjugates relative to $\mathfrak{F}$ has coefficients in Ra.

41. Algebraic root fields. An equation is called *separable* if it has no multiple root. Let $p(x) = 0$ be a separable equation of degree n with coefficients in a field $\mathfrak{F}$. We define the *root field* of $p(x) = 0$ to be the field $\mathfrak{R} = \mathfrak{F}(\rho, \rho', \cdots, \rho^{(n-1)})$ obtained by adjoining to $\mathfrak{F}$ all the roots of $p(x) = 0$. By Theorem 40.3 this field is uniquely determined and is the stem field of at least one algebraic number η. An irreducible equation satisfied by such a number η is called a *resolvent* of $p(x) = 0$.

Theorem 41.1. If $p(x) = 0$ is of degree n, the degree of the resolvent of its root field is $\leq n!$.

By Theorem 40.3 we should have the degree of the resolvent $\leq n^n$. But a modification of the proof, permissible because we are now considering roots of the same equation, reduces this degree to $\leq n!$. Let $\rho, \rho', \cdots, \rho^{(n-1)}$ be the roots of $p(x) = 0$ and define $\bar{\rho} = a_0\rho + a_1\rho' + \cdots + a_{n-1}\rho^{(n-1)}$. Let $\bar{\rho}, \bar{\rho}', \bar{\rho}'', \cdots, \bar{\rho}^{(n!-1)}$ be obtained from $\bar{\rho}$ by applying to the roots of $p(x) = 0$ the permutations of the symmetric group $\mathfrak{G}_{n!}$. The rest of the proof proceeds as in Theorem 40.3.

Generically, the root field of an equation of degree n is of degree exactly $n!$, but even an irreducible equation may have a root field of degree as low as n. Of course, if $p(x) = 0$ is completely reducible in $\mathfrak{F}$, its root field is $\mathfrak{F}$ itself.

A normal equation may be defined as an equation $p(x) = 0$ which is irreducible in $\mathfrak{F}$, but which is completely reducible into linear factors in $\mathfrak{F}(\rho)$ where ρ is any one of its roots. This means that all numbers of the stem field of a normal equation can be written as polynomials in any other root.

A (stem or root) field defined by a normal equation is called a *normal field*. If $\mathfrak{F}(\rho)$ is normal, each of the conjugates of ρ is in $\mathfrak{F}(\rho)$, so that the conjugate fields are all equal; and this condition is also sufficient that $\mathfrak{F}(\rho)$ be normal.

Corollary 41.1. Every root field of a separable equation is normal.

Let $p(x) = 0$ have the roots $\rho, \rho', \rho'', \cdots, \rho^{(n-1)}$. Then

$$\bar{\rho} = a_0\rho + a_1\rho' + \cdots + a_{n-1}\rho^{(n-1)},$$

and the numbers $\bar{\rho}, \bar{\rho}', \bar{\rho}'', \cdots, \bar{\rho}^{(n!-1)}$, which are obtained from $\bar{\rho}$ by permutations of the roots, are all in the root field of $p(x) = 0$. These numbers are the conjugates of $\bar{\rho}$, and so $\mathfrak{F}(\bar{\rho})$ is normal.

EXERCISES

1. Find a resolvent for $x^3 + px + q = 0$.

HINT: Set $\bar{\rho} = \rho + 2\rho' + 3\rho'' = \rho'' - \rho$. Let $\bar{\rho}'$ and $\bar{\rho}''$ be obtained by cyclic permutations. Find the equation satisfied by $\bar{\rho}, \bar{\rho}'$, and $\bar{\rho}''$. The resolvent is $(x^3 + 3px)^2 - \Delta = 0$.

2. Use Ex. 1 to prove that an irreducible cubic equation is normal if and only if its discriminant is a rational square. See Ex. 5, § 37.

3. Find a resolvent for $x^3 + 2x + 1 = 0$, and find a birational Tschirnhaus transformation relating it to the given equation.

4. Prove Corollary 41.1 with the omission of the word *separable*.

42. Automorphisms.

A correspondence

$$\alpha \leftrightarrow \beta$$

of the numbers of $\mathfrak{F}(\rho)$ with themselves is called an *automorphism* of $\mathfrak{F}(\rho)$ if it is an automorphism of both the addition and multiplication groups of $\mathfrak{F}(\rho)$. If under an automorphism every number of an algebraic subfield $\mathfrak{F}_1$ of $\mathfrak{F}(\rho)$ corresponds to itself, the automorphism is said to be *relative* to $\mathfrak{F}_1$.

If $1, \rho, \rho^2, \cdots, \rho^{n-1}$ is a basis for $\mathfrak{F}(\rho)$, every automorphism of $\mathfrak{F}(\rho)$ relative to $\mathfrak{F}$ can be defined by stating the correspondence $\rho \leftrightarrow \rho'$ of ρ with the number ρ'. For, if

$$\alpha = a_0 + a_1\rho + a_2\rho^2 + \cdots + a_{n-1}\rho^{n-1}$$

is any number of $\mathfrak{F}(\rho)$, then

$$\alpha \leftrightarrow \alpha' = a_0 + a_1\rho' + a_2\rho'^2 + \cdots + a_{n-1}\rho'^{n-1}.$$

Theorem 42.1. If $\rho \leftrightarrow \rho'$ is an automorphism of $\mathfrak{F}(\rho)$ relative to $\mathfrak{F}$, then ρ' is one of the conjugates of ρ.

Let $p(x) = 0$ be the irreducible equation with coefficients in $\mathfrak{F}$ which ρ satisfies. Since ρ' corresponds to ρ under both addition and multiplication, and numbers of $\mathfrak{F}$ correspond to themselves, $p(\rho') = 0$.

Theorem 42.2. If ρ' is a conjugate of ρ, then $\rho \leftrightarrow \rho'$ is an automorphism of $\mathfrak{F}(\rho)$ relative to $\mathfrak{F}$ if and only if $\mathfrak{F}(\rho') = \mathfrak{F}(\rho)$.

In any case the correspondence $\rho \leftrightarrow \rho'$ is an isomorphism. For, if α and β are two polynomials in ρ, and α' and β' the corresponding polynomials in ρ', obviously $\alpha + \beta$ corresponds to $\alpha' + \beta'$. In forming the product $\alpha\beta$, higher powers of ρ are reduced by the relation $p(\rho) = 0$. Higher powers of ρ' in $\alpha'\beta'$ are reduced by $p(\rho') = 0$. Obviously the reduced form of $\alpha'\beta'$ can be obtained from the reduced form of $\alpha\beta$ by replacing ρ by ρ'.

The correspondence is an automorphism if and only if ρ' is in $\mathfrak{F}(\rho)$. But in that event $\mathfrak{F}(\rho) = \mathfrak{F}(\rho')$ by Theorem 40.1.

Corollary 42.2. A normal equation of degree n has exactly n automorphisms.

This follows from the fact that

$$\mathfrak{F}(\rho) = \mathfrak{F}(\rho') = \cdots = \mathfrak{F}(\rho^{(n-1)}).$$

Theorem 42.3. The automorphisms of $\mathfrak{F}(\rho)$ form a group.

For the automorphisms of $\mathfrak{F}(\rho)$ are the intersection of the automorphism group of $\mathfrak{F}(\rho)$ relative to addition with the automorphism group relative to multiplication.

To see the exact meaning of this statement, let

$$I: \qquad \rho \leftrightarrow \rho^{(i)} = b_0 + b_1\rho + b_2\rho^2 + \cdots + b_{n-1}\rho^{n-1} = b(\rho),$$

$$J: \qquad \rho \leftrightarrow \rho^{(j)} = c_0 + c_1\rho + c_2\rho^2 + \cdots + c_{n-1}\rho^{n-1} = c(\rho)$$

be two automorphisms. The product IJ is evidently obtained by applying J to I,

$$IJ = b_0 + b_1\rho^{(j)} + b_2\rho^{(j)2} + \cdots + b_{n-1}\rho^{(j)n-1} = b(\rho^{(j)})$$

$$= b[c(\rho)] = d_0 + d_1\rho + d_2\rho^2 + \cdots + d_{n-1}\rho^{n-1}.$$

If the automorphisms form a group, there is an automorphism

$$IJ: \qquad \rho \leftrightarrow \rho^{(ij)} = d_0 + d_1\rho + d_2\rho^2 + \cdots + d_{n-1}\rho^{n-1}.$$

EXERCISES

1. Show that the field defined by $x^4 + 4x^2 + 2 = 0$ is normal with the automorphisms ρ, $\theta_1(\rho) = -\rho$, $\theta_2(\rho) = \rho^3 + 3\rho$, $\theta_3(\rho) = -\rho^3 - 3\rho$. What is the automorphism group of this field?

2. Show that the field defined by $x^4 + 3x^2 + 9 = 0$ is normal with the automorphisms ρ, $\theta_1(\rho) = -\rho$, $\theta_2(\rho) = \rho^3/3 + \rho$, $\theta_3(\rho) = -\rho^3/3 - \rho$. What is the automorphism group of this field?

43. The Galois group. Let $p(x) = 0$ be a separable equation with coefficients in $\mathfrak{F}$, and let $\mathfrak{N}$ be its root field. The automorphism group of $\mathfrak{N}$ relative to $\mathfrak{F}$ is called the *Galois group* of $\mathfrak{N}$ relative to $\mathfrak{F}$, or of $p(x) = 0$ relative to $\mathfrak{F}$.

Under the identity automorphism every element of the normal field $\mathfrak{N}$ corresponds to itself. Under the Galois group $\mathfrak{G}$ of $\mathfrak{N}$ relative to $\mathfrak{F}$, every number of $\mathfrak{F}$ corresponds to itself. More generally, we have

Theorem 43.1. If $\mathfrak{H}$ is a subset of $\mathfrak{G}$, all the elements of $\mathfrak{N}$ which correspond to themselves under the automorphisms $\mathfrak{H}$ form a subfield $\mathfrak{F}_1$ of $\mathfrak{N}$.

For, by the definition of automorphism, if two numbers are in the set $\mathfrak{F}_1$, then their sum and their product are in $\mathfrak{F}_1$. Also 1 is in $\mathfrak{F}_1$ and the negatives and reciprocals of numbers of $\mathfrak{F}_1$ are in $\mathfrak{F}_1$. Thus $\mathfrak{F}_1$ is a field all of whose numbers are in $\mathfrak{N}$.

Corollary 43.1. The field $\mathfrak{F}$ consists of those numbers of $\mathfrak{N} = \mathfrak{F}(\rho)$ which correspond to themselves under the group $\mathfrak{G}$.

If $\alpha = a_0 + a_1\rho + a_2\rho^2 + \cdots + a_{n-1}\rho^{n-1}$ corresponds to itself under all the automorphisms of $\mathfrak{G}$, it is a symmetric function in the roots ρ, ρ', $\cdots$, $\rho^{(n-1)}$, and hence is in $\mathfrak{F}$.

Theorem 43.2. If $\mathfrak{N}$ is a normal field of order n over $\mathfrak{F}$ with Galois group $\mathfrak{G}$ relative to $\mathfrak{F}$, and if $\mathfrak{F} \subset \mathfrak{F}_1 \subset \mathfrak{N}$, then the subgroup $\mathfrak{G}_1$ of $\mathfrak{G}$ which leaves every element of $\mathfrak{F}_1$ invariant is the Galois group of $\mathfrak{N}$ relative to $\mathfrak{F}_1$. If $\mathfrak{F}_1$, $\mathfrak{F}_1'$, $\mathfrak{F}_1''$, $\cdots$ are conjugate in $\mathfrak{N}$, then $\mathfrak{G}_1$, $\mathfrak{G}_1'$, $\mathfrak{G}_1''$, $\cdots$ are conjugate subgroups in $\mathfrak{G}$, and conversely.

Obviously those elements of $\mathfrak{G}$ which leave $\mathfrak{F}_1$ invariant form a subgroup $\mathfrak{G}_1$ of $\mathfrak{G}$. By definition it is the automorphism group of $\mathfrak{N}$ relative to $\mathfrak{F}_1$.

Every element g of $\mathfrak{G}$ carries $\mathfrak{F}_1$ into one of the conjugate fields $\mathfrak{F}_1$, $\mathfrak{F}_1'$, $\mathfrak{F}''$, $\cdots$, say into $\mathfrak{F}_1'$. Then $g\mathfrak{G}_1 g^{-1}$ carries $\mathfrak{F}_1'$ into itself and hence is contained in $\mathfrak{G}_1'$. Similarly $g^{-1}\mathfrak{G}_1' g$ carries $\mathfrak{F}_1$ into itself, and so it is contained in $\mathfrak{G}_1$. Thus $g\mathfrak{G}_1 g^{-1} = \mathfrak{G}_1'$. In general, $\mathfrak{G}_1$, $\mathfrak{G}_1'$, $\mathfrak{G}_1''$, $\cdots$ are a set of conjugate subgroups of $\mathfrak{G}$.

It is similarly proved that, if $\mathfrak{G}_1$ leaves $\mathfrak{F}_1$ invariant, then the conjugates of $\mathfrak{G}_1$ leave invariant each element of some conjugate field.

Corollary 43.2. A subfield $\mathfrak{F}_1$ of $\mathfrak{N}$ is normal if and only if $\mathfrak{G}_1$ is an invariant subgroup of $\mathfrak{G}$.

Theorem 43.3. If $\mathfrak{N}$ and $\mathfrak{N}_1$ are normal fields, $\mathfrak{F} \subset \mathfrak{N}_1 \subset \mathfrak{N}$, and if $\mathfrak{G}$ and $\mathfrak{H}$ are the Galois groups of $\mathfrak{N}$ with respect to $\mathfrak{F}$ and $\mathfrak{N}_1$, respectively, then $\mathfrak{G}/\mathfrak{H}$ is the Galois group of $\mathfrak{N}_1$ with respect to $\mathfrak{F}$.

Let

$$\mathfrak{G} = \mathfrak{H} + g_1\mathfrak{H} + g_2\mathfrak{H} + \cdots.$$

If every h in $\mathfrak{H}$ leaves every element of $\mathfrak{N}_1$ invariant, then the effect of $g_i\mathfrak{H}$ upon $\mathfrak{N}_1$ is the same as the effect of g_i. Thus the automorphism group of $\mathfrak{N}_1$ relative to $\mathfrak{F}$ is $\mathfrak{G}/\mathfrak{H}$.

Theorem 43.4. If $\mathfrak{H}$ is a maximal invariant subgroup of the Galois group $\mathfrak{G}$ of $\mathfrak{N}$, then there exists a normal field $\mathfrak{N}_1$, $\mathfrak{F} \subset \mathfrak{N}_1 \subset \mathfrak{N}$, such that the Galois group of $\mathfrak{N}$ relative to $\mathfrak{N}_1$ is $\mathfrak{H}$.

The field exists by Theorem 43.1. It is normal by Corollary 43.2.

EXERCISES

1. In Ex. 1, § 42, find the subfield composed of the numbers which correspond to themselves under $\rho \leftrightarrow \theta_1$. Do the same for $\rho \leftrightarrow \theta_2$.

2. In Ex. 2, § 42, find the subfield composed of the numbers which correspond to themselves under $\rho \leftrightarrow \theta_1$. Do the same for $\rho \leftrightarrow \theta_2$, and for $\rho \leftrightarrow \theta_3$. (Cf. Ex. 2, § 39.)

3. Solve $x^4 + 4x^2 + 2 = 0$ as a quadratic in x^2. What is the intermediate field $\mathfrak{F}_1$?

4. Solve $x^4 + 3x^2 + 9 = 0$: (a) As a quadratic in x^2; what is $\mathfrak{F}_1$? (b) By adding and subtracting $3x^2$; what is $\mathfrak{F}_1$? (c) By subtracting and adding $9x^2$; what is $\mathfrak{F}_1$?

44. The Galois group as a permutation group. Let us return to the proof of Theorem 41.1. The root field of $p(x) = 0$ was seen to be $\mathfrak{F}(\eta)$, where η was of the form

$$\eta = a_0\rho + a_1\rho' + a_2\rho'' + \cdots + a_{n-1}\rho^{(n-1)}.$$

The resolvent of $p(x) = 0$ was the irreducible equation $r(x) = 0$ satisfied by η. Moreover, $r(x)$ was an irreducible factor of $f(x) = \Pi(x - \eta^{(i)})$.

The polynomial $r(x)$ is of the form

$$(x - \eta)(x - \eta^{(i_1)})(x - \eta^{(i_2)}) \cdots (x - \eta^{(i_{k-1})}),$$

where each conjugate of η is obtained from η by applying some permutation to $\rho, \rho', \rho'', \cdots, \rho^{(n-1)}$. Let us consider the correspondence

$$\eta^{(i)} \leftrightarrow p_i \qquad\qquad (i = 0, 1, \cdots, k - 1)$$

between the conjugates of η and the permutations on the ρ's by which they are obtained.

Theorem 44.1. The permutations $p_0, p_1, p_2, \cdots, p_{k-1}$ form a group isomorphic with the Galois group $\mathfrak{G}$ of $p(x) = 0$ relative to $\mathfrak{F}$.

By definition $\mathfrak{G}$ is the group of automorphisms of $\mathfrak{F}(\eta)$. Let $p_i\eta$ denote that conjugate of η which is obtained by applying the permutation p_i to η. If I and J are two automorphisms

$$I\colon \eta \leftrightarrow \eta^{(i)} = p_i\eta, \quad J\colon \eta \leftrightarrow \eta^{(j)} = p_j\eta,$$

then IJ is the result of substituting $\eta^{(j)}$ for η in $\eta^{(i)}$, namely,

$$IJ\colon \eta \leftrightarrow \eta^{(ij)} = p_i(p_j\eta) = (p_ip_j)\eta.$$

Hence the correspondences

$$\eta^{(i)} \leftrightarrow p_i, \quad \eta^{(j)} \leftrightarrow p_j$$

imply that $\eta^{(ij)} \leftrightarrow p_ip_j$, thus establishing the isomorphism.

Theorem 44.2. The Galois group $\mathfrak{G}$ relative to the coefficient field $\mathfrak{F}$ of a separable equation $p(x) = 0$ is uniquely defined by the following properties:

A: Every rational function with coefficients in $\mathfrak{F}$ of the roots of $p(x) = 0$ which is invariant under $\mathfrak{G}$ is equal to a number of $\mathfrak{F}$.

B: *Every rational function with coefficients in $\mathfrak{F}$ of the roots of $p(x) = 0$ which is equal to a number of $\mathfrak{F}$ is invariant under $\mathfrak{G}$.*

This theorem is but a restatement of Corollary 43.1. The rational functions with coefficients in $\mathfrak{F}$ of the roots of $p(x) = 0$ are the numbers of the (normal) root field $\mathfrak{N}$ of $p(x) = 0$. The numbers of $\mathfrak{F}$ are precisely the numbers of $\mathfrak{N}$ which are invariant under the Galois group of $\mathfrak{N}$ relative to $\mathfrak{F}$.

If $\mathfrak{G}_1$ is any group having Property A, then $\mathfrak{G}_1 \supseteq \mathfrak{G}$. If $\mathfrak{G}_2$ is any group having Property B, then $\mathfrak{G}_2 \subseteq \mathfrak{G}$. Note that the symmetric group has Property A by the fundamental theorem on symmetric functions.

The Galois group is often defined by these properties.

Theorem 44.3.   If $f(x) = 0$ is a normal equation of degree n (defining the normal field $\mathfrak{N}$) with the Galois group $\mathfrak{G}$ relative to $\mathfrak{F}$ which has an invariant subgroup $\mathfrak{H}$ of order h (defining the normal subfield $\mathfrak{N}_1$), then $f(x)$ factors into k factors, each of degree h with coefficients in $\mathfrak{N}_1$.

Let $\mathfrak{G}$ be broken up into cosets,

$$\mathfrak{G} = \mathfrak{H} + \mathfrak{H}g_1 + \mathfrak{H}g_2 + \cdots + \mathfrak{H}g_{k-1}.$$

In the field $\mathfrak{N}$, $f(x)$ can be written

$$f(x) = (x - \rho)(x - \rho') \cdots (x - \rho^{(n-1)}).$$

Denote by

$$\rho^{(i)} \qquad\qquad (i = 0, 1, \cdots, h - 1)$$

the roots obtained from ρ by the correspondences of $\mathfrak{H}$.   Form

$$f_1(x) = \prod (x - \rho^{(i)}).$$

Since $\mathfrak{H}$ merely permutes the ρ's, $f_1(x)$ has coefficients in $\mathfrak{N}_1$.

Let g_1 carry ρ into $\rho^{(h)}$.   Let the elements of the coset $\mathfrak{H}g_1$ carry ρ into

$$\rho^{(h+i)} \qquad\qquad (i = 0, 1, \cdots, h - 1)$$

and form

$$f_2(x) = \prod (x - \rho^{(h+i)}) \quad (i = 0, 1, \cdots, h - 1).$$

Since $h_i\mathfrak{H}g_1 = \mathfrak{H}g_1$, $\mathfrak{H}$ merely permutes these roots also, so that $f_2(x)$ has coefficients in $\mathfrak{N}_1$. Thus, continuing,

$$f(x) = f_1(x) \cdot f_2(x) \cdots f_k(x)$$

where each $f_i(x)$ has coefficients in $\mathfrak{N}_1$.

Let the equation $p(x) = 0$ have the root field $\mathfrak{N}$ and the Galois group $\mathfrak{G}$ relative to $\mathfrak{F}$, and let $\mathfrak{H}_1$ be a maximal invariant subgroup of $\mathfrak{G}$.

Then $\mathfrak{H}_1$ leaves invariant some normal field $\mathfrak{N}_1$, $\mathfrak{N} \supset \mathfrak{N}_1 \supset \mathfrak{F}$, and is the Galois group of $\mathfrak{N}$ relative to $\mathfrak{N}_1$. Then $\mathfrak{G}/\mathfrak{H}_1$ is the Galois group of $\mathfrak{N}_1$ relative to $\mathfrak{F}$, and is simple.

Let $\mathfrak{H}_2$ be a maximal invariant subgroup of $\mathfrak{H}_1$ leaving invariant the field $\mathfrak{N}_2$ which is normal relative to $\mathfrak{N}_1$, $\mathfrak{N} \supset \mathfrak{N}_2 \supset \mathfrak{N}_1 \supset \mathfrak{F}$. Then $\mathfrak{H}_2$ is the Galois group of $\mathfrak{N}$ relative to $\mathfrak{N}_2$, and $\mathfrak{H}_1/\mathfrak{H}_2$ is the (simple) Galois group of $\mathfrak{N}_2$ relative to $\mathfrak{N}_1$.

Thus, in general, if $\mathfrak{G}$ has the series of composition $\mathfrak{G}$, $\mathfrak{H}_2$, $\mathfrak{H}_2$, $\cdots$, $\mathfrak{H}_{s-1}$, $\mathfrak{H}_s$, I and the prime quotient groups

$$\frac{\mathfrak{G}}{\mathfrak{H}_1}, \frac{\mathfrak{H}_1}{\mathfrak{H}_2}, \cdots \frac{\mathfrak{H}_{s-1}}{\mathfrak{H}_s}, \mathfrak{H}_s,$$

then there exists a sequence of fields

$$\mathfrak{N} \supset \mathfrak{N}_s \supset \mathfrak{N}_{s-1} \supset \cdots \supset \mathfrak{N}_2 \supset \mathfrak{N}_1 \supset \mathfrak{F},$$

where $\mathfrak{N}_i$ is normal relative to $\mathfrak{N}_{i-1}$ and such that $\mathfrak{H}_{i-1}/\mathfrak{H}_i$ is the Galois (or automorphism) group of $\mathfrak{N}_i$ relative to $\mathfrak{N}_{i-1}$.

EXERCISES

1. By the method of this paragraph find the Galois group of $x^3 + 2x + 1 = 0$ as a permutation group (Cf. Ex. 1, § 41.) Do the same for $x^3 - 3x + 1 = 0$.

2. Let ρ_1, ρ_2, ρ_3, ρ_4 be the roots of $x^4 + 3x^2 + 9 = 0$. Show that $\rho_1\rho_2 + \rho_3\rho_4$ is equal to a rational number. Why is this so? (See Ex. 2, § 42.)

3. Let ρ_1, ρ_2, ρ_3, ρ_4 be the roots of $x^4 + 4x^2 + 2 = 0$. Show that $\rho_1^2\rho_3 + \rho_2^2\rho_4 + \rho_3^2\rho_1 + \rho_4^2\rho_2$ is equal to a rational number. Why is this so? (See Ex. 1, § 42.)

4. Prove that the Galois group of an equation of degree n is the alternating group of order $\frac{1}{2}n!$ or a subgroup of this group if and only if the discriminant of the equation is a rational square.

45. Roots of unity. The solutions of the equation

$$(45.1) \qquad f(x) = x^n - 1 = 0$$

are called the nth roots of unity. As is well known, the n complex roots of this equation form n equally spaced spokes of the unit circle. That is to say,

Theorem 45.1. The nth roots of unity form a cyclic group of order n relative to multiplication.

That they form an abelian group $\mathfrak{G}_n$ is quite obvious, since, if $\rho_1^n = 1$ and $\rho_2^n = 1$, then $(\rho_1\rho_2)^n = 1$ and $(\rho_1/\rho_2)^n = 1$. Also $1^n = 1$, so the identity is present.

Since $f'(x) = nx^{n-1} = 0$ has only zero roots, $f'(x)$ and $f(x)$ are relatively prime and $f(x) = 0$ is separable. Thus the group of the nth roots of unity is of order n.

Let $n = p_1^{n_1} p_2^{n_2} \cdots p_k^{n_k}$, where the p's are distinct primes. By Corollary 31.3 the group can be written

$$\mathfrak{G}_n = \mathfrak{H}_1 \times \mathfrak{H}_2 \times \cdots \times \mathfrak{H}_k,$$

where $\mathfrak{H}_i$ is of order $p_i^{n_i}$ and consists of all elements of $\mathfrak{G}_n$ whose periods are powers of p_i. To prove that $\mathfrak{G}_n$ is cyclic, it is sufficient to prove that each $\mathfrak{H}_i$ is cyclic. But there are at most $p_i^{n_i-1}$ elements whose periods divide $p_i^{n_i-1}$, for the equation

$$x^{p_i^{n_i-1}} - 1 = 0$$

has at most $p_i^{n_i-1}$ roots. Hence there is at least one element of period $p_i^{n_i}$, and therefore $\mathfrak{H}_i$ is cyclic.

A generator of the cyclic group $\mathfrak{G}_n$ is called a *primitive nth root of unity*.

Theorem 45.2. There are exactly $\varphi(n)$ primitive nth roots of unity.

This follows from Ex. 1, § 31.

Let $\rho_1, \rho_2, \cdots, \rho_{\varphi(n)}$ be the primitive nth roots of unity. The polynomial

$$\psi_n(x) = (x - \rho_1)(x - \rho_2) \cdots (x - \rho_{\varphi(n)})$$

of degree $\varphi(n)$ is called a *cyclotomic polynomial*.

We now need a theorem universally known as the *Lemma of Gauss*.

Theorem 45.3. If $f(x)$ is a polynomial with rational integral coefficients, the leading coefficient being 1, and if

$$f(x) = g(x) \cdot h(x),$$

where $g(x)$ and $h(x)$ have rational coefficients, the leading coefficient being 1, then all the coefficients of $g(x)$ and $h(x)$ are rational integers.

Let b be the least common denominator of the coefficients of $g(x)$ so that

$$b \cdot g(x) = \sum_{i=0}^{m} b_i x^i,$$

where the b_i are relatively prime integers. Similarly set

$$c \cdot h(x) = \sum_{j=0}^{n} c_j x^j, \quad bc \cdot f(x) = bc \sum_{k=0}^{m+n} a_k x^k.$$

Then

$$bc \cdot h(x) \cdot g(x) = \sum_{k=0}^{m+n} \left[\sum_{i+j=k} b_i c_j \right] x^k.$$

Unless $b = c = 1$ (which we wish to prove), there would exist a prime p dividing bc which would not divide all the b_i or all the c_j. Let

$$p \mid b_i \ (i = 0, \cdots, s - 1), \ p \nmid b_s, \quad p \mid c_j \quad (j = 0, \cdots, \ t - 1), \ p \nmid c_t.$$

Then p divides every term of

$$bca_{s+t} = b_0 c_{s+t} + \cdots + b_s c_t + \cdots + b_{s+t} c_0$$

except $b_s c_t$, and is prime to it. This is absurd.

Theorem 45.4. Every cyclotomic polynomial has rational integral coefficients, the leading coefficient being 1.

The proof can be made by induction. Evidently $\psi_1(x) = x - 1$ is of this type. Let $d_1 = 1, d_2, d_3, \cdots, d_k$ be the divisors of n less than n, and assume the theorem for each of these divisors. Every root of $x^n - 1 = 0$ is a primitive nth root or a primitive d_ith root of unity for just one d_i. Hence

$$(45.2) \qquad \psi_n(x) = \frac{x^n - 1}{\psi_1(x)\psi_{d_2}(x) \cdots \psi_{d_k}(x)}.$$

By Theorem 45.3, $\psi_n(x)$ has rational integral coefficients, the leading coefficient being 1.

Theorem 45.5. Every cyclotomic polynomial is irreducible.[*]

Let $m(x)$ be the irreducible polynomial of degree $s \leqq \varphi(n)$ with rational integral coefficients satisfied by the primitive nth root of unity ρ. By Theorem 38.1, $m(x) \mid \psi_n(x)$. By Theorem 45.3, $m(x)$ has rational integral coefficients, the coefficient of x^s being 1. Since the other primitive nth roots of unity are the $\varphi(n)$ powers ρ^r where $r < n$, $(r, n) = 1$, the theorem will be proved if we can show that

$$m(\rho^r) = 0 \qquad\qquad (r, n) = 1.$$

For every integer k, we can write

$$(45.3) \qquad m(x^k) = q_k(x) \cdot m(x) + r_k(x),$$

where $r_k(x)$ is of degree $< s$ and has rational integral coefficients. Then

$$m(\rho^k) = r_k(\rho).$$

Since $\rho^{n+k} = \rho^k$, $r_{n+k}(\rho) = r_k(\rho)$; and since each r is of degree $< s$, it follows from Theorem 38.3 that corresponding coefficients are equal. That is,

$$r_{n+k}(x) = r_k(x).$$

[*] Proof by E. Landau, *Math. Zeitschrift*, 1929.

Thus while k takes on all positive integral values, only n distinct $r_k(x)$ are obtained.

Now, by Theorem 11.3,

$$m(x^p) \equiv [m(x)]^p \qquad \text{mod } p,$$

for every prime p, so that

$$m(x^p) = q_p(x) \cdot m(x) + r_p(x) \equiv [m(x)]^p \qquad \text{mod } p,$$

$$r_p(x) \equiv - \bar{q}_p(x) \cdot m(x) \qquad \text{mod } p.$$

But $r_p(x)$ is of degree $< s$ mod p while $m(x)$ is of degree s mod p, since its leading coefficient is 1. That is,

$$r_p(x) \equiv 0 \qquad \text{mod } p,$$

so that every coefficient of $r_p(x)$ is $\equiv 0$ mod p.

Let A be the greatest absolute value of all coefficients of all $r_k(x)$. For every prime $p > A$,

$$r_p(x) = 0,$$

since each coefficient is $\equiv 0$ modulo a prime greater than itself. Then from (45.3)

$$m(\rho^p) = 0 \qquad\qquad p > A.$$

Let $t = p_1 p_2 \cdots p_h$ be any integer each of whose prime factors exceeds A. By the above proof, $m(\rho) = 0$ implies that $m(\rho^{p_1}) = 0$. By a repetition of the above proof with ρ^{p_1} in place of ρ, it follows that $m(\rho^{p_1 p_2}) = 0$, and finally that $m(\rho^t) = 0$.

Let r be any integer $< n$ and prime to n. Set

$$t = r + n p_1' p_2' \cdots p_k',$$

where p_1', p_2', $\cdots$, p_k' are the primes $\leq A$ which do not divide r. No prime $\leq A$ divides t, for, if p is such a prime, either it divides r and is prime to $n p_1' p_2' \cdots p_k'$, or it is prime to r and divides $p_1' p_2' \cdots p_k'$. Hence

$$m(\rho^t) = 0.$$

But $t \equiv r$ mod n, so $m(\rho^r) = 0$.

EXERCISES

1. Show that there are exactly $p_i^{n_i} - p_i^{n_i-1}$ generators of $\mathfrak{H}_i$. Thus prove Theorem 45.2 directly.

2. Show by an examination of the process of long division, without Theorem 45.3, that $\psi_n(x)$ has rational integral coefficients, the leading coefficient being 1.

3. Calculate the degree of $\psi_n(x)$ from (45.2) and Theorem 10.3.

4. Find $\psi_3(x)$, $\psi_5(x)$.

46. Cyclotomic fields. The field $\mathfrak{F}(\rho) = \mathfrak{C}_n$ where ρ is a primitive nth root of unity is called a *cyclotomic field*. It is defined by the equation $\psi_n(x) = 0$, where $\psi_n(x)$ is the (irreducible) cyclotomic function of degree $\varphi(n)$. Since the other roots of this equation are the other primitive nth roots of unity, and every primitive nth root is a power of every other primitive nth root, the conjugate fields

$$\mathfrak{F}(\rho), \ \mathfrak{F}(\rho'), \ \cdots, \ \mathfrak{F}(\rho^{(\varphi(n)-1)})$$

are all equal, and we have

Theorem 46.1.   *Every cyclotomic field is normal.*

In fact, we can show further,

Theorem 46.2.   *The automorphism group of $\mathfrak{C}_n$ is abelian and is isomorphic with the group of reduced residues modulo n.*

Let ρ be any root of $\psi_n(x) = 0$. The other roots are ρ^r, where r ranges over a reduced set of residues modulo n. The correspondences

$$\rho \leftrightarrow \rho^r, \ \rho \leftrightarrow \rho^s, \ \cdots,$$

where $r, s, \cdots$ are distinct numbers of a reduced residue system modulo n, are the automorphisms of $\mathfrak{C}_n$. Let the first automorphism correspond to r, the second to s. Their product in the automorphism group, namely,

$$\rho \leftrightarrow \rho^{rs},$$

corresponds to $rs \bmod n$.

Theorem 46.3.   *The automorphism group of $\mathfrak{C}_n$ is a direct product of cyclic groups.*

This follows from Theorem 31.4.

EXERCISES

1. Show that every nth root of unity is in $\mathfrak{C}_n$.

2. Find a quadratic subfield of $\mathfrak{C}_5$.

3. Prove in general that the rational functions of $\rho + 1/\rho$ constitute a subfield of degree $\frac{1}{2}\varphi(n)$ of $\mathfrak{C}_n$, where ρ is a primitive nth root of unity.

4. Show that the odd prime p factors in $\mathfrak{C}_p$ into $p - 1$ factors.

HINT: Factor $\psi_p(x)$, and set $x = 1$.

47. Solution by radicals. The notation $\sqrt[p]{a}$ is used to represent one definite root of the equation

(47.1) $$x^p = a,$$

usually chosen according to a definite scheme. Thus, if a is in the real field and is positive, $\sqrt[p]{a}$ denotes the positive solution. If a is negative and p odd, $\sqrt[p]{a}$ is the negative solution. In other cases the definition of the principal value is not so clear, but some one solution of (47.1) must always be selected and named $\sqrt[p]{a}$.

If we set $x = y\sqrt[p]{a}$, then (47.1) become $y^p = 1$, so that the p solutions of (47.1) are

$$\sqrt[p]{a}, \quad \rho\sqrt[p]{a}, \quad \rho^2\sqrt[p]{a}, \cdots, \rho^{p-1}\sqrt[p]{a}$$

in the field $\mathfrak{F}(\rho, \sqrt{a})$, where ρ is a primitive pth root of unity.

We shall say that an equation $p(x) = 0$ with coefficients in a field $\mathfrak{F}$ is *solvable by radicals relatively to* $\mathfrak{F}$ if all the roots of $p(x) = 0$ can be obtained in a finite number of steps from the numbers of $\mathfrak{F}$ by the rational operations and root extractions.

If, corresponding to the prime quotient groups

$$\frac{\mathfrak{G}}{\mathfrak{H}_1}, \quad \frac{\mathfrak{H}_1}{\mathfrak{H}_2}, \quad \cdots, \mathfrak{H}_s$$

of the Galois group $\mathfrak{G}$ of $p(x) = 0$, we have the normal fields

$$\mathfrak{N} \supset \mathfrak{N}_s \supset \cdots \supset \mathfrak{N}_1 \supset \mathfrak{F},$$

then $p(x) = 0$ is solvable by radicals relatively to $\mathfrak{F}$ if and only if the resolvent of $\mathfrak{N}_i$ is solvable by radicals relatively to $\mathfrak{N}_{i-1}$ for every i. The particular resolvent selected is immaterial, for the roots of any one resolvent are polynomials in each root of every other resolvent.

An equation is called *cyclic* if its Galois group is cyclic.

Theorem 47.1. *Every cyclic equation $p(x) = 0$ of degree n is solvable by radicals relatively to the field $\mathfrak{F}(\rho)$ where ρ is a primitive nth root of unity.*

Let $p(x) = 0$ have the roots

$$\xi, \xi', \xi'', \cdots, \xi^{(n-1)},$$

and set

$$\eta_i = \xi + \rho^i \xi' + \rho^{2i} \xi'' + \cdots + \rho^{ni-i} \xi^{(n-1)}.$$

Let P be the permutation

$$\begin{pmatrix} \xi & \xi' & \cdots & \xi^{(n-2)} & \xi^{(n-1)} \\ \xi' & \xi'' & \cdots & \xi^{(n-1)} & \xi \end{pmatrix}$$

generating the cyclic group. Then

$$P\eta_i = \xi' + \rho^i \xi'' + \rho^{2i} \xi''' + \cdots + \rho^{ni-i} \xi = \frac{\eta_i}{\rho^i}.$$

Hence

$$P(\eta_i)^n = (P\eta_i)^n = \frac{\eta_i^n}{\rho^{ni}} = \eta_i^n,$$

so that $\eta_i^n = \zeta_i$, $(i = 0, 1, \cdots, n - 1)$, is a number of the field $\mathfrak{F}(\rho)$.

If
$$p(x) = x^n - p_1 x^{n-1} + \cdots,$$
then

$$\xi + \xi' + \xi'' + \cdots + \xi^{(n-1)} = \sqrt[n]{\zeta_0} = p_1,$$
$$\xi + \rho\xi' + \rho^2\xi'' + \cdots + \rho^{n-1}\xi^{(n-1)} = \sqrt[n]{\zeta_1},$$
$$\xi + \rho^2\xi' + \rho^4\xi'' + \cdots + \rho^{2(n-1)}\xi^{(n-1)} = \sqrt[n]{\zeta_2},$$
$$\cdots\cdots\cdots\cdots\cdots\cdots\cdots\cdots$$
$$\xi + \rho^{n-1}\xi' + \rho^{2(n-1)}\xi'' + \cdots + \rho^{(n-1)^2}\xi^{(n-1)} = \sqrt[n]{\zeta_{n-1}}.$$

The determinant of this system of equations is
$$\prod_{i=0}^{n-2} (\rho^i - \rho^j) \neq 0, \qquad\qquad j > i,$$

so that $\xi, \xi', \cdots, \xi^{(n-1)}$ can be expressed as linear functions of $\sqrt[n]{\zeta_i}$ with coefficients in $\mathfrak{F}(\rho)$.

Theorem 47.2. Every root of unity can be expressed in terms of radicals relatively to the rational field.

Clearly, if $n = hk$ is not prime, the solutions of $x^{hk} = 1$ are of the form $\rho^i \sqrt[h]{u}$, where ρ is a primitive nth root of unity and $u^k = 1$. Thus the theorem will be proved if we show that every primitive pth root of unity, where p is a prime, can be expressed in terms of radicals.

The theorem is known for $p = 2, 3$, and 5 at least. Suppose that it holds for every prime $< p$. Let b be a primitive root modulo p in the sense of Corollary 15.3, so that
$$b, b^2, \cdots, b^{p-1} \equiv 1$$
are all incongruent modulo p, and hence are congruent in some order to
$$1, 2, \cdots, p - 1.$$
The equation
$$\psi_p = \frac{x^p - 1}{x - 1} = x^{p-1} + x^{p-2} + \cdots + x + 1 = 0$$
is irreducible by Theorem 45.5, and its roots are the primitive pth roots of unity. If ρ is one such root, all the roots are given by
$$\rho, \rho^2, \cdots, \rho^{p-1},$$
which are equal in some order to
$$\rho, \rho^b, \rho^{b^2}, \cdots, \rho^{b^{p-2}}.$$

Hence, if $\chi(\rho) = \rho^b$, all the roots are the iterates of this function, so that $\psi_p = 0$ is cyclic. Since $\psi_p = 0$ is a reciprocal equation, it can be written

$$\left(x + \frac{1}{x}\right)^q + c_1\left(x + \frac{1}{x}\right)^{q-1} + \cdots + c_{q-1}\left(x + \frac{1}{x}\right) + c_q = 0,$$

where $q = \dfrac{p-1}{2}$ and the c's are rational.

Let $\mathfrak{F}_1$ denote the root field of

(47.2) $$y^q + c_1 y^{q-1} + \cdots + c_{q-1}y + c_q = 0,$$

and let $\sigma_1, \sigma_2, \cdots, \sigma_q$ denote its roots. Then in $\mathfrak{F}_1$ we can write

$$x^{p-1} + x^{p-2} + \cdots + x + 1$$
$$= (x^2 - \sigma_1 x + 1)(x^2 - \sigma_2 x + 1) \cdots (x^2 - \sigma_q x + 1).$$

The Galois group $\mathfrak{H}$ of $\mathfrak{F}(\rho)$ relative to $\mathfrak{F}_1$ is cyclic of order 2, and so the quotient group $\mathfrak{G}/\mathfrak{H}$, which is the Galois group of (47.2) relative to $\mathfrak{F}$, is cyclic, by Theorem 26.4.

Since (47.2) is cyclic, by Theorem 47.1 its roots can be expressed in terms of radicals relatively to a field $\mathfrak{F}(\rho_1)$, where ρ_1 is a primitive qth root of unity. But we assumed that, for every prime $p_1 < p$, every primitive p_1th root of unity was expressible in terms of radicals relatively to the rational field. Thus the roots of (47.2) are so expressible, and so are the roots of (47.1).

Corollary 47.2. Every cyclic equation $p(x) = 0$ of degree n is solvable by radicals relatively to the field of its coefficients.

Theorem 47.3. If $\mathfrak{G}$ is the Galois group of an equation $p(x) = 0$ relative to its coefficient field $\mathfrak{F}$, a necessary and sufficient condition that $p(x) = 0$ be solvable by radicals relatively to $\mathfrak{F}$ is that the factors of composition of $\mathfrak{G}$ consist entirely of primes.

Suppose first that the equation is solvable by radicals. Its roots are obtainable from $\mathfrak{F}$ by the solution of a chain of linear and binomial equations of prime degrees, each of the latter being cyclic. Thus the condition is necessary.

Now suppose that

$$\frac{\mathfrak{G}}{\mathfrak{H}_1}, \frac{\mathfrak{H}_1}{\mathfrak{H}_2}, \frac{\mathfrak{H}_2}{\mathfrak{H}_3}, \cdots$$

are all of prime order. Then they are cyclic, and the roots of $p(x) = 0$ are obtainable from the coefficient field by the solution of a chain of cyclic equations. By Corollary 47.2 every root of each of these equations is expressible in terms of radicals in the field of the coefficients of the preceding equation.

EXERCISES

1. The discriminant of $x^3 + bx^2 + cx + d = 0$ is $D = 18bcd - 4b^3d + b^2c^2 - 4c^3 - 27d^2$. If the equation is cyclic, with roots ρ_1, ρ_2, ρ_3, compute

$$A = \rho_1\rho_2^2 + \rho_2\rho_3^2 + \rho_3\rho_1^2, \quad B = \rho_1^2\rho_2 + \rho_2^2\rho_3 + \rho_3^2\rho_1.$$

HINT: Find $A + B$ and $A - B$.

2. Solve the cyclic cubic $x^3 + x^2 - 2x - 1 = 0$ by the method used to prove Theorem 47.1.

3. Find in terms of radicals the seventh roots of unity.

4. Show that $\mathfrak{C}_7$ is the direct product of two cyclic fields, one cubic and one quadratic.

HINT: If $\rho^6 + \rho^5 + \rho^4 + \rho^3 + \rho^2 + \rho + 1 = 0$, then $\sigma^3 + \sigma^2 - 2\sigma - 1 = 0$ where $\sigma = \rho + 1/\rho = \rho + \rho^6$, and $\tau^2 + \tau + 2 = 0$ where $\tau = \rho^4 + \rho^2 + \rho$. Show that $\sigma^i\tau^j$ are linearly independent.

5. Assuming the fact that the alternating group of order 60 is simple, prove that a fifth-degree equation whose Galois group is the symmetric group of order 5! cannot be solved by radicals.

SUGGESTED READINGS

WEISNER, L. *Introduction to the Theory of Equations.* Macmillan, 1938.

DICKSON, L. E. *Modern Algebraic Theories*, Chapters VII–XIV. Sanborn, 1926.

MILLER, G. A., BLICHFELDT, H. F., and DICKSON, L. E. *Theory and Applications of Finite Groups*, Part III. Wiley, 1916.

NETTO, E., trans. by COLE, F. N. *The Theory of Substitutions and Its Applications to Algebra*, Part II. Wahr, Ann Arbor, 1892.

HAUPT, O. *Einführung in die Algebra*, Vol. II. Akad. Verlag., Leipzig, 1929.

HASSE, H. *Höhere Algebra*, Vol. II. de Gruyter, Berlin, 1927.

ALBERT, A. A. *Modern Higher Algebra*, Chapters VI, VII, VIII, IX. University of Chicago Press, 1937.

VAN DER WAERDEN, B. L. *Moderne Algebra*, Vol. I, Chapters V, VI, VII. Springer, Berlin, 1937.

CHAPTER IV

INTEGRAL ALGEBRAIC DOMAINS

48. Quadratic domains. It was seen in Theorem 34.3 that every quadratic field is of the type $Ra(\sqrt{m})$, where m is an integer with distinct prime factors. It was also seen (Theorem 35.1) that every number $\alpha = a + b\sqrt{m}$ of $Ra(\sqrt{m})$ satisfies a principal equation

$$(48.1) \qquad x^2 - 2ax + a^2 - b^2 m = 0$$

with rational coefficients.

The set of all numbers of $Ra(\sqrt{m})$ the coefficients of whose principal equations are rational integers (the coefficient of x^2 being 1) constitute the *integral domain* $Ra[\sqrt{m}]$ of $Ra(\sqrt{m})$. Numbers of $Ra[\sqrt{m}]$ will be called *integral numbers* of $Ra(\sqrt{m})$.

This definition requires some justification, which will be furnished by the theorems of the present paragraph.

Theorem 48.1. Every rational integer is in $Ra[\sqrt{m}]$. Every number of $Ra[\sqrt{m}]$ which is rational is an ordinary integer.

If a is an ordinary integer, its principal equation is

$$x^2 - 2ax + a^2 = 0.$$

If, conversely, $a + b\sqrt{m}$ is rational, then $b = 0$; if also a^2 is an integer, so is a.

Thus ordinary integers are properly termed *rational integers*.

Theorem 48.2. The conjugate of a number of $Ra[\sqrt{m}]$ is in $Ra[\sqrt{m}]$.

For α and $\bar{\alpha}$ have the same principal equation.

Theorem 48.3. If $m \equiv 2$ or 3 modulo 4, the numbers of $Ra[\sqrt{m}]$ are given by $a + b\sqrt{m}$, where a and b range over all rational integers. If $m \equiv 1$ modulo 4, the numbers of $Ra[\sqrt{m}]$ are given by $a + b\sqrt{m}$, where a and b are both integers or both halves of odd integers.

By the definition of $Ra[\sqrt{m}]$,

$$2a = h, \quad a^2 - b^2 m = k$$

are rational integers. Then

$$h^2 - 4k = 4b^2 m$$

113

is a rational integer. If $2b = l$ were not an integer, the square of its denominator would divide m, whereas m is without a square factor. Hence

$$4k = h^2 - l^2 m \equiv 0 \qquad \text{mod } 4.$$

If h is even, $h^2 \equiv 0$ mod 4, while if h is odd, $h^2 \equiv 1$ mod 4, and similarly for l. The last displayed congruence is satisfied for all m's if both h and l are even, and for no m if one is even and the other odd, since $m \not\equiv 0$ mod 4. However, if both h and l are odd, it is satisfied when and only when $m \equiv 1$ mod 4. This proves the theorem.

Consider the sets of numbers

$$S_1: \ a_1 + b_1 \sqrt{m}, \quad S_2: \ a_2 + b_2(\tfrac{1}{2} + \tfrac{1}{2}\sqrt{m})$$

where a_1, b_1 are both rational integers or both halves of odd integers, and a_2, b_2 are rational integers. If a number of S_1 equals a number of S_2,

$$b_2 = 2b_1, \quad a_2 = a_1 - b_1, \quad 2a_1 = 2a_2 + b_2.$$

If a_1 and b_1 are rational integers, so are a_2 and b_2. If a_1 and b_1 are halves of odd integers, a_2 and b_2 are integers. Thus $S_1 \subseteq S_2$.

If a_2 and b_2 are rational integers and b_2 is even, then a_1 and b_1 are integers; if b_2 is odd, $2a_1$ and $2b_1$ are both odd. Then $S_2 \subseteq S_1$.

Two numbers θ_1 and θ_2 form a *basis* for the domain $Ra[\sqrt{m}]$ if every number of the domain is given without repetition in the form $a\theta_1 + b\theta_2$, where a and b range independently over all rational integers, and if, conversely, every such number is in the domain. We have, therefore, proved

Theorem 48.4. The numbers 1 *and* θ *form a basis for* $Ra[\sqrt{m}]$ *where* $\theta = \sqrt{m}$ *if* $m \equiv 2, 3$ *mod 4 and* $\theta = \tfrac{1}{2} + \tfrac{1}{2}\sqrt{m}$ *if* $m \equiv 1$ *mod 4.*

That the numbers are given without repetition follows from the fact that 1 and θ are linearly independent.

Theorem 48.5. The set of numbers $Ra[\sqrt{m}]$ *is closed under addition, subtraction, and multiplication.*

For

$$(a_1 + b_1\theta) \pm (a_2 + b_2\theta) = (a_1 \pm a_2) + (b_1 \pm b_2)\theta.$$

Also

$$(a_1 + b_1\theta)(a_2 + b_2\theta) = a_1 a_2 + b_1 b_2 \theta^2 + (a_1 b_2 + a_2 b_1)\theta.$$

In Case I, where $m \equiv 2, 3$ mod 4, $\theta^2 = m$. In Case II, where $m \equiv 1$ mod 4,

$$\theta^2 = \theta + m', \quad m' = \tfrac{1}{4}(m - 1).$$

In each case, then, the product is again in the set.

EXERCISES

1. Find bases for $Ra[\sqrt{2}]$, $Ra[\sqrt{5}]$, and $Ra[\sqrt{-7}]$.
2. Prove that all the third and fourth roots of unity are quadratic integers.
3. Give a formal proof that 1 and θ are linearly independent.
4. Define integral quadratic number in terms of norm and trace.
5. What is the principal equation of 3α? of α^2?

49. The discriminant.

Theorem 49.1. If θ_1, θ_2 is a basis for $Ra[\sqrt{m}]$, every basis of $Ra[\sqrt{m}]$ is given by

$$\theta_1' = a_{11}\theta_1 + a_{12}\theta_2, \quad \theta_2' = a_{21}\theta_1 + a_{22}\theta_2$$

where the a_{ij} are rational integers with determinant equal to ± 1. Conversely, every such pair θ_1', θ_2' constitutes a basis for $Ra[\sqrt{m}]$.

Let θ_1, θ_2 and θ_1', θ_2' be two bases for $Ra[\sqrt{m}]$. Since θ_1' and θ_2' are integral numbers and θ_1, θ_2 form a basis,

$$\theta_1' = a_{11}\theta_1 + a_{12}\theta_2, \quad \theta_2' = a_{21}\theta_1 + a_{22}\theta_2$$

where the a's are rational integers. Since θ_1 and θ_2 are integral numbers and θ_1', θ_2' form a basis,

$$\theta_1 = b_{11}\theta_1' + b_{12}\theta_2', \quad \theta_2 = b_{21}\theta_1' + b_{22}\theta_2',$$

where the b's are rational integers. That is,

$$\theta_1 = (b_{11}a_{11} + b_{12}a_{21})\theta_1 + (b_{11}a_{12} + b_{12}a_{22})\theta_2,$$

$$\theta_2 = (b_{21}a_{11} + b_{22}a_{21})\theta_1 + (b_{21}a_{12} + b_{22}a_{22})\theta_2.$$

Since θ_1 and θ_2 are linearly independent, we equate coefficients and obtain four equations which can be written as a single matric equation

$$\begin{pmatrix} 1 & 0 \\ 0 & 1 \end{pmatrix} = \begin{pmatrix} b_{11} & b_{12} \\ b_{21} & b_{22} \end{pmatrix} \begin{pmatrix} a_{11} & a_{12} \\ a_{21} & a_{22} \end{pmatrix}.$$

Since the determinant of each matrix is an integer which divides 1, each determinant is $+1$ or each is -1.

The sufficiency of the condition is more immediate. Let θ_1, θ_2 be a basis and define

$$\theta_1' = a_{11}\theta_1 + a_{12}\theta_2, \quad \theta_2' = a_{21}\theta_1 + a_{22}\theta_2.$$

Clearly every linear combination of θ_1', θ_2' with rational integral coefficients is in $Ra[\sqrt{m}]$. If $a_{11}a_{22} - a_{12}a_{21} = \pm 1$, there exist rational integral b's such that

$$\theta_1 = b_{11}\theta_1' + b_{12}\theta_2', \quad \theta_2 = b_{21}\theta_1' + b_{22}\theta_2'.$$

Thus every number of $Ra[\sqrt{m}]$ can be written as a linear combination of θ_1', θ_2' with rational integral coefficients.

Finally, if θ_1', θ_2' were linearly dependent, and θ_1, θ_2 were linearly independent, we should have $a_{11}a_{22} - a_{12}a_{21} = 0$.

If θ_1, θ_2 is any basis for $Ra[\sqrt{m}]$, and if

$$\alpha_1 = a_1\theta_1 + b_1\theta_2, \quad \alpha_2 = a_2\theta_1 + b_2\theta_2$$

are any two numbers of $Ra[\sqrt{m}]$, we define the *discriminant* of the two numbers to be

$$\Delta(\alpha_1, \alpha_2) = \begin{vmatrix} a_1\theta_1 + b_1\theta_2 & a_2\theta_1 + b_2\theta_2 \\ a_1\bar{\theta}_1 + b_1\bar{\theta}_2 & a_2\bar{\theta}_1 + b_2\bar{\theta}_2 \end{vmatrix}^2.$$

Clearly

(49.1) $$\Delta(\alpha_1, \alpha_2) = \begin{vmatrix} \theta_1 & \theta_2 \\ \bar{\theta}_1 & \bar{\theta}_2 \end{vmatrix}^2 \begin{vmatrix} a_1 & a_2 \\ b_1 & b_2 \end{vmatrix}^2.$$

By Theorem 49.1, α_1, α_2 form a basis for $Ra[\sqrt{m}]$ if and only if $a_1b_2 - a_2b_1 = \pm 1$. Thus $\Delta(\theta_1, \theta_2)$ is an invariant under change of basis, and will be called the *discriminant of the domain* $Ra[\sqrt{m}]$, written $\Delta[\sqrt{m}]$.

The discriminant is, in fact, a rational integer. In Case I (where $m \equiv 2, 3 \bmod 4$) we may take $\theta_1 = 1$, $\theta_2 = \sqrt{m}$ and obtain $\Delta[\sqrt{m}] = 4m$. In Case II (where $m \equiv 1 \bmod 4$), we may take 1 and $\frac{1}{2} + \frac{1}{2}\sqrt{m}$ as a basis and obtain $\Delta[\sqrt{m}] = m$.

If α_1 and α_2 are any two linearly independent numbers of $Ra[\sqrt{m}]$ which do not form a basis, it follows from (49.1) that

$$\left| \Delta(\alpha_1, \alpha_2) \right| > \left| \Delta[\sqrt{m}] \right|,$$

where the bars indicate absolute value. This completes the proof of

Theorem 49.2. The discriminant $\Delta[\sqrt{m}]$ of $Ra[\sqrt{m}]$ is a rational integer $\neq 0$ independent of the basis. A necessary and sufficient condition that θ_1, θ_2 form a basis for $Ra[\sqrt{m}]$ is that $\left| \Delta(\theta_1, \theta_2) \right|$ be positive and minimal, and hence equal to $\Delta[\sqrt{m}]$.

EXERCISES

1. Prove in full the last step in the proof of Theorem 49.1.
2. If θ_1, θ_2 is any basis for $Ra[\sqrt{m}]$, prove that the conjugate of $\alpha = a\theta_1 + b\theta_2$ is $\bar{\alpha} = a\bar{\theta}_1 + b\bar{\theta}_2$.
3. Prove that $\Delta(1, \alpha)$ is the discriminant of the principal equation of α.
4. Show that $\theta_1 = 4 + \sqrt{5}$, $\theta_2 = \frac{11}{2} + \frac{3}{2}\sqrt{5}$ constitute a basis for $Ra[\sqrt{5}]$.
5. If $\theta_1 = a + b\sqrt{5}$, where $(a, b) = 1$, show how to construct another number θ_2 such that θ_1, θ_2 form a basis for $Ra[\sqrt{5}]$.

50. The complex domain. By Theorem 48.4 the numbers of $Ra[\sqrt{-1}] = Ra[i]$ are given by $a + bi$.

If $\alpha\beta = \gamma$, where α, β, γ are in $Ra[i]$, then α and β are *divisors* of γ, written $\alpha \mid \gamma$, $\beta \mid \gamma$. By Theorem 35.4

$$N(\alpha) \cdot N(\beta) = N(\gamma),$$

so that we have

Theorem 50.1. $\alpha \mid \gamma$ *implies that* $N(\alpha) \mid N(\gamma)$.

In $Ra[i]$, $N(a + bi) = a^2 + b^2$, so that every norm except $N(0)$ is a positive integer.

A *unit* ϵ of $Ra[i]$ is an integral number which divides 1. Since $\epsilon_1 \epsilon_2 = 1$ implies that

$$N(\epsilon_1) \cdot N(\epsilon_2) = N(1) = 1,$$

and $N(\epsilon_1)$ and $N(\epsilon_2)$ are both positive integers, $N(\epsilon_1) = N(\epsilon_2) = 1$. If $a^2 + b^2 = 1$, then either $a = 0$, $b = \pm 1$, or $b = 0$, $a = \pm 1$. Hence we have

Theorem 50.2. *A number* ϵ *of* $Ra[i]$ *is a unit if and only if* $N(\epsilon) = 1$. *The units are* $1, -1, i, -i$.

The numbers of $Ra[i]$ are conveniently separated into four classes: (1) Zero. (2) The units. (3) Primes. (4) Composite numbers.

A number π is a *prime* if it is neither 0 nor a unit, and if $\pi = \alpha\beta$ implies that α or β is a unit. A number not in any of the first three classes is *composite*.

If $\alpha_1 = \epsilon\alpha$, where ϵ is a unit, then α_1 and α are *associated numbers*, and α_1 is an *associate* of α. The relation is symmetric, for, if ϵ is a unit, there exists another unit ϵ_1 such that $\epsilon\epsilon_1 = 1$, and $\alpha = \epsilon_1\alpha_1$. Every number of $Ra[i]$ except 0 has just four associates including itself.

Theorem 50.3. *If* $\beta \neq 0$ *and* α *are two numbers of* $Ra[i]$, *there exist two numbers* κ *and* ρ *of* $Ra[i]$ *such that*

$$\alpha = \beta\kappa + \rho, \qquad\qquad N(\rho) < N(\beta).$$

On the complex plane (page 118) let x represent any number of the field $Ra(i)$. With x as a center, draw a circle of radius 1. There will always be at least one lattice point corresponding to a number of $Ra[i]$ within this circle.

Take for x the algebraic number α/β, and let κ be an integral number within the unit circle about x. Then $\alpha/\beta = \kappa + \nu$, where $\nu = x - \kappa$. Let

$$x = x_1 + x_2 i, \quad \kappa = k_1 + k_2 i,$$

where x_1, x_2, k_1, k_2 are rational. Then

$$N(\nu) = (x_1 - k_1)^2 + (x_2 - k_2)^2$$

is the square of the distance from x to κ and hence is < 1. Let $\nu\beta = \rho$.

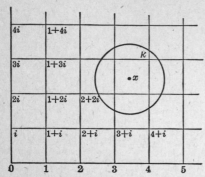

Since $\rho = \alpha - \beta\kappa$, ρ is integral. Since

$$N(\rho) = N(\nu) \cdot N(\beta),$$

we have $N(\rho) < N(\beta)$, thus completing the proof.

If $\delta \mid \alpha$ and $\delta \mid \beta$, and if, furthermore, every common divisor of α and β divides δ, then δ is called a *greatest common divisor* (g.c.d.) of α and β, written (α, β).

Theorem 50.4. Every pair of numbers of $Ra[i]$ not both 0 has a g.c.d. δ. It is unique up to an associate, and is expressible linearly in terms of the given numbers.

If $N(\alpha) > N(\beta)$, determine ρ by Theorem 50.3 so that

$$\alpha = \kappa\beta + \rho, \qquad\qquad N(\rho) < N(\beta).$$

Continue the process, obtaining

$$\beta = \kappa_1\rho + \rho_1, \qquad\qquad N(\rho_1) < N(\rho),$$

$$\rho = \kappa_2\rho_1 + \rho_2, \qquad\qquad N(\rho_2) < N(\rho_1),$$

$$\cdots\cdots\cdots\qquad\qquad\cdots\cdots\cdots$$

until we arrive at a ρ_k with norm 0. Since $N(\beta) > N(\rho) > N(\rho_1) > \cdots$ form a sequence of decreasing positive integers, this point will be reached in a finite number of steps. Then $\rho_k = 0$, and $\rho_{k-1} = (\alpha, \beta)$ as in the proof of Theorem 3.3.

Also as in the proof of Theorem 3.4, two numbers μ, ν of $Ra[i]$ can be determined such that

$$\rho_{k-1} = \delta = \mu\alpha + \nu\beta.$$

If δ_1 is also a g.c.d. of α and β,

$$\delta = \lambda_1\delta_1, \quad \delta_1 = \lambda_2\delta, \quad \delta = \lambda_1\lambda_2\delta, \quad N(\delta) = N(\lambda_1) \cdot N(\lambda_2) \cdot N(\delta).$$

Since $N(\delta) \neq 0$, $N(\lambda_1) = N(\lambda_2) = 1$, and λ_1 and λ_2 are units by Theorem 50.2. Thus δ and δ_1 are associated.

If every common divisor of two numbers α and β is a unit, the numbers are said to be *relatively prime*. Evidently every unit is a g.c.d. of two relatively prime numbers, and we have in particular

Corollary 50.4. *If α and β are relatively prime, there exist numbers* μ, ν *in* $Ra[i]$ *such that* $\mu\alpha + \nu\beta = 1$.

EXERCISES

1. Find a g.c.d. of $-23 + 2i$ and $13i$.
2. Find a g.c.d. of $112 + i$ and $-57 + 79i$.
3. Show that every number of $Ra[i]$ is associated with one and only one number in the first quadrant.
4. Prove that if $\alpha_1, \alpha_2, \cdots, \alpha_n$ are integers of $Ra[i]$ not all 0, there exists a g.c.d. δ expressible in the form

$$\delta = \mu_1\alpha_1 + \mu_2\alpha_2 + \cdots + \mu_n\alpha_n.$$

5. Prove Theorem 50.4 as follows: Let $\delta = \mu_1\alpha + \nu_1\beta$ be a number of minimum positive norm which can be represented linearly in terms of α and β. Show that $\delta = (\alpha, \beta)$. (See Ex. 5, § 3.)
6. If $\delta = (\alpha, \beta)$, prove that $N(\delta)$ is a common divisor of $N(\alpha)$ and $N(\beta)$ but is not necessarily their g.c.d.

HINT: Take $\alpha = 18 + i$, $\beta = 5$.

51. Complex primes.

Theorem 51.1. *If $\alpha \mid \beta\gamma$ and is relatively prime to β, then $\alpha \mid \gamma$.*

For, if α is prime to β, there are a μ and a ν such that

$$1 = \mu\alpha + \nu\beta, \quad \gamma = \gamma\mu\alpha + \gamma\beta\nu,$$

Since α divides the right member, it divides γ.

Corollary 51.1. *If the prime π divides $\beta_1\beta_2 \cdots \beta_k$, it divides some β_i.*

Theorem 51.2. *Every composite number can be factored into a finite number of primes.*

Suppose that α is neither 0 nor a unit. If it is not a prime, it can be written as a product, and each factor which is not prime can be written as a product, and so on. But

$$\alpha = \alpha_1\alpha_2 \cdots \alpha_n$$

implies that

$$N(\alpha) = N(\alpha_1) \cdot N(\alpha_2) \cdots N(\alpha_n)$$

by Theorem 35.4, and, unless α_i is a unit, $N(\alpha_i)$ is an integer > 1. But $N(\alpha)$ can have but a finite number of factors each > 1.

Theorem 51.3. *If a composite complex integer is written*

$$\lambda = \alpha_1\alpha_2 \cdots \alpha_k = \beta_1\beta_2 \cdots \beta_l,$$

where each α and each β is a prime, then $k = l$, and the α's and β's can be grouped into associated pairs $\beta_i = \epsilon_i \alpha_i$.

This is the analogue of the Fundamental Theorem of Arithmetic (Theorem 4.2).

Since α_1 is a prime, it divides some β (Corollary 51.1), say β_1. Since β_1 is also a prime, $\beta_1 = \epsilon_1 \alpha_1$, where ϵ_1 is a unit. Then

$$\alpha_2 \alpha_3 \cdots \alpha_k = \epsilon_1 \beta_2 \beta_3 \cdots \beta_l.$$

Then α_2 divides one of the remaining β's, say β_2, and $\beta_2 = \epsilon_2 \alpha_2$. Suppose that $l < k$. After l steps we should have a product of α's equal to a unit, which is impossible. Similarly $k < l$ is impossible.

Every complex prime π divides its norm and therefore divides some smallest positive integer. This smallest integer is a rational prime, for, if $\pi \mid n_1 n_2$, then $\pi \mid n_1$ or $\pi \mid n_2$ by Corollary 51.1. We obtain all primes of $Ra[i]$, then, if we factor all rational primes into their complex factors.

Theorem 51.4. If p is a rational prime $\equiv 3 \bmod 4$, then p is a complex prime. If $p \equiv 1 \bmod 4$, p is a product of two conjugate complex primes. And $2 = (1 + i)(1 - i) = i(1 - i)^2$. Every complex prime is thus obtained.

Let p be the smallest rational prime which the complex prime π divides. Then

$$p = \pi\alpha, \quad p^2 = N(\pi) \cdot N(\alpha).$$

Either α is a unit, or $N(\alpha) > 1$ so that $N(\pi) = N(\alpha) = p$. If $\pi = a + bi$, then $p = a^2 + b^2$. Since the square of every rational integer is $\equiv 0$ or $1 \bmod 4$ according as the integer is even or odd, and since every odd prime is $\equiv 1$ or $3 \bmod 4$, we must have

$$p = a^2 + b^2 \equiv 1 \qquad \bmod 4.$$

Hence every prime of the form $p = 4k + 3$ is a complex prime.

Let $p \equiv 1 \bmod 4$. Then $(-1/p) = 1$ (Theorem 18.5), and there exists a rational integer a such that

$$a^2 + 1 \equiv 0 \qquad \bmod p.$$

Then $(a + i)(a - i) = kp$. If p were a complex prime it would divide either $a + i$ or $a - i$ by Corollary 51.1. But, if

$$p(c + di) = a \pm i,$$

we should have $pd = \pm 1$, whereas p is a rational prime. Since p is neither a complex prime nor a unit, it is composite.

Evidently α is also a prime, for $\beta \mid \alpha$ implies $N(\beta) \mid N(\alpha)$ by Theorem 35.4, and $N(\alpha) = p$, a prime. Now $N(\pi) = \pi\bar{\pi} = p = \pi\alpha$. Hence, by Theorem 51.3, $\alpha = \bar{\pi}$.

The only rational prime $\not\equiv 1$ or $3 \bmod 4$ is 2, and clearly $2 = (1 + i)(1 - i)$.

EXERCISES

1. Factor 65 into its complex prime factors.

2. Show that 2 and all odd primes of the type $4k + 1$ can be uniquely expressed as a sum of two squares of rational integers, and that no prime of the type $4k + 3$ can be so expressed.

3. Let $n = p_1 p_2 \cdots p_l$ where the p's are distinct odd primes. Then n can be represented as a sum of two squares if and only if each p_i is $\equiv 1 \bmod 4$. The number of representations is then 2^{l-1}.

4. Extend the definition of the Legendre symbol (see § 18) so that $(a/p) = 0$ means $p \mid a$. Prove that p is a complex prime, the product of two conjugate non-associated complex primes, or associated with the square of a complex prime, according as $(\Delta[i]/p) = -1$ or 1 or 0.

52. The concept of ideal. Since $-5 \equiv 3 \bmod 4$, the integral numbers of $Ra[\sqrt{-5}]$ are $a + b\sqrt{-5}$, where a and b are rational integers. Since

$$N(a + b\sqrt{-5}) = a^2 + 5b^2$$

is never negative, $\alpha\beta = 1$ implies that $N(\alpha) \cdot N(\beta) = 1$, which in turn implies that $N(\alpha) = N(\beta) = 1$. The units, then, are $+1$ and -1.

Theorem 52.1. Unique factorization into primes does not exist in $Ra[\sqrt{-5}]$

A single instance will establish this fact. Evidently

$$9 = 3\cdot 3 = (2 + \sqrt{-5})(2 - \sqrt{-5}).$$

It is clear that neither $2 + \sqrt{-5}$ nor $2 - \sqrt{-5}$ is associated with 3, and we shall show that none of these three numbers can be factored. Suppose that

$$(x_1 + y_1\sqrt{-5})(x_2 + y_2\sqrt{-5}) = \beta,$$

where β is either 3 or $2 + \sqrt{-5}$ or $2 - \sqrt{-5}$. Then

$$N(x_1 + y_1\sqrt{-5})\cdot N(x_2 + y_2\sqrt{-5}) = N(\beta) = 9.$$

Unless one of the factors of β is a unit,

$$N(x_1 + y_1\sqrt{-5}) = x_1^2 + 5y_1^2 = 3.$$

This equation is not solvable in integers.

In order to overcome the difficulties occasioned by the lack of unique factorization, Kummer postulated the existence of ideal numbers into which the indecomposable factors should factor. Thus he would set

$$3 = jk, \quad 2 + \sqrt{-5} = j^2, \quad 2 - \sqrt{-5} = k^2,$$

so that

$$9 = 3 \cdot 3 = (jk)^2 = j^2 k^2 = (2 + \sqrt{-5})(2 - \sqrt{-5}).$$

The theory was placed upon a rigorous foundation by Dedekind, whose development will be followed essentially.

If every pair of numbers of $Ra[\sqrt{-5}]$ not both 0 had a g.c.d. expressible linearly in terms of the numbers, we could prove unique factorization. (See Theorems 51.1, 51.2, 51.3.) It is this lack of a g.c.d. which is the fundamental difficulty.

Dedekind's point of attack may be seen from a simple example from ordinary number theory. Consider the set S of positive integers which are $\equiv 1$ modulo 7. This set is closed under multiplication. A number of S may be called prime if it cannot be written as a product of two numbers of S. Factorization into primes is not unique, e.g.,

$$792 = 22 \cdot 36 = 8 \cdot 99,$$

where 22, 36, 8, 99 are all primes.

Of course, the difficulty is due to the absence from S of the other integers. The problem is to introduce these missing numbers in a notation involving only the numbers of S. Let (a, b) denote the g.c.d. of a and b. Then

$$2 = (22, 36), \quad 4 = (8, 36), \quad 9 = (36, 99), \quad 11 = (22, 99).$$

Thus

$$792 = (22, 36)(8, 36)(36, 99)(22, 99)$$

is uniquely factored into "ideal" numbers.

Since the set S is not closed under addition, we can carry the analogy no further. But Ex. 5, § 50, gives a further clue. The set of numbers $\mu\alpha + \nu\beta$ of $Ra[i]$ consists exactly of the multiples of $\delta = (\alpha, \beta)$. Set up the correspondence

$$\mu\alpha + \nu\beta \leftrightarrow (\alpha, \beta).$$

The problem is so to define multiplication of sets that this correspondence shall be an isomorphism. In $Ra[\sqrt{-5}]$, two numbers α and β do not necessarily have a g.c.d. The sets $\mu\alpha + \nu\beta$ where μ and ν range independently over $Ra[\sqrt{-5}]$ do exist, however, and are the "ideals" of $Ra[\sqrt{-5}]$. We shall see later that Kummer's ideal numbers are representable in this way.

EXERCISES

1. Show that, in the set of numbers of the form $5k + 1$, 336 is factorable into primes in two ways. Find the ideal factors.

2. Show that the numbers of the set $\mu\alpha + \nu\beta$ of $Ra[\sqrt{-5}]$ form an additive abelian group, and that the set is also closed under multiplication by the numbers of $Ra[\sqrt{-5}]$.

3. In the domain of rational integers, show that

$$I_1 = x_1 a + y_1 b \leftrightarrow (a, b), \quad I_2 = x_2 c + y_2 d \leftrightarrow (c, d)$$

is an isomorphism if we define

$$I_1 I_2 = xac + ybc + zad + wbd,$$

where x, y, z, w range independently over all rational integers.

53. Quadratic ideals. An *ideal* of $Ra[\sqrt{m}]$ is a set of integral numbers of $Ra[\sqrt{m}]$ not all 0 which is a group relative to addition, and which is closed under multiplication by all the numbers of $Ra[\sqrt{m}]$.

Theorem 53.1.   In every ideal there exist two numbers ω_1, ω_2 such that the numbers of the ideal are given by

$$k_1 \omega_1 + k_2 \omega_2$$

where k_1, k_2 range over the rational integers.

These numbers form a *minimal basis* for the ideal.

Let 1, θ be a basis for $Ra[\sqrt{m}]$. If $\alpha \neq 0$ is a number of the ideal A, then A contains $\pm \alpha\bar{\alpha} = \pm N(\alpha)$, and so A contains positive integers. Let ω_1 be the smallest positive integer in A. Of all numbers $l_1 + l_2\theta$ in A having $l_2 \neq 0$, choose as ω_2 one such in which l_2 is positive and minimal. Let $\alpha = a_1 + a_2\,\theta$ be any number of A.   Write

$$a_2 = l_2 k_2 + r_2, \qquad\qquad 0 \leqq r_2 < l_2.$$

Then

$$\alpha - k_2\omega_2 = (a_1 - k_2 l_1) + r_2\theta$$

is in A, and if r_2 were not zero, the definition of ω_2 would be violated. Thus $\alpha - k_2\omega_2 = a_1 - k_2 l_1 = b$. Now write

$$b = \omega_1 k_1 + r_1, \qquad\qquad 0 \leqq r_1 < \omega_1,$$

so that $\alpha - k_2\omega_2 - k_1\omega_1 = r_1$. Since ω_1 was minimal, $r_1 = 0$, and

$$\alpha = k_1\omega_1 + k_2\omega_2.$$

Corollary 53.1.   Every rational integer in A is divisible by ω_1.

Theorem 53.2.   If ω_1, ω_2 is a minimal basis for an ideal A in $Ra[\sqrt{m}]$, every minimal basis is given by

$$\omega_1' = a_{11}\omega_1 + a_{12}\omega_2, \qquad \omega_2' = a_{21}\omega_1 + a_{22}\omega_2,$$

where the a's are rational integers such that

$$\begin{vmatrix} a_{11} & a_{12} \\ a_{21} & a_{22} \end{vmatrix} = \pm 1,$$

and every such pair ω_1', ω_2' is a minimal basis.

The proof follows as in Theorem 49.1.

Theorem 53.3.   Every ideal A has a minimal basis k, $l + r\theta$, where k is the smallest positive integer in A and $0 \leqq l < k$.

In the proof of Theorem 53.1, we saw that we could choose a basis $\omega_1 = k$, $\omega_2 = m + r\theta$, where k was the smallest positive integer in A. Set

$$m = qk + l, \qquad\qquad 0 \leqq l < k.$$

The transformation

$$\omega_1' = \omega_1 = k, \quad \omega_2' = \omega_2 - q\omega_1 = l + r\theta$$

is of determinant 1, so the result follows from Theorem 53.2.

Theorem 53.4.   Every ideal A has a minimal basis of the form

$$\omega_1 = ra, \qquad \omega_2 = r(b + \theta),$$

where r and a are positive integers, and $0 \leqq b < a$, and θ is defined as in Theorem 48.4.   Moreover,

$$b^2 - m \equiv 0 \qquad \mod a, \qquad b^2 + b + \tfrac{1}{4}(1 - m) \equiv 0 \qquad \mod a,$$

in Cases I and II, respectively.

Such a basis is called a *canonical basis*.

We shall prove this for Case I.   Use the notation of Theorem 53.3. Since k is in A, $k\theta$ is in A.   Set

$$k = ar + t, \qquad\qquad 0 \leqq t < r.$$

Then

$$k\theta - a\omega_2 = -al + t\theta$$

is in A.   This is impossible unless $t = 0$, in which case $r \mid k$.   Hence

$$\omega_1 = ra, \qquad \omega_2 = l + r\theta.$$

Since $l + r\theta$ is in A, so is $l\theta + r\theta^2 = rm + l\theta$. Set

$$l = br + t_1, \qquad\qquad 0 \le t_1 < r.$$

Then

$$rm + l\theta - b\omega_2 = rm - bl + t_1\theta$$

is in A, so $t_1 = 0$ and $r \mid l$. Hence there is a basis

$$\omega_1 = ra, \quad \omega_2 = r(b + \theta),$$

where r and a are positive. Since, by Theorem 53.3, $0 \le rb < ra$, we have $0 \le b < a$.

Since $\theta\omega_2 - b\omega_2 = rm - rb^2$ is a rational integer in A, it is divisible by ra by Corollary 53.1. That is,

$$b^2 - m \equiv 0 \qquad \bmod a.$$

EXERCISES

1. An ideal has a minimal basis $(13 + 4\sqrt{-5},\ 9 + 3\sqrt{-5})$. Find a canonical basis.

2. Show that, if ω_1, ω_2 is a minimal basis for A, the numbers of A are given by both forms

$$k_1\omega_1 + k_2\omega_2, \quad \mu\omega_1 + \nu\omega_2,$$

where k_1, k_2 range over all rational integers while μ, ν range over the numbers of $Ra[\sqrt{m}]$.

3. Prove Theorem 53.4 for Case II.

4. Prove that every two numbers ω_1, ω_2 satisfying the conditions of Theorem 53.4 form a minimal basis of an ideal.

5. The ideal (α) is composed of the multiples of α. Show that $(\alpha, \alpha\theta)$ is a minimal basis for (α), and that, if α is a positive rational integer, this basis is canonical.

54. Multiplication of ideals. The *product* AB of two ideals A and B is defined to be the set of all numbers obtained by multiplying every number of A by every number of B, and then adding and subtracting these numbers until no new ones are obtained. This set of numbers satisfies the definition of ideal.

If $A = (\omega_1, \omega_2)$, and $B = (\chi_1, \chi_2)$, then AB consists of the numbers

$$k_1\omega_1\chi_1 + k_2\omega_1\chi_2 + k_3\omega_2\chi_1 + k_4\omega_2\chi_2,$$

where k_1, k_2, k_3, k_4 range over all rational integers, or over all numbers of $Ra[\sqrt{m}]$. We shall sometimes use one representation and sometimes the other.

It is evident that ideal multiplication is associative and commutative. If all the numbers of an ideal A are multiples by numbers of $Ra[\sqrt{m}]$

of one number α, the ideal A is called *principal* and is written (α). We shall see that, in those and only those domains in which every ideal is principal, we have unique factorization into primes (Theorem 58.2).

Theorem 54.1. If every number of an ideal A is replaced by its conjugate, the resulting set is an ideal $\bar{A}$.

This ideal $\bar{A}$ is called the *conjugate* of A.
The theorem follows from Corollary 35.3 and the definition of ideal.

Theorem 54.2. $\overline{AB} = \bar{A}\bar{B}$.

If $A = (\omega_1, \omega_2)$ and $B = (\chi_1, \chi_2)$, then

$$AB = (\overline{\omega_1\chi_1}, \overline{\omega_1\chi_2}, \overline{\omega_2\chi_1}, \overline{\omega_2\chi_2}),$$

$$\bar{A}\bar{B} = (\overline{\omega_1}\,\overline{\chi_1}, \overline{\omega_1}\,\overline{\chi_2}, \overline{\omega_2}\,\overline{\chi_1}, \overline{\omega_2}\,\overline{\chi_2}).$$

Theorem 54.3. If $A = (ra, r(b + \theta))$, then $A\bar{A} = (r^2a)$.

The number r^2a is called the *norm* of A, written $N(A)$.

In Case I the product $A\bar{A}$ consists of all numbers

(54.1) $\kappa r^2 a^2 + \lambda r^2 a(b + \theta) + \mu r^2 a(b - \theta) + \nu r^2(b^2 - m)$,

where κ, λ, μ, ν range over all numbers of $Ra[\sqrt{m}]$. By Theorem 53.4 $c = (b^2 - m)/a$ is an integer. The transformation

$$\kappa = \kappa_1, \quad \lambda = \lambda_1 + \nu_1, \quad \mu = \lambda_1, \quad \nu = \mu_1$$

takes the set of numbers (54.1) into the set

(54.2) $\kappa_1 r^2 a^2 + \lambda_1 2r^2 ab + \mu_1 r^2 ac + \nu_1 r^2 a(b + \theta)$.

Hence every number of (54.2) is in (54.1). The converse is true, since

$$\kappa_1 = \kappa, \quad \lambda_1 = \mu, \quad \mu_1 = \nu, \quad \nu_1 = \lambda - \mu.$$

Suppose that a and c were both even. Then $b^2 - m = ac \equiv 0 \bmod 4$. But $b^2 \equiv 0$ or $1 \bmod 4$ according as b is even or odd, and neither of these agrees with the fact that $m \equiv 2$ or $3 \bmod 4$. Hence a and c are not both even.

Let $g = (a, 2b, c)$. Since a and c are not both even, g is odd and so $g \mid b$. Then

$$b^2 - m \equiv ac \equiv 0 \qquad \bmod g^2$$

implies $m \equiv 0 \bmod g^2$. Since m has no square factor > 1, $g = 1$.
We can now see that the set of numbers

(54.3) $\kappa_1 r^2 a^2 + \lambda_1 2r^2 ab + \mu_1 r^2 ac$

is the same as the set $\rho r^2 a$. Obviously every number of (54.3) is in $\rho r^2 a$.
Since a, $2b$, and c are relatively prime, there exist rational integers
p, q, t such that

$$1 = pa + 2qb + tc.$$

Multiply through by $r^2 a$. Then

$$r^2 a = pr^2 a^2 + 2qr^2 ab + tr^2 ac$$

so that every number of $\rho r^2 a$ is in (54.3).

The set (54.2) is now seen to be equal to the set

(54.4) $\qquad\qquad\qquad \rho r^2 a + \nu_1 r^2 a(b + \theta).$

But obviously every number of this set is a multiple of $r^2 a$, and, conversely, every multiple of $r^2 a$ is in the set, indeed with $\nu_1 = 0$. Thus
$A\bar{A} = (r^2 a)$ in Case I.

The proof in Case II is similar.

*Theorem 54.4. The norm of the product of two ideals is equal to the
product of their norms.*

By Theorems 54.2 and 54.3,

$$(N(AB)) = AB \cdot \overline{AB} = A\bar{A} \cdot B\bar{B} = (N(A)) \cdot (N(B)).$$

The numbers of $(N(AB))$ are the multiples of $N(AB)$. By the definition of ideal multiplication, the numbers of $(N(A)) \cdot (N(B))$ are the multiples of $N(A) \cdot N(B)$. Thus $N(AB)$ and $N(A) \cdot N(B)$ divide each other.
Since they are positive integers, they are equal.

In reducing an ideal to a simpler form, any bi-integral transformation
may be applied. That is, two ideals $(\alpha_1, \alpha_2, \cdots, \alpha_k)$ and $(\beta_1, \beta_2, \cdots, \beta_l)$
are equal if there exists a transformation

$$\alpha_i = \sum_j \kappa_{ij}\beta_j, \quad \beta_i = \sum_j \lambda_{ij}\alpha_j,$$

where the κ's and λ's belong to $Ra[\sqrt{m}]$. In particular we may:

1. Multiply any α_i by a unit.
2. Add to any α_i a linear combination of the other α's.
3. Replace any set of α's by their g.c.d.

Thus, if δ is a g.c.d. of α_1, α_2, α_3, we have

$$\alpha_1 = \kappa_1 \delta, \quad \alpha_2 = \kappa_2 \delta, \quad \alpha_3 = \kappa_3 \delta, \quad \delta = \lambda_1 \alpha_1 + \lambda_2 \alpha_2 + \lambda_3 \alpha_3,$$

so that every linear combination of α_1, α_2, α_3 is a multiple of δ, and
conversely. In a domain without unique factorization, (3) must be

used with care. However, any set of rational integers in the ideal may be replaced by their g.c.d., and, if $\alpha_1 \mid \alpha_2$, then α_2 may be deleted.

EXERCISES

1. Let $A = (a_{11} + a_{12}\theta, a_{21} + a_{22}\theta)$. Prove that $N(A) = \mid a_{11}a_{22} - a_{12}a_{21} \mid$.
2. Prove Case II of Theorem 54.3.
3. Find a canonical basis for $(\sqrt{-5})$ in $Ra[\sqrt{-5}]$.
4. Show that $(3, \frac{1}{2}(1 + \sqrt{13}))$ is principal in $Ra[\sqrt{13}]$.
5. Prove that $(3, 1 + \sqrt{-5})(3, 1 - \sqrt{-5}) = (3)$.
6. Prove that $(3, 1 + \sqrt{-5})^2 = (2 - \sqrt{-5})$.
7. If (α) is a principal ideal, show that $N((\alpha)) = \alpha\bar{\alpha}$.

55. Division of ideals.

Theorem 55.1. If $SA = SB$, where S, A, and B are ideals, then $A = B$.

The numbers of A are given by

$$\kappa_1\omega_1 + \kappa_2\omega_2,$$

where ω_1, ω_2 form a basis for A and κ_1, κ_2 are in $Ra[\sqrt{m}]$. Let $s = N(S)$. The numbers of (s) are given by λs. Thus the numbers of $(s)A$ consist of the numbers

$$\lambda\kappa_1 s\omega_1 + \lambda\kappa_2 s\omega_2 = \eta_1 s\omega_1 + \eta_2 s\omega_2$$

where η_1, η_2 range over $Ra[\sqrt{m}]$. Thus every number of $(s)A$ is of the form $s\alpha$ where α is in A.

If $SA = SB$, then $\bar{S}SA = \bar{S}SB$, and by Theorem 54.3,

$$(s)A = (s)B,$$

where s is a rational integer. That is, for every number α in A there is a number β in B such that

$$s\alpha = s\beta, \quad \alpha = \beta,$$

and conversely. Hence every α is in B and every β is in A, so that $A = B$.

If three ideals A, B, C of the same domain are in the relation $AB = C$, we say that $A \mid C$ and $B \mid C$. A and B are called *factors* of C.

Theorem 55.2. $A \mid C$ if and only if every number of C is in A.

If $A = (\omega_1, \omega_2)$ and $B = (\chi_1, \chi_2)$, then $AB = C$ consists of all numbers

$$\kappa\omega_1\chi_1 + \lambda\omega_1\chi_2 + \mu\omega_2\chi_1 + \nu\omega_2\chi_2,$$

where κ, λ, μ, ν vary over $Ra[\sqrt{m}]$. But this form can be written in either of the two ways

$$(\kappa\chi_1 + \lambda\chi_2)\omega_1 + (\mu\chi_1 + \nu\chi_2)\omega_2, \quad (\kappa\omega_1 + \mu\omega_2)\chi_1 + (\lambda\omega_1 + \nu\omega_2)\chi_2,$$

so that every number of C is in A and also in B.

Conversely, suppose that every number of C is in A. Then every number of $C\bar{A}$ is in $A\bar{A} = (a)$, where a is a positive integer (Theorem 54.3). That is, all numbers of $C\bar{A}$ are given by βa, where β varies over a certain set B of numbers of the domain. We shall prove that B is an ideal.

Since $C\bar{A}$ is an ideal, for every two numbers $\beta_1 a$ and $\beta_2 a$ of $C\bar{A}$ there are numbers $\beta_3 a$, $\beta_4 a$, and $\beta_5 a$ of $C\bar{A}$ such that

$$\beta_1 a + \beta_2 a = \beta_3 a, \quad \beta_1 a - \beta_2 a = \beta_4 a, \quad \kappa\beta_1 a = \beta_5 a$$

for every κ in $Ra[\sqrt{m}]$. Hence

$$\beta_1 + \beta_2 = \beta_3, \quad \beta_1 - \beta_2 = \beta_4, \quad \kappa\beta_1 = \beta_5,$$

so that B is an ideal.

It follows from Theorem 55.1 and

$$\bar{A}C = (a)\cdot B = \bar{A}AB$$

that

$$C = AB.$$

Theorem 55.3. *A positive integer t occurs in but a finite number of ideals.*

Let the ideal A containing t have a canonical basis $(ra, rb + r\theta)$, where $r > 0$, $a > 0$, $0 \leqq b < a$. By Corollary 53.1, $ra \mid t$. For a given t, there are not more than t choices for each of the positive integers r, a, and b, and therefore not more than t^3 such ideals A.

Theorem 55.4. *An ideal C is divisible by only a finite number of ideals.*

By Theorem 54.3, $C\bar{C} = (c)$, where c is a positive integer. By Theorem 55.2, c is in C and also in every ideal which divides C. By Theorem 55.3, there is but a finite number of such divisors.

EXERCISES

1. Prove that the set of all numbers of $Ra[\sqrt{m}]$ constitute the unit ideal (1).
2. Prove that $(\alpha) = (\beta)$, where α and β are in $Ra[\sqrt{m}]$ if and only if α and β are associated.
3. Show that $A = (1)$ if and only if $N(A) = 1$.
4. Show that $(3, 1 + \sqrt{-5})$ is a prime ideal.

56. Factorization of ideals. If an ideal P different from the unit ideal (1) is divisible by no ideal other than itself and (1), it is called a *prime ideal*. All other ideals except (1) are *composite*.

An ideal G is called a *greatest common divisor* of A and B if $G \mid A$ and $G \mid B$, and if every common divisor of A and B divides G.

Theorem 56.1. *Every pair of ideals A and B possesses a unique g.c.d., G. It is composed of all numbers $\alpha + \beta$ where α ranges over A and β over B.*

The set G of all numbers $\alpha + \beta$ satisfies the definition of ideal. Since every number of A is in G and every number of B is in G, G is a common divisor of A and B.

Let E be any common ideal divisor of A and B—that is, any ideal containing all the numbers of A and all the numbers of B. Since it is closed under addition, it contains all numbers $\alpha + \beta$ of G and hence divides G.

Suppose that G and G_1 are two g.c.d.'s of A and B. Then $G = K_1 G_1$, $G_1 = KG$, so that $(1)G = K_1 KG$. Hence $K_1 K = (1)$ by Theorem 55.1. Since $N(K_1) \cdot N(K) = 1$,

$$K_1 = K = (1)$$

by Ex. 3, § 55.

Two ideals are called *relatively prime* if their g.c.d. is (1).

Corollary 56.1. *If A and B are relatively prime, there exists an α in A and a β in B such that $\alpha + \beta = 1$.*

Theorem 56.2. *If $A \mid BC$ and is prime to B, then $A \mid C$.*

If A is prime to B, by Corollary 56.1

$$\alpha + \beta = 1, \quad \gamma\alpha + \gamma\beta = \gamma,$$

for every γ in C. Since $A \mid BC$, the number $\gamma\beta$ of BC is in A. So is $\gamma\alpha$, and so therefore is γ. Then $A \mid C$ by Theorem 55.2.

Theorem 56.3. *Every composite ideal can be factored into prime ideals in one and, except for order of the factors, in only one way.*

That every ideal can be factored into a finite number of prime ideals follows from Theorem 55.4. The uniqueness follows from Theorem 56.2. The proof is entirely similar to that of Theorem 4.2.

EXERCISES

1. Find the g.c.d. of (3) and $(2 + \sqrt{-5})$. (See § 52.)
2. Find the g.c.d. of $(5, -4 + \sqrt{-14})$ and $(13, 5 - 12\sqrt{-14})$.
3. Prove that every pair of ideals A and B possesses a *least common multiple* $[A, B]$ composed of all numbers common to A and B.
4. If $A\bar{A} = (p)$ where p is a rational prime, then A is a prime ideal.

57. Determination of all prime ideals.

Theorem 57.1. *If P is a prime ideal, either $P = (p)$ or else $P\overline{P} = (p)$, where p is a rational prime.*

By Theorem 54.3, $P\overline{P} = (c)$, where c is a positive integer. Let $c = p_1 p_2 \cdots p_k$, where the p's are positive primes. Then

$$P\overline{P} = (c) = (p_1)(p_2) \cdots (p_k).$$

Since P is a prime ideal, P divides some (p_i) by Theorem 56.2. Let $PQ = (p)$. Then

$$N(P) \cdot N(Q) = N((p)) = p^2$$

by Theorem 54.4 and Ex. 7, § 54. If $N(Q) = 1$, $Q = (1)$ by Ex. 3, § 55, and $P = (p)$. If $N(Q) \neq 1$, $N(P) = p$, $P\overline{P} = (N(P)) = (p)$.

Theorem 57.2. *Let p be an odd positive prime. If $p \mid m$, then (p) is the square of a prime ideal. Otherwise (p) is the product of two distinct prime ideals or is a prime ideal according as $(m/p) = +1$ or -1.*

If $(p) = P\overline{P}$, where $P = (ra, r(b + \theta))$, then $N(P) = r^2 a = p$, so that $r = 1$, $a = p$. Then $P = (p, b + \theta)$, where $b < p$ is a root of one of the congruences

(57.1) $\qquad x^2 \equiv m \quad \mod p, \qquad x^2 + x + \tfrac{1}{4}(1 - m) \equiv 0 \quad \mod p,$

in Cases I and II, respectively, by Theorem 53.4. Since p is odd, this second congruence is equivalent to

(57.2) $\qquad\qquad\qquad (2x + 1)^2 \equiv m \quad \mod p.$

In each case, then, if $(m/p) = -1$, there exists no b, and (p) cannot be factored.

In Case I, if $p \mid m$ there is a value of b which satisfies (57.1), namely, $b = 0$. Then $P = (p, \theta)$, $\overline{P} = (p, -\theta) = (p, \theta)$, and by Theorem 54.3, $(p) = P\overline{P} = P^2$. We leave Case II as an exercise.

If $(m/p) = 1$, (57.1) has a root $b \not\equiv 0$. The ideals $P = (p, b + \theta)$ and $\overline{P} = (p, b - \theta)$ are unequal, for their equality would imply the existence of rational integers k and l such that

$$b + \theta = kp + lb - l\theta.$$

This would imply that $l = -1$, $2b = kp$, $p \mid b$, whereas $b < p$.

Theorem 57.3. *If $m \equiv 2 \mod 4$, (2) is the square of the prime ideal $(2, \theta)$. If $m \equiv 3 \mod 4$, (2) is the square of the prime ideal $(2, 1 + \theta)$. If $m \equiv 1 \mod 8$, (2) is the product of the distinct prime ideals $(2, \theta)$ and $(2, 1 - \theta)$. If $m \equiv 5 \mod 8$, (2) is prime.*

If $m \equiv 2 \bmod 4$, (57.1) becomes $x^2 \equiv 0 \bmod 2$, so that $b \equiv 0$ and $P = (2, \theta)$, $\overline{P} = (2, -\theta) = (2, \theta)$.

If $m \equiv 3 \bmod 4$, (57.1) becomes $x^2 \equiv 1 \bmod 2$ so that $b \equiv 1$ and $P = (2, 1 + \theta)$, $\overline{P} = (2, 1 - \theta) = (2, 1 + \theta)$.

If $m \equiv 1 \bmod 8$, $m' = \frac{1}{4}(m - 1) \equiv 0 \bmod 2$, so that (57.1) gives $x^2 + x \equiv 0 \bmod 2$. This has a solution $b \equiv 0$, so that

$$P = (2, \theta), \quad \overline{P} = (2, 1 - \theta) \neq P.$$

If $m \equiv 5 \bmod 8$, $m' \equiv 1 \bmod 2$, and the congruence $x^2 + x + 1 \equiv 0 \bmod 2$ has no solution, so that (2) is prime.

EXERCISES

1. Complete the proof for Case II of Theorem 57.2.

2. Prove that (p) is a square if and only if p divides the discriminant of $Ra[\sqrt{m}]$.

3. Show that Theorem 51.4 is a special case of Theorems 57.2 and 57.3.

4. Find six units of the domain $Ra[\sqrt{2}]$. Prove that the number of units is infinite.

58. The laws of arithmetic for ideals. The principal ideals in $Ra[\sqrt{m}]$ are homomorphic (see § 24) under multiplication with the numbers of $Ra[\sqrt{m}]$ (0 excepted), for $\alpha\beta = \gamma$ implies that $(\alpha)(\beta) = (\gamma)$. The correspondence between numbers α of the domain and principal ideals (α) is k-to-1, where k is the cardinal number (finite or infinite) of units in the domain, for $(\alpha) = (\epsilon\alpha)$, where ϵ is a unit. Thus associated numbers determine the same principal ideal.

Theorem 58.1. A necessary and sufficient condition that α and β have a g.c.d. δ such that $\delta = \kappa\alpha + \lambda\beta$ is that the ideal (α, β) shall be principal.

If the numbers $\mu\alpha + \nu\beta$ constitute a principal ideal $C = (\delta)$, we have

$$(58.1) \qquad \mu\alpha + \nu\beta = \eta\delta$$

in the sense that: (1) for every pair of integral numbers (μ, ν) there exists an integral number η such that (58.1) holds; and (2) for every integral number η there exists a pair (μ, ν) of integral numbers such that (58.1) holds. Take $(\mu, \nu) = (1, 0)$ so that $\alpha = \eta_1\delta$. Thus $\delta \mid \alpha$. Similarly $\delta \mid \beta$. Now take $\eta = 1$ so that $\delta = \mu_1\alpha + \nu_1\beta$. Thus every common divisor of α and β divides δ, and δ is a g.c.d. of α and β.

Conversely, if $\alpha = \eta_1\delta$, $\beta = \eta_2\delta$, $\delta = \mu_1\alpha + \nu_1\beta$, evidently every number of

$$\mu\alpha + \nu\beta = (\mu\eta_1 + \nu\eta_2)\delta$$

is in (δ), and every number

$$\eta\delta = \eta\mu_1\alpha + \eta\nu_1\beta$$

is a number of the set $\mu\alpha + \nu\beta$, so that the given ideal is equal to (δ).

It follows, then, that in domains such as $Ra[i]$, where every pair of numbers not both 0 has a g.c.d. expressible as a linear function of the numbers, every ideal is principal, for, if the ideal A has the basis ω_1, ω_2, and if δ is a g.c.d. of ω_1 and ω_2, then $A = (\delta)$.* In such fields factorization into primes is unique except for unit factors. If, conversely, α and β do not have a g.c.d. expressible linearly in terms of them, then the ideal $\mu\alpha + \nu\beta$ cannot be principal.

Theorem 58.2. A necessary and sufficient condition that factorization into primes in $Ra[\sqrt{m}]$ be unique is that every ideal shall be principal.

As in Theorem 51.2, every number α of $Ra[\sqrt{m}]$ can be factored into a finite number of primes.   Uniqueness of factorization is now equivalent to Theorem 51.1, namely that if $\alpha \mid \beta\gamma$ and is prime to β, then $\alpha \mid \gamma$. For if this theorem holds, unique factorization can be demonstrated as in Theorem 51.3; and conversely, if factorization is unique and $\pi \mid \alpha$, then any factorization of α into primes must involve π explicitly, so that Theorem 51.1 holds.

If every ideal in $Ra[\sqrt{m}]$ is principal, then, for every pair of relatively prime numbers α and β, numbers μ and ν exist, by Theorem 58.1, such that

$$1 = \mu\alpha + \nu\beta.$$

Then Theorem 51.1 holds, and factorization into primes is unique.

Conversely, suppose that factorization into primes is unique, so that Theorem 51.1 holds.   If π is a prime, then (π) is a prime ideal.   For, if

$$(\pi) = AB, \qquad\qquad A \neq (\pi), B \neq (\pi),$$

there would exist a number α of A, and a number β of B, which are not multiples of π.   Yet the product $\alpha\beta$ would be a multiple of π, in contradiction to Theorem 51.1.   Thus one of A, B is (π) and the other is (1).

Now let P be any prime ideal, and let

$$\alpha = \pi_1^{e_1}\pi_2^{e_2} \cdots \pi_k^{e_k}$$

be any number of P, the π's being primes.   Then

$$(\alpha) = (\pi_1)^{e_1} (\pi_2)^{e_2} \cdots (\pi_k)^{e_k},$$

---

* The notation (ω_1, ω_2) at first appears ambiguous, denoting either a g.c.d. of ω_1 and ω_2 or the ideal whose basis is ω_1 and ω_2.   We now see that the two concepts are the same.

where each (π_i) is a prime ideal, as we saw above. But $(\alpha) \subseteq P$ so that $P \mid (\alpha)$. By Theorem 56.3, P is equal to one of the principal ideals (π_i).

EXERCISES

1. Two numbers α and β of $Ra[\sqrt{m}]$ are congruent mod A if $\alpha - \beta$ is in the ideal A. Show that congruence mod A is an equals relation. Show that this concept generalizes that of congruence in elementary number theory.

2. Prove that the number of residue classes mod A is $N(A)$.

59. The field of all algebraic numbers. If the coefficients of an algebraic equation

$$(59.1) \qquad x^n + a_{n-1}x^{n-1} + \cdots + a_1 x + a_0 = 0$$

are rational numbers, its roots are called *algebraic numbers*. We have seen that each root ρ satisfies a unique irreducible equation (Corollary 38.11), and that every equation satisfied by ρ is divisible by this irreducible function (Theorem 38.1).

Theorem 59.1. *The reciprocal of an algebraic number $\neq 0$ is an algebraic number.*

For, if $\rho \neq 0$ satisfies (59.1), $1/\rho$ satisfies

$$1 + a_{n-1}x + \cdots + a_1 x^{n-1} + a_0 x^n = 0.$$

Theorem 59.2. *If α and β are algebraic numbers, so is $f(\alpha, \beta)$, where f is any polynomial.*

Suppose that α is a root of an equation $A(x) = 0$ of degree h, and β is a root of an equation $B(x) = 0$ of degree k. Set $hk = n$, and denote by $\lambda_1, \lambda_2, \cdots, \lambda_n$ the numbers

$$\alpha^i \beta^j, \qquad (i = 0, 1, \cdots, h-1;\ j = 0, 1, \cdots, k-1)$$

in any convenient order. Since $A(\alpha) = 0$ and $B(\beta) = 0$, we can write

$$(59.2) \qquad \begin{aligned} \alpha^h &= -a_{h-1}\alpha^{h-1} - a_{h-2}\alpha^{h-2} - \cdots - a_0, \\ \beta^k &= -b_{k-1}\beta^{k-1} - b_{k-2}\beta^{k-2} - \cdots - b_0. \end{aligned}$$

Therefore

$$\lambda_i f = c_{i1}\lambda_1 + c_{i2}\lambda_2 + \cdots + c_{in}\lambda_n \qquad (i = 1, 2, \cdots, n),$$

where the c's are rational. These equations can be written

$$(c_{11} - f)\lambda_1 + c_{12}\lambda_2 + \cdots + c_{1n}\lambda_n = 0,$$

$$c_{21}\lambda_1 + (c_{22} - f)\lambda_2 + \cdots + c_{2n}\lambda_n = 0,$$

$$\cdots \cdots \cdots \cdots \cdots \cdots \cdots \cdots$$

$$c_{n1}\lambda_1 + c_{n2}\lambda_2 + \cdots + (c_{nn} - f)\lambda_n = 0.$$

A necessary and sufficient condition that such a system of equations be consistent where $\lambda_1, \lambda_2, \cdots, \lambda_n$ are not all zero is that

$$(59.3) \qquad \begin{vmatrix} c_{11} - f & c_{12} & \cdots & c_{1n} \\ c_{21} & c_{22} - f & \cdots & c_{2n} \\ \cdot & \cdot \cdot \cdot \cdot \cdot \cdot \cdot \cdot & \cdot & \cdot \\ c_{n1} & c_{n2} & \cdots & c_{nn} - f \end{vmatrix} = 0.$$

This is an algebraic equation satisfied by f.

Theorem 59.3.   The set of all algebraic numbers constitutes a field.

For, by Theorems 59.2 and 59.1, every rational function of two algebraic numbers is an algebraic number, with the usual exclusion of division by 0.

This field is commonly denoted by H.

Theorem 59.4.   If ρ is a root of an equation whose coefficients are algebraic numbers, then ρ is an algebraic number.

Let ρ satisfy (59.1), where each a_i belongs to an algebraic field $\mathfrak{F}_i$. Let $\mathfrak{F}$ denote a field containing each $\mathfrak{F}_i$ as a subfield (Theorem 40.3). Let $a_i, a_i', a_i'', \cdots, a_i^{(t-1)}$ denote the conjugates of a_i in $\mathfrak{F}$. If by $p(x)$ we denote the left member of (59.1), and by $p'(x)$ the same polynomial with each a primed, then

$$p(x) \cdot p'(x) \cdots p^{(t-1)}(x) = 0$$

is an equation satisfied by ρ. Every automorphism of $\mathfrak{F}$ leaves this equation identically unaltered, and so each coefficient is a rational number. Thus ρ is an algebraic number.

A field $\mathfrak{F}$ is called *algebraically closed* if it has the property that every algebraic equation with coefficients in $\mathfrak{F}$ has a root in $\mathfrak{F}$. We have therefore proved

Theorem 59.5.   The field H of all algebraic numbers is algebraically closed.

It should be noted that H is not *an* algebraic field. Algebraic fields (over the rational field) are not algebraically closed.

EXERCISES

1. Find an equation with rational coefficients satisfied by $\sqrt[3]{2} + \sqrt{3}$.

2. If ρ is a root of $x^2 + \sqrt{2}\, x + 1 = 0$, find an equation with rational coefficients satisfied by ρ.

3. Prove Theorem 59.2 with the aid of Theorem 40.3.

60. Integral algebraic numbers. If all the coefficients of a polynomial or equation are rational integers, and the coefficient of the highest power of the indeterminate is 1, we shall say that it is of *integral type*.

If θ is a root of an equation (59.1) of integral type, then θ is called an *algebraic integer*, or an *integral number* of the field H. The set of all such numbers will be denoted by $[H]$. A set of integral numbers closed under addition and multiplication, and containing 1, is called an *integral domain* or *domain of integrity*.

Theorem 60.1. If $f(\alpha, \beta)$ is a polynomial with rational integral coefficients of two numbers α and β of $[H]$, then $f(\alpha, \beta)$ is a number of $[H]$.

The proof is like that of Theorem 59.2. If $A(x)$ and $B(x)$ are of integral type, then the a's and b's of (59.2) will be integral, and so will the c's of (59.3). It is clear that the coefficient of f^n in (59.3) is ± 1, so that $f(\alpha, \beta)$ is integral.

Corollary 60.1. The numbers of $[H]$ constitute an integral domain in H.

Theorem 60.2. If θ is an integral algebraic number, its irreducible equation is of integral type.

Let θ satisfy $g(x) = 0$ of integral type. By Theorem 38.1, $p(x) \mid g(x)$, where $p(x) = 0$ is the irreducible equation satisfied by θ. By Theorem 45.3, $p(x)$ is of integral type.

Corollary 60.2. The conjugates of an integral algebraic number are integral algebraic numbers.

Theorem 60.3. Every algebraic field $Ra(\rho)$ can be written $Ra(\theta)$, where θ is integral.

Let ρ satisfy the equation

$$a_n x^n + a_{n-1}x^{n-1} + \cdots + a_0 = 0, \qquad a_n \neq 0,$$

where the a's are rational integers. Then $a_n\rho = \theta$ satisfies the equation

$$x^n + a_{n-1}x^{n-1} + a_{n-2}a_n x^{n-2} + \cdots + a_0 a_n^{n-1} = 0$$

and is therefore integral. Clearly $Ra(\rho) = Ra(\theta)$.

EXERCISES

1. A number of $[H]$ is a unit if it divides 1. Prove that ϵ is a unit if and only if its irreducible equation of integral type has the constant term ± 1.
2. If θ is a root of an equation (59.1) of integral type whose coefficients are algebraic integers, show that θ is an algebraic integer.

3. Show that there are no primes in $[H]$, so that the analogue of Theorem 51.2 is not valid.

4. Prove Theorem 45.3 by means of Theorem 60.1.

61. Integral domains of algebraic fields.

Let $Ra(\rho)$ be an algebraic field. We shall denote by $[Ra(\rho)]$, or by $Ra[\rho]$, the set of all numbers of $[H]$ which are in $Ra(\rho)$.

Theorem 61.1. The numbers of $Ra[\rho]$ form an integral domain.

Let α, β be two numbers of $Ra[\rho]$. Since they are in $Ra(\rho)$, their sum, difference, and product are in $Ra(\rho)$. By Theorem 60.1, their sum, difference, and product are in $[H]$, and hence are in $Ra[\rho]$.

Let α be a number of an algebraic field $Ra(\rho)$ of degree n. The *norm* of α is defined to be

$$N(\alpha) = \alpha\alpha'\alpha'' \cdots \alpha^{(n-1)},$$

where α', α'', $\cdots$ are the conjugates of α in $Ra(\rho)$. Clearly $N(\alpha)$ is equal to $(-1)^n f_0$, where f_0 is the constant term of the principal equation of α. (See Theorem 39.1.)

The *trace* of α is defined to be

$$T(\alpha) = \alpha + \alpha' + \alpha'' + \cdots + \alpha^{(n-1)}.$$

Evidently $T(\alpha) = -f_{n-1}$. If α is integral, $N(\alpha)$ and $T(\alpha)$ are rational integers.

Theorem 61.2. $N(\alpha\beta) = N(\alpha) \cdot N(\beta)$. $T(\alpha + \beta) = T(\alpha) + T(\beta)$.

Since the correspondence $\alpha \leftrightarrow \alpha'$ is an isomorphism,

$$N(\alpha\beta) = (\alpha\beta)(\alpha\beta)' \cdots (\alpha\beta)^{(n-1)} = \alpha\beta\alpha'\beta' \cdots \alpha^{(n-1)}\beta^{(n-1)}$$

$$= \alpha\alpha' \cdots \alpha^{(n-1)}\beta\beta' \cdots \beta^{(n-1)} = N(\alpha) \cdot N(\beta).$$

The second part follows similarly.

EXERCISES

1. Prove that if $\mathfrak{F}_1$ is a subfield of $\mathfrak{F}$, the integral domain $[\mathfrak{F}_1]$ consists of those numbers of $[\mathfrak{F}]$ which lie in $\mathfrak{F}_1$.

2. Show that if $\mathfrak{F}_1$ and $\mathfrak{F}_2$ are conjugate subfields of $\mathfrak{F}$, then $[\mathfrak{F}_2]$ consists of the numbers of $\mathfrak{F}_2$ which correspond to the numbers of $[\mathfrak{F}_1]$ by the isomorphism $\mathfrak{F}_1 \leftrightarrow \mathfrak{F}_2$.

3. If a is a rational number in $Ra(\rho)$ of degree n, what is $T(a)$ and what is $N(a)$?

4. Prove that $N(\alpha) = 0$ if and only if $\alpha = 0$.

62. The discriminant. Let

$$\alpha = a_0 + a_1\rho + \cdots + a_{n-1}\rho^{n-1},$$
$$\beta = b_0 + b_1\rho + \cdots + b_{n-1}\rho^{n-1},$$
$$\cdots\cdots\cdots\cdots\cdots\cdots\cdots\cdots$$
$$\kappa = k_0 + k_1\rho + \cdots, + k_{n-1}\rho^{n-1}$$

be n numbers of $Ra(\rho)$, and let $\alpha', \alpha'', \cdots, \beta', \beta'', \cdots$, etc., be their conjugates. We define

$$\Delta(\alpha, \beta, \cdots, \kappa) = \begin{vmatrix} \alpha & \alpha' & \cdots & \alpha^{(n-1)} \\ \beta & \beta' & \cdots & \beta^{(n-1)} \\ \cdots & \cdots & \cdots & \cdots \\ \kappa & \kappa' & \cdots & \kappa^{(n-1)} \end{vmatrix}^2$$

as the *discriminant* of the n numbers $\alpha, \beta, \cdots, \kappa$. It is evidently independent of the order of the numbers.

Theorem 62.1.

$$\Delta(\alpha, \beta, \cdots, \kappa) = \begin{vmatrix} T(\alpha^2) & T(\alpha\beta) & \cdots & T(\alpha\kappa) \\ T(\beta\alpha) & T(\beta^2) & \cdots & T(\beta\kappa) \\ \cdots & \cdots & \cdots & \cdots \\ T(\kappa\alpha) & T(\kappa\beta) & \cdots & T(\kappa^2) \end{vmatrix}.$$

Multiplying row by column, we have

$$\begin{vmatrix} \alpha & \alpha' & \cdots & \alpha^{(n-1)} \\ \beta & \beta' & \cdots & \beta^{(n-1)} \\ \cdots & \cdots & \cdots & \cdots \\ \kappa & \kappa' & \cdots & \kappa^{(n-1)} \end{vmatrix} \begin{vmatrix} \alpha & \beta & \cdots & \kappa \\ \alpha' & \beta' & \cdots & \kappa' \\ \cdots & \cdots & \cdots & \cdots \\ \alpha^{(n-1)} & \beta^{(n-1)} & \cdots & \kappa^{(n-1)} \end{vmatrix}$$

$$= \begin{vmatrix} \alpha^2 + \alpha'^2 + \cdots + \alpha^{(n-1)2} & \cdots & \alpha\kappa + \alpha'\kappa' + \cdots + \alpha^{(n-1)}\kappa^{(n-1)} \\ \beta\alpha + \beta'\alpha' + \cdots + \beta^{(n-1)}\alpha^{(n-1)} & \cdots & \beta\kappa + \beta'\kappa' + \cdots + \beta^{(n-1)}\kappa^{(n-1)} \\ \cdots & \cdots & \cdots \\ \kappa\alpha + \kappa'\alpha' + \cdots + \kappa^{(n-1)}\alpha^{(n-1)} & \cdots & \kappa^2 + \kappa'^2 + \cdots + \kappa^{(n-1)2} \end{vmatrix}.$$

But

$$T(\alpha\beta) = \alpha\beta + \alpha'\beta' + \cdots + \alpha^{(n-1)}\beta^{(n-1)},$$

and similarly for each element of the last determinant.

Corollary 62.1. If $\alpha, \beta, \cdots, \kappa$ are integral numbers, $\Delta(\alpha, \beta, \cdots, \kappa)$ is a rational integer.

Theorem 62.2. If

$$\beta_i = \sum_{j=1}^{n} a_{ij}\alpha_j \qquad (i = 1, 2, \cdots, n),$$

then

$$\Delta(\beta_1, \beta_2, \cdots, \beta_n) = a^2 \Delta(\alpha_1, \alpha_2, \cdots, \alpha_n),$$

where $a = |a_{rs}|$.

From the given equations

$$\beta_r \beta_s = \sum_{i, j} a_{ri} a_{sj} \alpha_i \alpha_j,$$

so that by Theorem 61.2

$$T(\beta_r \beta_s) = \sum_{i, j} a_{ri} a_{sj} T(\alpha_i \alpha_j).$$

Passing to determinants, we have

$$\left| T(\beta_r \beta_s) \right| = \left| a_{rs} \right| \left| T(\alpha_r \alpha_s) \right| \left| a_{sr} \right|,$$

$$\Delta(\beta_1, \beta_2, \cdots, \beta_n) = a^2 \Delta(\alpha_1, \alpha_2, \cdots, \alpha_n).$$

Theorem 62.3. $\Delta(\alpha_1, \alpha_2, \cdots, \alpha_n) = 0$ *if and only if* $\alpha_1, \alpha_2, \cdots, \alpha_n$ *are linearly dependent.*

If

$$\alpha_i = \sum_{j=0}^{n-1} a_{ij} \rho^j \qquad (i = 1, 2, \cdots, n),$$

then by the last theorem

$$\Delta(\alpha_1, \alpha_2, \cdots, \alpha_n) = a^2 \Delta(1, \rho, \rho^2, \cdots, \rho^{n-1})$$

where

$$\Delta(1, \rho, \rho^2, \cdots, \rho^{n-1}) = \begin{vmatrix} 1 & \rho & \rho^2 & \cdots & \rho^{n-1} \\ 1 & \rho' & \rho'^2 & \cdots & \rho'^{n-1} \\ \cdot & \cdot & \cdot & \cdots & \cdot \\ 1 & \rho^{(n-1)} & \rho^{(n-1)2} & \cdots & \rho^{(n-1)n-1} \end{vmatrix}^2$$

is the discriminant of the equation (59.1). Since this equation is separable, its discriminant is $\neq 0$. Hence $\Delta(\alpha_1, \alpha_2, \cdots, \alpha_n) = 0$ if and only if $a = 0$, i.e., if and only if $\alpha_1, \alpha_2, \cdots, \alpha_n$ are linearly dependent.

EXERCISES

1. Find $\Delta(1, \rho, \rho^2)$ where ρ is a root of $x^3 + px + q = 0$.
2. Show that, if ρ is a root of an equation of degree n,

$$\Delta(1, \rho, \rho^2, \cdots, \rho^{n-1}) = \prod_{i<j} (\rho^{(i)} - \rho^{(j)})^2 = \begin{vmatrix} s_0 & s_1 & s_2 & \cdots & s_{n-1} \\ s_1 & s_2 & s_3 & \cdots & s_n \\ \cdot & \cdot & \cdot & \cdots & \cdot \\ s_{n-1} & s_n & s_{n+1} & \cdots & s_{2n-2} \end{vmatrix},$$

where $s_i = \rho^i + \rho'^i + \cdots + \rho^{(n-1)i}$.

63. The basis.   If there exist in $Ra[\rho]$ n numbers $\theta_1, \theta_2, \cdots, \theta_n$ such that every number of $Ra[\rho]$ is given uniquely by the form

$$k_1\theta_1 + k_2\theta_2 + \cdots + k_n\theta_n,$$

where the k's are rational integers, then $\theta_1, \theta_2, \cdots, \theta_n$ are said to form a *basis* for $Ra[\rho]$.

   Theorem 63.1.   If $\theta_1, \theta_2, \cdots, \theta_n$ are n linearly independent numbers of $Ra[\rho]$ such that the absolute value of $\Delta(\theta_1, \theta_2, \cdots, \theta_n)$ is as small as possible, then $\theta_1, \theta_2, \cdots, \theta_n$ form a basis for $Ra[\rho]$.   Thus every domain has a basis.

   Let $\theta_1, \theta_2, \cdots, \theta_n$ be as described in the theorem.   Since they are in $Ra(\rho)$, they can be written

$$\theta_i = \sum_{j=0}^{n-1} b_{ij}\rho^j \qquad (i = 1, 2, \cdots, n),$$

where the b_{ij} are rational and $\mid b_{rs} \mid \neq 0$.   We can, then, solve for the ρ^j in terms of the θ_i, and write every number of $Ra[\rho]$ in the form

$$\gamma = c_1\theta_1 + c_2\theta_2 + \cdots + c_n\theta_n,$$

where the c's are rational.

   Suppose some coefficient c_i were not a rational integer, and let $[c_i]$ denote the numerically greatest integer in c_i.   Set

$$d_i = c_i - [c_i], \qquad\qquad 0 < \mid d_i \mid < 1.$$

Then $\delta_i = \gamma - [c_i]\theta_i$ is a number of $Ra[\rho]$.   By Theorem 62.2,

$$\mid \Delta(\theta_1, \cdots, \theta_{i-1}, \delta_i, \theta_{i+1}, \cdots, \theta_n) \mid = \begin{vmatrix} 1 & \cdots & 0 & \cdots & 0 \\ & \cdots & \cdots & \cdots & \\ c_1 & \cdots & d_i & \cdots & c_n \\ & \cdots & \cdots & \cdots & \\ 0 & \cdots & 0 & \cdots & 1 \end{vmatrix}^2 \cdot \mid \Delta(\theta_1, \theta_2, \cdots, \theta_n) \mid$$

$$< \mid \Delta(\theta_1, \theta_2, \cdots, \theta_n) \mid.$$

But $\mid \Delta(\theta_1, \cdots, \theta_n) \mid$ is minimal, so our assumption that c_i was not a rational integer is contradicted.   Hence, $\theta_1, \theta_2, \cdots, \theta_n$ form a basis.

   Theorem 63.2.   If $\theta_1, \theta_2, \cdots, \theta_n$ form a basis for $Ra[\rho]$, then every basis is given by $\theta'_1, \theta'_2, \cdots, \theta'_n$, where

$$\theta'_i = \sum_{j=1}^{n} b_{ij}\theta_j \qquad (i = 1, 2, \cdots, n),$$

where the b_{ij} are rational integers such that $\mid b_{rs} \mid = \pm 1$.

Since every linear combination of the θ'_i with rational integral coefficients is a linear combination of the θ_i with rational integral coefficients, and conversely (since the determinant is ± 1), it follows that the θ'_i form a basis for $Ra[\rho]$.

Let $\theta'_1, \theta'_2, \cdots, \theta'_n$ be any basis for $Ra[\rho]$. There exist rational integers b_{ij} and c_{jk} such that

$$\theta'_i = \sum b_{ij}\theta_j, \quad \theta_j = \sum c_{jk}\theta'_k,$$

so that

$$\theta'_i = \sum b_{ij}c_{jk}\theta'_k.$$

But the θ'_k are linearly independent so that

$$\sum_{j=1}^{n} b_{ij}c_{jk} = \delta_{ik},$$

where δ_{ik} is Kronecker's δ. Taking determinants, we have

$$|\, b_{rs}\, |\,|\, c_{rs}\, | = 1.$$

Since the b's and c's are rational integers,

$$|\, b_{rs}\, | = |\, c_{rs}\, | = \pm 1.$$

Corollary 63.2. If $\theta_1, \theta_2, \cdots, \theta_n$ is a basis for $Ra[\rho]$, $\Delta(\theta_1, \theta_2, \cdots, \theta_n)$ is a rational integer which is invariant under change of basis.

This rational integer is called the *discriminant of the domain* and is written $\Delta[\rho]$.

EXERCISES

1. Given that the domain of integrity of the stem field of $x^3 + 3x + 5 = 0$ has the basis $1, \rho, \frac{1}{3}(1 + \rho + \rho^2)$, find $\Delta[\rho]$.

2. Let ρ be a root of $x^3 + px + q = 0$, where p and q are rational integers. If $\Delta(1, \rho, \rho^2)$ has no square factor, prove that $1, \rho, \rho^2$ is a basis for $Ra[\rho]$.

3. Show that the definition of basis could have read: If there exist in $Ra[\rho]$ a certain finite number of numbers $\theta_1, \theta_2, \cdots$, such that every number of $Ra[\rho]$ is given uniquely by the form $k_1\theta_1 + k_2\theta_2 + \cdots$, where the k's are rational integers, then $\theta_1, \theta_2, \cdots$ form a basis for $Ra[\rho]$.

64. Units. A number of $Ra[\rho]$ is called a *unit* if it divides 1.

Theorem 64.1. A number ϵ of $Ra[\rho]$ is a unit if and only if $N(\epsilon) = \pm 1$.

If ϵ is a unit, there exists an integer ϵ_1 (also a unit) such that $\epsilon\epsilon_1 = 1$. Then from Theorem 61.2

$$N(\epsilon) \cdot N(\epsilon_1) = 1.$$

But $N(\epsilon)$ and $N(\epsilon_1)$ are rational integers, and so $N(\epsilon) = N(\epsilon_1) = \pm 1$.

Let ϵ be a number of $Ra[\rho]$ such that

$$N(\epsilon) = \epsilon\epsilon'\epsilon'' \cdots \epsilon^{(n-1)} = \pm 1.$$

Set $\epsilon_1 = \pm \epsilon'\epsilon'' \cdots \epsilon^{(n-1)}$. Then ϵ is clearly a unit.

Theorem 64.2. The units of $Ra[\rho]$ form an abelian subgroup of the multiplication group of $Ra(\rho)$.

For, if ϵ and ϵ_1 are units, by Theorem 61.2

$$N(\epsilon\epsilon_1) = N(\epsilon)\cdot N(\epsilon_1) = \pm 1,$$

so that $\epsilon\epsilon_1$ is a unit. Clearly 1 is a unit and is the identity element of multiplication. If ϵ is a unit and $\epsilon\epsilon_1 = 1$, then $\epsilon_1 = \epsilon^{-1}$.

It is evident that the roots of unity (± 1 at least) which lie in $Ra[\rho]$ are units. Usually, however, there are units which are not roots of unity.

Theorem 64.3. A domain $Ra[\rho]$ contains but a finite number of roots of unity.

Every root of unity is a root of some irreducible cyclotomic equation $\psi_k = 0$. If the root of unity is in $Ra[\rho]$, the degree of ψ_k cannot exceed n, since ψ_k must be a factor of the principal equation for $Ra(\rho)$ of this root of unity (Theorem 39.2). There is but a finite number of cyclotomic polynomials of degrees $\leq n$.

Theorem 64.4. If $Ra[\rho]$ contains a unit which is not a root of unity, then $Ra[\rho]$ contains infinitely many units.

Either ϵ, ϵ^2, ϵ^3, $\cdots$ are all distinct, or else $\epsilon^m = \epsilon^n$ for some $m > n$. In the latter case $\epsilon^{m-n} = 1$, so that ϵ is a root of unity.

Two numbers α and β of $Ra[\rho]$ are called *associates* if there exists a unit ϵ such that $\alpha = \epsilon\beta$. A subset S of $Ra[\rho]$ is called a *complete set of non-associates* if no two numbers of S are associates, yet every number of $Ra[\rho]$ is associated with a number of S.

EXERCISES

1. Prove that the non-negative integers form a complete set of non-associates in $[Ra]$.

2. Find graphically a complete set of non-associates for $Ra[i]$, also for $Ra[\sqrt{-3}]$.

3. Show that every unit of $Ra[\sqrt{m}]$ is a root of unity if $m < 0$.

4. Show that, if $Ra[\rho]$ has a unit ϵ of absolute value $\neq 1$, a unit can be found whose absolute value is arbitrarily small.

65. Ideal and its basis. An *ideal* of $Ra[\rho]$ is defined to be a set of numbers of $Ra[\rho]$ not all 0 which form an abelian group relative to addition, and which is closed under multiplication by the numbers of $Ra[\rho]$.

If $\alpha_1, \alpha_2, \cdots, \alpha_s$ are any numbers of $Ra[\rho]$ not all 0, then the set of numbers

$$\lambda_1\alpha_1 + \lambda_2\alpha_2 + \cdots + \lambda_s\alpha_s,$$

where $\lambda_1, \lambda_2, \cdots, \lambda_s$ range over $Ra[\rho]$, evidently constitutes an ideal $A = (\alpha_1, \alpha_2, \cdots, \alpha_s)$. If there exists a single number α such that $A = (\alpha)$, then A is *principal*.

Theorem 65.1. Every ideal contains rational integers $\neq 0$.

Let $\alpha \neq 0$ be a number of A. It is a root of its principal equation

$$x^n + a_{n-1}x^{n-1} + \cdots + a_1x + N(\alpha) = 0,$$

all of whose coefficients are rational integers. Then

$$N(\alpha) = -(\alpha^{n-1} + a_{n-1}\alpha^{n-2} + \cdots + a_1)\alpha$$

is in A. By Ex. 4, § 61, $N(\alpha) \neq 0$.

Theorem 65.2. If $Ra[\rho]$ is of degree n and A is an ideal of this domain, there exist n linearly independent numbers $\omega_1, \omega_2, \cdots, \omega_n$ of A such that A is given by the form

$$k_1\omega_1 + k_2\omega_2 + \cdots + k_n\omega_n,$$

where $k_1, k_2, \cdots, k_n$ range over $[Ra]$.

Such a set of numbers is called a *minimal basis* for A.

By Theorem 65.1, A contains positive integers, so it contains a smallest positive integer a, or a_{11}. Then A contains $a_{11}\theta_1$ which we shall denote by ω_1. Since A contains $a\theta_2$, it contains numbers of the form $a_{21}\theta_1 + a_{22}\theta_2$, where $a_{22} > 0$. Denote by ω_2 one such number where a_{22} is minimal. Since A contains $a\theta_3$, it contains numbers of the form $a_{31}\theta_1 + a_{32}\theta_2 + a_{33}\theta_3$, where $a_{33} > 0$. Denote by ω_3 one such number where a_{33} is minimal, etc. Then $\omega_1, \omega_2, \cdots, \omega_n$ constitute a basis for A.

For, if

$$\alpha = b_1\theta_1 + b_2\theta_2 + \cdots + b_n\theta_n$$

is any number of A, set

$$b_n = q_n a_{nn} + r_n, \qquad 0 \leqq r_n < a_{nn}.$$

Then

$$\alpha - q_n\omega_n = (b_1 - q_n a_{n1})\theta_1 + \cdots + (b_{n-1} - q_n a_{n,n-1})\theta_{n-1} + r_n\theta_n$$

is in A. But, of all such numbers, ω_n had the smallest coefficient of θ_n, and so $r_n = 0$. Thus $\alpha - q_n\omega_n$ is of the form

$$\alpha - q_n\omega_n = c_1\theta_1 + c_2\theta_2 + \cdots + c_{n-1}\theta_{n-1}.$$

Now set

$$c_{n-1} = q_{n-1}a_{n-1,n-1} + r_{n-1}, \qquad 0 \leqq r_{n-1} < a_{n-1,n-1}.$$

Then

$$\alpha - q_n\omega_n - q_{n-1}\omega_{n-1} = d_1\theta_1 + d_2\theta_2 + \cdots + d_{n-2}\theta_{n-2} + r_{n-1}\theta_{n-1},$$

and, as before, $r_{n-1} = 0$. We continue until we have

$$\alpha - q_n\omega_n - \cdots - q_1\omega_1 = 0,$$

so that

$$\alpha = q_1\omega_1 + q_2\omega_2 + \cdots + q_n\omega_n,$$

where the q's are rational integers.

Since the determinant of these linear forms is $a_{11}a_{22} \cdots a_{nn} \neq 0$, they are linearly independent.

Corollary 65.2. *If a is the smallest positive integer in A, then each $a_{ii} \leqq a$.*

Theorem 65.3. *If $\omega_1, \omega_2, \cdots, \omega_n$ is a basis for A, every basis is given by*

$$\omega'_i = \sum_{j=1}^{n} b_{ij}\omega_j, \qquad |b_{rs}| = \pm 1,$$

where the b's are rational integers.

The proof is like that of Theorem 63.2.

Theorem 65.4. *Every ideal A has a canonical basis*

$$\omega_i = a_{i1}\theta_1 + a_{i2}\theta_2 + \cdots + a_{ii}\theta_i, \qquad (i = 1, \cdots, n),$$

where $0 \leqq a_{ij} < a_{jj} \leqq a_{11}$ for $j < i$.

In the basis of Theorem 65.2, $0 < a_{ii} \leqq a_{11} = a$, where a is the smallest positive integer in A. By Theorem 65.3 we may subtract from any basis number a rational integral multiple of another basis number, thereby getting a new basis. Now set

$$a_{n,n-1} = q_{n,n-1}a_{n-1,n-1} + r_{n,n-1}, \qquad 0 \leqq r_{n,n-1} < a_{n-1,n-1}.$$

Then

$$\omega'_n = \omega_n - q_{n,n-1}\omega_{n-1} = a'_{n1}\theta_1 + \cdots + r_{n,n-1}\theta_{n-1} + a_{nn}\theta_n.$$

Then both ω_{n-1} and ω'_n can be replaced by basis numbers whose coefficients $a_{n-1,n-2}$ and $a_{n,n-2}$ are $\geqq 0$ and $< a_{n-2,n-2}$. The process can be continued until the described basis is obtained.

Corollary 65.4. A positive integer $\neq 0$ occurs in but a finite number of ideals.

In fact, there are but $h^{n(n+1)/2}$ matrices satisfying the conditions of the theorem having $a \leq h$.

EXERCISES

1. Perform the reduction of Theorem 65.4 upon the linear forms

$$\omega_1 = 3\theta_1, \qquad\qquad \omega_2 = -\theta_1 + 2\theta_2,$$
$$\omega_3 = 10\theta_1 + 13\theta_2 + \theta_3, \qquad \omega_4 = 2\theta_1 - 2\theta_2 - \theta_3 + 2\theta_4,$$

and show that there exists a transformation of determinant ± 1 carrying the new basis into the old.

2. For $n = 3$, prove that the canonical basis of Theorem 65.4 is unique.

3. Given that the domain of $x^3 + px + q = 0$ has the basis 1, θ, θ^2, prove that every canonical basis of an ideal is subject to the additional conditions

$$a_{33} \mid a_{22} \mid a_{11}, \qquad a_{33} \mid a_{31}, \qquad a_{33} \mid a_{32}, \qquad a_{22} \mid a_{21}.$$

66. Multiplication of ideals. If

$$A = (\alpha_1, \alpha_2, \cdots, \alpha_l), \quad B = (\beta_1, \beta_2, \cdots, \beta_m)$$

are two ideals, the set of numbers

$$C = \sum \kappa_{ij}\alpha_i\beta_j,$$

where the κ_{ij} range over $Ra[\rho]$, is evidently an ideal, and is called the *product* of A and B. If $AB = C$, then A and B are *divisors* of C.

Theorem 66.1. Hurwitz' extension of the Lemma of Gauss. Let

$$f(x) = \alpha_0 x^m + \alpha_1 x^{m-1} + \cdots + \alpha_m, \qquad \alpha_0 \neq 0,$$
$$g(x) = \beta_0 x^n + \beta_1 x^{n-1} + \cdots + \beta_n, \qquad \beta_0 \neq 0,$$

be two polynomials in x whose coefficients are algebraic integers. Let

$$f(x) \cdot g(x) = \gamma_0 x^{m+n} + \gamma_1 x^{m+n-1} + \cdots + \gamma_{m+n}, \qquad \gamma_0 = \alpha_0\beta_0.$$

If each γ is divisible by the algebraic integer v, then $v \mid \alpha_i\beta_k$.

Let $x_1, x_2, \cdots, x_m$ be the roots of $f(x) = 0$, and $y_1, y_2, \cdots, y_n$ the roots of $g(x) = 0$. Let $z_1, z_2, \cdots, z_{m+n}$ denote the x's and y's together. Let E_i denote the ith elementary symmetric function, i.e.,

$$E_1(z_1, z_2, \cdots, z_m) = z_1 + z_2 + \cdots + z_m,$$

etc. Define

$$u_{ik}^{(p)} = E_i(z_1, z_2, \cdots, z_m) \cdot E_k(z_{m+1}, \cdots, z_{m+n}),$$

where p ranges over the $\binom{m+n}{n}$ ways in which $z_1, z_2, \cdots, z_m$ can be selected from among $x_1, x_2, \cdots, x_m, y_1, y_2, \cdots, y_n$. In particular

$$u_{ik}^{(1)} = E_i(x_1, x_2, \cdots, x_m)\, E_k(y_1, y_2, \cdots, y_n) = \pm \frac{\alpha_i \beta_k}{\alpha_0 \beta_0}.$$

For i and k fixed, the polynomials $u_{ik}^{(p)}$ satisfy an equation

(66.1) $$u^M + d_1 u^{M-1} + \cdots + d_M = 0, \qquad M = \binom{m+n}{n}.$$

The permutations of $z_1, z_2, \cdots, z_{m+n}$ are obtained by taking all separations into two sets $z_1, z_2, \cdots, z_m$ and $z_{m+1}, \cdots, z_{m+n}$, and then considering all permutations within each set. Hence every d_h, being a symmetric function of the $u_{ik}^{(p)}$, is unaltered by every permutation of the z's, and hence is a polynomial in the coefficients γ_i/γ_0.

As every E_i is linear in each z which it involves, so d_1 is linear in each z and hence in γ_i/γ_0. Similarly each d_h is a sum of products of just h of the $u_{ik}^{(p)}$, and hence contains each z to exactly the power h. Thus d_h is of degree h in the γ_i/γ_0. It is also homogeneous, so that $D_h = \gamma_0^h d_h$ is a polynomial in the γ_i.

Since $u_{ik}^{(1)} = \pm \alpha_i \beta_k/\gamma_0$ is a root of (66.1), $\pm \alpha_i \beta_k$ is a root of

$$u^M + D_1 u^{M-1} + \cdots + D_M = 0.$$

Consider the equation

$$\left(\frac{u}{\nu}\right)^M + \frac{D_1}{\nu}\left(\frac{u}{\nu}\right)^{M-1} + \cdots + \frac{D^M}{\nu^M} = 0.$$

Since $\nu \mid \gamma_i$, $\nu^h \mid D_h$, so that this equation has integral coefficients. By Ex. 2, § 60, $\pm \alpha_i \beta_k/\nu$ is an algebraic integer, so that $\nu \mid \alpha_i \beta_k$.

Theorem 66.2. *If A is an ideal, there exists an ideal B such that $AB = (a)$ where a is a rational integer.*

Let $A = (\alpha_1, \alpha_2, \cdots, \alpha_l)$, and define

$$f(x) = \alpha_1 + \alpha_2 x + \cdots + \alpha_l x^{l-1}.$$

Also define $\alpha_i, \alpha_i', \cdots, \alpha_i^{(n-1)}$ to be the conjugates of α_i, and set

$$g(x) = \prod_{k=1}^{n-1} (\alpha_1^{(k)} + \alpha_2^{(k)} x + \cdots + \alpha_l^{(k)} x^{l-1})$$

$$= \beta_1 + \beta_2 x + \cdots + \beta_m x^{m-1},$$

where x is an indeterminate.   Then

$$f(x) \cdot g(x) = \gamma_1 + \gamma_2 x + \cdots + \gamma_{l+m-1} x^{l+m-2},$$

where

$$\gamma_i = \sum_{j+k=i+1} \alpha_j \beta_k.$$

This function $f(x) \cdot g(x)$ is symmetric in the conjugates of each α_i, so the γ's are rational integers.

Define the ideal $B = (\beta_1, \beta_2, \cdots, \beta_m)$.   Let a be the positive g.c.d. of the γ's.   By Theorem 66.1, a divides every $\alpha_i \beta_j$.   Then

$$AB = (\alpha_1 \beta_1, \cdots, \alpha_l \beta_m) = (\gamma_1, \cdots, \gamma_{l+m-1}, \alpha_1 \beta_1, \cdots, \alpha_l \beta_m)$$

$$= (a, \alpha_1 \beta_1, \cdots, \alpha_l \beta_m) = (a).$$

EXERCISES

Consider the domain $Ra[\rho]$, where ρ is a root of the equation $x^3 + 6x + 8 = 0$. This has a minimal basis $1, \rho, \rho^2/2$.

1. Prove that $(3, \rho - 1)^3 = (3)$.
2. Let $A = (5, \rho - 1)$. Show that Theorem 66.2 yields $B = (5, 2 + \rho + \rho^2)$.
3. Find B so that $AB = (7)$ when $A = (7, \rho - 2)$. Reduce B to two components.
4. Prove an analogue of Theorem 58.1.

67. Unique factorization of ideals.

Theorem 67.1.   If $SA = SB$,   where $S, A,$ and B are ideals, then $A = B$.

Let S' be the ideal of Theorem 66.2 such that $SS' = (s)$.   Then

$$S'SA = S'SB, \quad (s) \cdot A = (s) \cdot B, \quad A = B.$$

Theorem 67.2. $A \mid C$ if and only if every number of C is in A.

The proof of this theorem is similar to that of Theorem 55.2.

Theorem 67.3.   An ideal C is divisible by only a finite number of ideals.

By Theorem 66.2 there exists an ideal C' such that $CC' = (c)$, where c is a positive integer.   By Theorem 67.2, c is in C and also in every ideal which divides C.   By Corollary 65.4, there is but a finite number of such divisors.

Theorem 67.4.   Every pair of ideals A and B has a unique g.c.d., G. It is composed of the numbers $\alpha + \beta$, where α ranges over A and β ranges over B.

The proof that the set of numbers $\alpha + \beta$ is a g.c.d. of A and B is the same as in Theorem 56.1. Suppose that G and G_1 are two g.c.d.'s of A and B. Then $G = K_1G_1$, $G_1 = KG$ so that $(1)G = K_1KG$. Hence $K_1K = (1)$ by Theorem 67.1. Since 1 is in (1), 1 is in K_1 and also in K by Theorem 67.2. Thus every number of $R\alpha[\rho]$ is in K_1 and also in K. Thus $K_1 = K = (1)$.

Corollary 67.4. If A and B are relatively prime ideals, there exists an α in A and a β in B such that $\alpha + \beta = 1$.

Theorem 67.5. If $A \mid BC$ and is prime to B, then $A \mid C$.

The proof is entirely similar to that of Theorem 56.2.

Theorem 67.6. The principal theorem of ideal theory. Every composite ideal can be factored into prime ideals in one and, except for order of the factors, in only one way.

The proof is analogous to that of Theorem 56.3. By Theorem 67.3, an ideal can be factored into but a finite number of prime ideals. The uniqueness follows from Theorem 67.5.

Theorem 67.7. A necessary and sufficient condition that factorization into primes in $Ra[\rho]$ be unique is that every ideal shall be principal.

The proof is like that of Theorem 58.2.

EXERCISES

Consider the domain $Ra[\theta]$, where θ is a root of the equation $x^3 + 6x + 1 = 0$.
1. Find the g.c.d. of (2) and $(2\theta, \theta^2 - 5\theta - 1)$.
2. Find the g.c.d. of $(6, \theta + 1)$ and $(6, 2\theta + 2, \theta^2 + \theta + 3)$.
3. Factor (2) into its prime factors.
4. Show that $(2, \theta^2 + \theta + 1)$ and $(2, \theta + 1)$ are relatively prime. Find an α in the first ideal and a β in the second ideal such that $\alpha + \beta = 1$.
5. Prove the converse of Corollary 67.4.

SUGGESTED READINGS

REID, L. W.   *The Elements of the Theory of Algebraic Numbers*, Chapters V–XIV. Macmillan, 1910.

SOMMER, J.   *Vorlesungen über Zahlentheorie*.   Teubner, Leipzig, 1907.

HANCOCK, H.   *Foundations of the Theory of Algebraic Numbers*.   Macmillan, 1931.

HECKE, E.   *Vorlesungen über die Theorie der algebraischen Zahlen*.   Akad. Verlag., Leipzig, 1923.

LANDAU, E.   *Vorlesungen über Zahlentheorie*, Vol. III.   Hirzel, Leipzig, 1927.

VAN DER WAERDEN, B. L.   *Moderne Algebra*, Vol. II, Chapter XIV.   Springer, Berlin, 1931.

CHAPTER V

RINGS AND FIELDS

68. Algebraic varieties. The definition of field was given in § 33. By altering these postulates, various *algebraic varieties* other than field are obtained.

A *ring* is the most general algebraic variety which we shall consider. It is a mathematical system composed of elements $a, b, \cdots$, an equals relation, and two single-valued operations, addition ($+$) and multiplication ($\times$), relative to which the system is closed. We assume further:

A. The elements constitute an abelian group relative to the operation $+$, the identity element being denoted by z, and the inverse of a by $-a$.

D. Multiplication is distributive with respect to addition. That is,

$$a \times (b + c) = a \times b + a \times c,$$
$$(b + c) \times a = b \times a + c \times a.$$

M_2: *Multiplication is associative. That is,*

$$(a \times b) \times c = a \times (b \times c).$$

The other postulates regarding multiplication (besides M_1, which merely assumes closure) which hold for fields are not assumed for rings.

If also M_5 holds,

M_5: $$a \times b = b \times a,$$

the ring is called a *commutative ring*.

If the elements of the ring satisfy

M_3: *There exists an identity element i of multiplication such that*

$$a \times i = i \times a = a$$

for every a,

then the ring is called a *ring with unit element*.

Clearly a field is a commutative ring with unit element which also satisfies the postulate

M_4: *Every element $a \neq z$ has an inverse a^{-1} such that*

$$a \times a^{-1} = a^{-1} \times a = i.$$

A ring with unit element, whether commutative or not, which satisfies M_4 is called a *non-commutative field*. According to this terminology, a field is a special case of a non-commutative field.

If $ab = z$ while $b \neq z$, a is called a *divisor of zero*. Evidently z is a divisor of zero. Numbers $a \neq z$ which have this property are called *proper divisors of zero*. Rings may contain proper divisors of zero.

It was proved in Theorem 33.1 that a field contains no proper divisors of zero. In the proof of this theorem, the postulate that every element except z has an inverse was basic. The theorem is considerably weaker than the postulate, however.

An *integral domain* $\mathfrak{D}$ (or *domain of integrity*) is defined to be a commutative ring with unit element which is not necessarily a field because M_4 is replaced by the weaker condition

M'_4: *There are no proper divisors of zero.*

EXERCISES

1. Show that the integers modulo m form a ring.
2. Prove that, in the ring of integers modulo m, a number is a proper divisor of zero if and only if it has a factor > 1 in common with m.
3. Show that, in the definition of field, Postulate A_5, the commutative law of addition, is provable from the other postulates. Is this also true for the definition of ring?

HINT: Expand $(a + b)(i + i)$ in two ways by the distributive laws.
4. Prove that $ab = ac$, $a \neq 0$, imply $b = c$, by M'_4.

69. Integral domains. The proof that a product is z if one factor is z follows as in the proof of Theorem 33.1. Hence, with Postulate M'_4, we have

Theorem 69.1. A product in an integral domain $\mathfrak{D}$ is equal to z if and only if at least one of the factors is equal to z.

We shall separate the numbers of $\mathfrak{D}$ into four mutually exclusive classes:

1. The identity z of addition.
2. Those numbers which have an inverse with respect to the unit element i. These will be called *units*.
3. Those numbers p, distinct from z and the units, for which $p = p_1 p_2$ implies that p_1 or p_2 is a unit. These will be called *primes*.
4. All other numbers not in Classes 1, 2, or 3. These will be called *composite numbers*.

While a field is an instance of a domain of integrity, it is a trivial instance in the sense that every number except z is a unit.

Note that all the theorems of § 33 which relate to addition hold for rings as well as for fields.

If $a \mid b$ and the quotient is a unit, then b is called an *associate* of a. The relationship is symmetric. If $a \mid b$ and the quotient is not a unit, then a is a *proper divisor* of b.

A number d is called a *greatest common divisor* of a and b if

  1. It divides both a and b,

and if

  2. Every common divisor of a and b divides d.

A domain of integrity $\mathfrak{P}$ is called a *principal ideal ring* if the following additional postulates hold.

P_1: *Every pair of numbers a and b not both z have a greatest common divisor d.*

P_2: *There exist two numbers r and s in $\mathfrak{P}$ such that*

$$d = ra + sb.$$

P_3: *If in the sequence*

$$a_1, a_2, a_3, \cdots$$

every number is a proper divisor of the preceding, there are but a finite number of a's in the sequence.

Two numbers a and b of a principal ideal ring $\mathfrak{P}$ are *relatively prime* if their greatest common divisors are units. If a and b are relatively prime, there exist numbers r and s of $\mathfrak{P}$ such that

$$ra + sb = i.$$

Theorem 69.2. *If a prime p divides a product bc, it divides either b or c.*

If p does not divide b, it is prime to b. Then

$$rp + sb = i, \qquad rpc + sbc = c.$$

Since $p \mid bc$, then $p \mid c$.

Theorem 69.3. *Every composite number of $\mathfrak{P}$ is expressible as a product of primes. Except for order and for unit factors, this representation is unique.*

The proof is like that of Theorem 4.2.

EXERCISES

1. Give an example of a ring, not a field, in which P_3 fails.
2. Give an example of a ring in which P_3 holds but P_1 fails.
3. Show that an algebraic integral domain is a principal ideal ring if and only if every ideal of the domain is principal.
4. Prove that in a principal ideal ring the g.c.d. is unique up to a unit factor.

70. Modular fields. Let $GF(p)$ be a mathematical system whose elements are the rational integers. Let equality be congruence modulo the prime p. Let addition and multiplication be defined as usual.

Theorem 70.1. *The mathematical system $GF(p)$ is a field.*

The postulates A are obviously satisfied, the identity being 0. The only postulate which is not obviously satisfied is M_4, the existence of the inverse. But by Theorem 6.2 the congruence

$$ax \equiv 1 \mod p$$

has a solution when p is a prime.

Theorem 70.2. *Every field with a prime number p of elements is isomorphic with $GF(p)$.*

Since p is a prime, the addition group of the field $\mathfrak{F}$ is cyclic of order p. Since $i \neq z$, this group is generated by i (see § 31). That is,

$$i, 2i, 3i, \cdots, pi$$

are the elements of $\mathfrak{F}$. Consider the correspondence

$$ki \leftrightarrow k$$

between the elements ki of $\mathfrak{F}$ and the element k of $GF(p)$. By Theorem 33.10,

$$ki + li = (k + l)i,$$

so the correspondence is an isomorphism relative to addition. By Theorem 33.13,

$$ki \times li = kli^2 = kli,$$

so the correspondence is an isomorphism relative to multiplication.

Theorem 70.3. *The field $GF(p)$ has no automorphism except the identity.*

Let $a_i \leftrightarrow a_i'$ be an automorphism of $GF(p)$. Then, for every a,

$$0 \cdot a \equiv 0, \quad 1 \cdot a \equiv a \mod p,$$

so that

$$0' \cdot a' \equiv 0', \quad 1' \cdot a' \equiv a \quad \mod p,$$

for every element a' of $GF(p)$. But by Theorem 33.3, the identities are unique, so that

$$0 \equiv 0', \quad 1 \equiv 1' \quad \mod p.$$

Then, for any a,

$$a \equiv 1 + 1 + \cdots + 1 \equiv 1' + 1' + \cdots + 1' \equiv a' \quad \mod p.$$

EXERCISES

1. Construct an addition table and a multiplication table for $GF(7)$.
2. Prove that the multiplication group of $GF(p)$ is cyclic.
3. What is the condition that a quadratic equation with coefficients in $GF(p)$ have a solution in $GF(p)$?

71. Quotient fields. Let $\mathfrak{D}$ be any domain of integrity. Consider the set $Q\mathfrak{D}$ of ordered pairs $[a, b]$ of numbers of $\mathfrak{D}$, where $b \neq z$. We shall say that $[a, b]$ equals $[c, d]$ if and only if $ad = bc$.

We must show that this definition of equality satisfies the postulates of § 21. Clearly (a), (b) and (c) hold. To establish (d), we assume

$$[a, b] = [c, d], \quad [c, d] = [e, f], \qquad bdf \neq z.$$

Then $ad = bc$, $cf = de$, so that

$$adf = bcf = bde, \quad d(af - be) = z.$$

Since $d \neq z$, $af - be = z$ by Postulate M_4'. Hence $[a, b] = [e, f]$.

Addition is defined by the identity

$$[a, b] + [c, d] = [ad + bc, bd],$$

and multiplication by the identity

$$[a, b] \times [c, d] = [ac, bd].$$

Theorem 71.1. *The system $Q\mathfrak{D}$ is a field.*

We shall check each postulate.

A_1: If $b \neq z$ and $d \neq z$, then $bd \neq z$, so the sum exists. If $[a, b]$ is replaced by its equal $[e, f]$, the sum is replaced by $[ed + fc, fd]$. But

$$ebd^2 + bdfc = ad^2f + bcfd,$$

since $eb = af$, so the sum is well defined.

A_2: The associative law holds, since

$$[a, b] + [c, d] + [e, f] = [adf + bcf + bde, bdf]$$

for both manners of grouping.

A_3: The identity is $[z, b]$.

A_4: The inverse of $[a, b]$ is $[-a, b]$.

A_5: Since the commutative law holds in $\mathfrak{D}$,

$$[a, b] + [c, d] = [ad + bc, bd] = [cb + da, db] = [c, d] + [a, b].$$

The postulates on multiplication concern only elements $[a, b]$, where $a \neq z$ and $b \neq z$.

M_1: If $a \neq z$ and $c \neq z$, then $ac \neq z$. If $b \neq z$ and $d \neq z$, then $bd \neq z$. Hence the set $Q\mathfrak{D}$ is closed under multiplication. If $[a, b]$ is replaced by its equal $[e, f]$, the product $[ac, bd]$ is replaced by $[ec, fd]$. These will be equal if $acfd = bdec$. This is true, since $af = be$. Hence the product is well defined.

M_2: The associative law holds, since

$$[a, b] \times [c, d] \times [e, f] = [ace, bfd]$$

for both methods of grouping.

M_3: The identity is $[a, a]$, $\quad a \neq z$.

M_4: The inverse of $[a, b]$ is $[b, a]$.

M_5: The commutative law holds, for

$$[a, b] \times [c, d] = [ac, bd] = [ca, db] = [c, d] \times [a, b].$$

The distributive law must be proved without the restriction $a \neq z$.

$$[a, b] \times ([c, d] + [e, f]) = [a, b] \times [cf + de, df]$$
$$= [acf + ade, bdf].$$

$$[a, b] \times [c, d] + [a, b] \times [e, f] = [ac, bd] + [ae, bf]$$
$$= [acbf + bdae, bdbf]$$
$$= [acf + dae, bdf]$$

since $b \neq z$.

Theorem 71.2. *If d is a number of $\mathfrak{D}$, the subset of the numbers of $Q\mathfrak{D}$ which are of the form $[da, a]$ is isomorphic with $\mathfrak{D}$ with $[da, a] \leftrightarrow d$.*

For, if $[da, a] \leftrightarrow d$ and $[eb, b] \leftrightarrow e$, then

$$[da, a] + [eb, b] = [dab + eba, ab] \leftrightarrow d + e,$$
$$[da, a] \times [eb, b] = [deab, ab] \leftrightarrow de.$$

By virtue of this theorem, it is customary to write d for $[da, a]$.

Theorem 71.3. *The number $[p, q]$ is the unique solution of the equation*

$$qx = p, \qquad\qquad q \neq z,$$

in $Q\mathfrak{D}$.

For

$$q \times [p, q] = [qa, a] \times [p, q] = [pqa, qa] = p,$$

so $[p, q]$ is a solution. Let $[r, s]$ be any solution. Then

$$[qa, a] \times [r, s] = [pb, b], \qquad\qquad ab \neq z,$$

$$[qar, as] = [pb, b],$$

$$qarb = apbs, \qquad qr = ps.$$

This is the condition that $[r, s] = [p, q]$.

By virtue of this theorem, it is customary to write p/q for $[p, q]$.

The field $Q\mathfrak{D}$ is called the *quotient field* of the domain $\mathfrak{D}$. In particular, when $\mathfrak{D}$ is the domain $[Ra]$ of rational integers, $Q\mathfrak{D}$ is the rational field Ra. It is to be noted that Ra contains the rational integers $[Ra]$ only in the sense that Ra contains a subset of numbers which is isomorphic with $[Ra]$.

EXERCISES

The set $[Ra]$ of rational integers can be developed from the set of positive integers in a manner analogous to that of this paragraph. Consider all pairs $[a, b]$ of positive integers a, b. Two such pairs $[a, b]$ and $[c, d]$ are equal if $a + d = c + b$.

1. Show that this definition satisfies the postulates of § 21.

Addition and multiplication are defined as follows:

$$[a, b] + [c, d] = [a + c, b + d].$$

$$[a, b] \times [c, d] = [ac + bd, ad + bc].$$

2. Show that these operations are well defined.
3. Show that these pairs form a ring.
4. Show that the pairs $[a + 1, 1]$ form a subset which is isomorphic under both addition and multiplication with the set of positive integers.

72. The characteristic. A field is called a *prime field* if it contains no proper subfield.

Theorem 72.1. *The field* $GF(p)$ *is a prime field.*

For the addition group of $GF(p)$ is of prime order and can have no proper subgroup.

Theorem 72.2. *The rational field* Ra *is a prime field.*

Let $\mathfrak{F}$ be a subfield of Ra containing elements of Ra besides 0. Since it contains 1, it contains the positive integers and their inverses with respect to addition, the negative integers. It contains the inverses with respect to multiplication of both positive and negative integers, and their integral multiples. Thus $\mathfrak{F}$ contains all the numbers of Ra.

Let $\mathfrak{F}$ be any field.   Consider the set of elements

$$\cdots, \; -3i, \; -2i, \; -i, \; 0i = z, \; i, \; 2i, \; 3i, \; \cdots.$$

We recognize two types of field.

Type I.   There exist two rational integers s and t such that

$$si = ti, \qquad\qquad\qquad s > t.$$

Then

$$si - ti = (s - t)i = z.$$

Hence there is at least one positive integer n such that $ni = z$, and therefore a smallest positive integer p such that $pi = z$.   This number p is called the *characteristic* of the field of Type I.

Theorem 72.3.   *The characteristic of a field of Type I is a prime.*

The characteristic cannot be 1, for $i \neq z$.

Suppose that $p = p_1 p_2$, $p_1 > 1$, $p_2 > 1$.   Then

$$pi = p_1 i \times p_2 i = z,$$

and by Theorem 33.1, either $p_1 i = z$ or $p_2 i = z$, contradicting the definition of p.

Theorem 72.4.   *For a field of Type I of characteristic p, $ni = z$ if and only if $p \mid n$.*

If $n = kp$, $ni = kpi = kz = z$.

Let $n = pq + r, 0 \leqq r < p$.   Then

$$z = ni = (qp + r)i = qpi + ri = qz + ri = ri,$$

so that p is not the characteristic unless $r = 0$, and hence $p \mid n$.

Corollary 72.4.   *For a field of Type I,*

$$si = ti$$

if and only if $s \equiv t \bmod p$.

Type II.   The relation

$$si = ti$$

holds if and only if $s = t$.

It is possible to consider $s = t$ as a congruence modulo 0, for

$$s = t + k0$$

holds if and only if $s = t$.   By analogy with Corollary 72.4, we define the *characteristic* of a field of Type II to be 0.

Theorem 72.5. Every field contains as a subfield a prime field $\mathfrak{P}$ which is isomorphic either with Ra or with GF(p) according as its characteristic is 0 or p.

Let $\mathfrak{F}$ be a field of characteristic p. Then the elements

$$i, 2i, 3i, \cdots, pi$$

constitute a subfield of p elements which, by Theorem 70.2, is isomorphic with $GF(p)$.

Let $\mathfrak{F}$ be a field of characteristic 0. Then the elements qi are all distinct, q being a rational integer. Let qi of $\mathfrak{F}$ correspond to q of $[Ra]$. If $qi \neq z$, there are in $\mathfrak{F}$ elements satisfying every equation

$$qi \times x = ri, \qquad\qquad q \neq 0.$$

(Theorem 33.6.) Let x correspond to the number r/q of Ra. This correspondence is an isomorphism relative to both addition and multiplication. Thus let

$$q_1i \times x_1 = r_1i, \qquad\qquad q_2i \times x_2 = r_2i,$$

$$q_2q_1i \times x_1 = q_2r_1i, \qquad\qquad q_1q_2i \times x_2 = q_1r_2i,$$

$$q_1q_2i \times (x_1 + x_2) = (q_2r_1 + q_1r_2)i,$$

so that

$$x_1 + x_2 \leftrightarrow \frac{q_2r_1 + q_1r_2}{q_1q_2} = \frac{r_1}{q_1} + \frac{r_2}{q_2}.$$

The proof of the isomorphism relative to multiplication is left as an exercise. Then the set of all such numbers x of $\mathfrak{F}$ form a subfield of $\mathfrak{F}$ isomorphic with Ra.

Corollary 72.5. The only prime fields are Ra and the fields GF(p).

We shall henceforth use the symbols 0 and 1 instead of z and i for the identity elements of a field. We shall say that every field of characteristic 0 contains the rational field as a subfield, and that every field of characteristic p contains $GF(p)$.

EXERCISES

1. Complete the proof of Theorem 72.5.
2. Show that, in every field of characteristic p,

$$(a + b)^p = a^p + b^p.$$

3. Show that a prime field has no automorphism except the identity. Is the converse true?

73. Polynomial Rings. Let $\Re i$ be a ring with unit element i, and elements a, b, c, $\cdots$. Consider the following mathematical system which, for reasons to appear later, will be denoted by $\Re i[\lambda]$. The elements of $\Re i[\lambda]$ are the ordered sets

$$A = [a_0, a_1, a_2, \cdots, a_n], \qquad (n = 0, 1, 2, \cdots),$$

of elements of $\Re i$. We shall say that

$$[a_0, a_1, \cdots, a_n] = [b_0, b_1, \cdots, b_m],$$

in case $m \geq n$, if $a_i = b_i$ for $i = 0, 1, \cdots, n$ and $b_i = z$ for $i > n$; and similarly for $m \leq n$. Evidently the postulates for an equals relation are satisfied.

In considering any finite number of numbers of $\Re i[\lambda]$, we may assume that they consist of the same number of elements, for z's may be put in at the right as desired. If a_r is the last element of A which is not z, we say that A is of *degree* r. Note that $[a_0]$, $a_0 \neq z$, is of degree 0, while $[z, z, \cdots, z]$ has no degree, and is the only number which has no degree.

Addition is defined by the identity

$$[a_0, a_1, \cdots, a_n] + [b_0, b_1, \cdots, b_n] = [a_0 + b_0, a_1 + b_1, \cdots, a_n + b_n].$$

Multiplication is defined by the identity

$$[a_0, a_1, \cdots, a_m] \times [b_0, b_1, \cdots, b_n] = [c_0, c_1, \cdots, c_{m+n}],$$

where

$$c_k = \sum_{\alpha+\beta=k} a_\alpha b_\beta.$$

Theorem 73.1. The system $\Re i[\lambda]$ is a ring with unit element.

A_1, A_2, and A_5 are immediate. (See §§ 68, 33, and 21.)

A_3: The unit element Z of addition is $[z, z, \cdots, z]$.

A_4: The inverse $-A$ of $A = [a_0, a_1 \cdots, a_n]$ is $[-a_0, -a_1, \cdots, -a_n]$.

M_1 is evident.

M_2, the associative law: Let

$$[a_0, a_1, \cdots, a_l] \times [b_0, b_1, \cdots, b_m] = [d_0, d_1, \cdots, d_{l+m}],$$

$$d_i = \sum_{\alpha+\beta=i} a_\alpha b_\beta.$$

Let

$$[d_0, d_1, \cdots, d_{l+m}] \times [c_0, c_1, \cdots, c_n] = [e_0, e_1, \cdots, e_{l+m+n}],$$

$$e_j = \sum_{\gamma+\delta=j} d_\gamma c_\delta$$

$$= \sum_{\gamma+\delta=j} \left(\sum_{\alpha+\beta=\gamma} a_\alpha b_\beta \right) c_\delta$$

$$= \sum_{\alpha+\beta+\delta=j} a_\alpha b_\beta c_\delta.$$

This last step follows from the associative and distributive laws for $\Re i$. The same result is obtained from

$$[a_0, a_1, \cdots, a_l] \times \{ [b_0, b_1, \cdots, b_m] \times [c_0, c_1, \cdots, c_n] \},$$

so the associative law holds.

M_3, the identity of multiplication:

$$[a_0, a_1, \cdots, a_n] \times [i, z, \cdots, z] = [c_0, c_1, \cdots],$$

where

$$c_i = \sum_{\alpha+\beta=i} a_\alpha \delta_{0\beta} = a_i,$$

δ_{00} denoting i and $\delta_{0\beta}$ for $\beta \neq 0$ denoting z. Hence $[i, z, \cdots, z] = I$ is the identity element of $\Re i[\lambda]$.

D, the distributive law: Let $(A + B) \times C = D$. Then

$$d_i = \sum_{\alpha+\beta=i} (a_\alpha + b_\alpha) c_\beta,$$

$$= \sum_{\alpha+\beta=i} a_\alpha c_\beta + \sum_{\alpha+\beta=i} b_\alpha c_\beta,$$

so that $D = A \times C + B \times C$. The other distributive law is similarly proved.

Theorem 73.2. *If $\Re i$ is a commutative ring, then $\Re i[\lambda]$ is a commutative ring.*

This follows directly from the definition of multiplication.

Theorem 73.3. *If $\Re i$ is an integral domain, then $\Re i[\lambda]$ is an integral domain.*

It is sufficient to prove that $\Re i[\lambda]$ has no proper divisors of zero if $\Re i$ has none. If $A \neq Z$, it has a degree, say r. If $B \neq Z$, it has a degree, say s. If $A \times B = C$,

$$c_{r+s} = \sum_{\alpha+\beta=r+s} a_\alpha b_\beta = a_r b_s.$$

But $a_r \neq z$ and $b_s \neq z$, so that $a_r b_s \neq z$. Thus C has the degree $r + s$ and hence is not Z.

Corollary 73.3. If $\Re i$ is an integral domain, the degree of the product of two numbers of $\Re i[\lambda]$ is equal to the sum of their degrees.

Theorem 73.4. The subset of $\Re i[\lambda]$ composed of the numbers $[a, z, \cdots, z]$ forms a subring of $\Re i[\lambda]$ isomorphic with $\Re i$.

For the correspondence

$$A = [a, z, \cdots, z] \leftrightarrow a, \quad B = [b, z, \cdots, z] \leftrightarrow b,$$

is an isomorphism, since

$$A + B = [a + b, z, \cdots, z] \leftrightarrow a + b,$$
$$A \times B = [ab, z, \cdots, z] \leftrightarrow ab.$$

We shall therefore write a instead of $[a, z, \cdots, z]$.

Theorem 73.5.

$$a \times [b_0, b_1, \cdots, b_n] = [ab_0, ab_1, \cdots, ab_n].$$

This follows directly from the definition of multiplication. We shall now set

$$[z, i, z, \cdots, z] = \lambda.$$

Theorem 73.6.

$$\lambda^k = [z, \cdots, z, i, z, \cdots, z]$$

where the i is in the $(k + 1)th$ position.

For $k = 1$, the theorem is true by definition of λ. If it is true for k, then

$$\lambda^{k+1} = \lambda^k \times \lambda = [c_0, c_1, \cdots, c_n],$$

where

$$c_i = \sum_{\alpha + \beta = i} a_\alpha b_\beta.$$

Every a_α is z except a_k, which is i, and every b_β is z except b_1, which is i. Hence every c_i is z except c_{k+1}, which is i. This proves the theorem by induction.

Theorem 73.7. Every number of $\Re i[\lambda]$ of degree r is uniquely expressible in the form

$$[a_0, a_1, \cdots, a_r] = a_0 + a_1\lambda + \cdots + a_r\lambda^r, \qquad a_r \neq z.$$

By definition of addition,

$$[a_0, a_1, \cdots, a_r] = [a_0, z, \cdots, z] + [z, a_1, z, \cdots, z] + \cdots + [z, z, \cdots, a_r].$$

We agreed to write a_0 for $[a_0, z, \cdots, z]$. By Theorem 73.5, the second summand is $a_1\lambda$. By Theorems 73.5 and 73.6, the third summand is $a_2\lambda^2$, etc.

We shall call a number of $\Re i[\lambda]$ a *polynomial* in the *indeterminate* λ with coefficients in $\Re i$, and we shall call $\Re i[\lambda]$ the *polynomial ring* of $\Re i$.

EXERCISES

1. Let $\Re i$ be $[Ra]$. Find the product of $[1, 3, -2]$ with $[5, 3, 17, 4]$. What is the degree of the product?

2. Show that each of the properties of equality for $\Re i[\lambda]$ follows from the corresponding property for $\Re i$.

3. Prove the uniqueness stated in Theorem 73.7.

4. If $\mathfrak{D}$ is $GF(p)$, how many polynomials are there in $\mathfrak{D}[\lambda] = GF[p, \lambda]$ of degree r?

5. Prove that, if $\Re i$ is a domain of integrity, the units of $\Re i[\lambda]$ are the units of $\Re i$.

6. Show that, if $\Re i$ is the ring of integers modulo 4, the conclusion of Ex. 5 does not follow.

74. Polynomial domain of a domain of integrity in which factorization is unique. Let $\mathfrak{D}$ be a domain of integrity in which factorization into primes is unique. Then Postulates P_1 and P_3 for a principal ideal ring are satisfied, but not necessarily Postulate P_2. (See §69.) A prime divides a product if and only if it divides one of the factors, and every pair of numbers not both z have a g.c.d. unique up to a unit factor.

By the remark over Theorem 73.5, the identity element for addition of $\mathfrak{D}[\lambda]$ is $Z = (z, z, \cdots, z) = z$. The units of $\mathfrak{D}[\lambda]$ are of degree 0 by Corollary 73.3; therefore they are the units of $\mathfrak{D}$.

Let

$$A = a_t\lambda^t + a_{t-1}\lambda^{t-1} + \cdots + a_1\lambda + a_0$$

be a polynomial of $\mathfrak{D}[\lambda]$, and let a be a g.c.d. of $a_0, a_1, \cdots, a_t$. Let $a_i = aa_i'$. Then

$$A = aA' = a(a_t'\lambda^t + a_{t-1}'\lambda^{t-1} + \cdots + a_1'\lambda + a_0'),$$

where $(a_0', a_1', \cdots, a_t') = i$. The number a of $\mathfrak{D}$ is called the *content* of A, and A' is called a *primitive* polynomial.

Theorem 74.1. If $aA' = bB'$ where A' and B' are primitive, then $a = \epsilon b$ and $B' = \epsilon A'$, where ϵ is a unit.

For $a = (a_0, a_1, \cdots, a_t)$ is unique up to a unit factor, since factorization in $\mathfrak{D}$ is unique.

Theorem 74.2. The product of two primitive polynomials is primitive.

Let

$$A' = a'_t\lambda^t + a'_{t-1}\lambda^{t-1} + \cdots + a'_0, \quad B' = b'_s\lambda^s + b'_{s-1}\lambda^{s-1} + \cdots + b'_0,$$

be primitive. If $A'B'$ were not primitive, there would exist a prime p of $\mathfrak{D}$ dividing every coefficient of $A'B'$ but not every a'_i or every b'_j. Let

$$p \mid a'_i \ (i = 0, \cdots, k - 1), \ p \nmid a'_k, \ p \mid b'_j \ (j = 0, \cdots l - 1), \ p \nmid b'_l.$$

Then p would divide the coefficient of λ^{k+l} in $A'B'$, namely,

$$a'_0 b'_{k+l} + \cdots + a'_k b'_l + \cdots + a'_{k+l}b'_0,$$

and would divide every term of this sum except $a'_k b'_l$, which is absurd. Hence no such prime p exists, and $A'B'$ is primitive.

Theorem 74.3. The content of the product of two polynomials is equal to the product of their contents.

For, if $A = aA'$, $B = bB'$, where a is the content of A and b is the content of B, then $AB = abA'B'$. But, by Theorem 74.2, $A'B'$ is primitive, and so by Theorem 74.1 the content of AB is ab.

Corollary 74.3. If $A \mid B$, then $a \mid b$ and $A' \mid B'$.

For, if $aA' \mid bB'$, let $bB' = cC'aA'$. Then $b = \epsilon ca$ and $B' = \epsilon^{-1}C'A'$.

Theorem 74.4. If A and B are polynomials with coefficients in $\mathfrak{D}$, and B is of degree s, then there exist polynomials Q and R with coefficients in $\mathfrak{D}$, and a number $q \neq z$ in $\mathfrak{D}$, such that

$$qA = QB + R,$$

where R is either z or of degree $< s$.

If $A = z$, or if the degree t of A is $< s$, take $Q = z$ and $q = i$. If $t \geqq s$, let

$$A = a_t\lambda^t + a_{t-1}\lambda^{t-1} + \cdots + a_0, \qquad a_t \neq z,$$

$$B = b_s\lambda^s + b_{s-1}\lambda^{s-1} + \cdots + b_0, \qquad b_s \neq z.$$

Then

$$b_s A - a_t\lambda^{t-s}B$$

is a polynomial with coefficients in $\mathfrak{D}$ which is z or of degree $< t$. If its degree is $\geqq s$, continue the process (which is essentially long division) until we have

$$qA - QB = R$$

either z or of degree $r < s$. In fact, q is a power of b_s.

Theorem 74.5. Every two polynomials A and B not both z with coefficients in $\mathfrak{D}$ have a greatest common divisor.

If B is of degree s, by Theorem 74.4 we can write

$$q_1 A = Q_1 B + R_1 \qquad\qquad R_1 \text{ of degree } r_1 < s,$$

$$q_2 B = Q_2 R_1 + R_2 \qquad\qquad R_2 \text{ of degree } r_2 < r_1,$$

$$q_3 R_1 = Q_3 R_2 + R_3 \qquad\qquad R_3 \text{ of degree } r_3 < r_2,$$

. . . .

$$q_{k+2} R_k = Q_{k+2} R_{k+1} + R_{k+2} \qquad R_{k+2} \text{ of degree } r_{k+2} < r_{k+1},$$

$$q_{k+3} R_{k+1} = Q_{k+3} R_{k+2}.$$

The sequence

$$r_1, r_2, r_3, \cdots$$

is a sequence of decreasing positive integers which can contain but a finite number of terms. Hence at some state (say with R_{k+3}) the alternative condition of Theorem 74.4 must hold, namely, $R_{k+3} = z$.

Let C be any common divisor of A and B. By the first equation above, $C \mid R_1$; by the second equation, then, $C \mid R_2$, etc., so that $C \mid R_{k+2}$.

Let $R_{k+2} = rR'$, where r is the content of R_{k+2} and R' is primitive. By Corollary 74.3 and the last displayed equation, $R' \mid R_{k+1}$. Since R' divides both R_{k+2} and R_{k+1}, $R' \mid R_k$. Finally $R' \mid B$ and $R' \mid A$.

Set $A = aA'$, $B = bB'$, where A' and B' are primitive. Let $(a, b) = g$, and define $G = gR'$. Since $R' \mid A$, then $R' \mid A'$ by Corollary 74.3. Similarly $R' \mid B'$. Hence G is a common divisor of A and B.

Let $C = cC'$, where C' is primitive, be any common divisor of A and B. Then $c \mid a$, $c \mid b$ by Corollary 74.3, so that $c \mid g$. Since $C \mid R_{k+2} = rR'$, $C' \mid R'$. Hence $C \mid G$. That is, $G = (A, B)$.

Theorem 74.6. *If G is a g.c.d. of A and B, then every g.c.d. of A and B is associated with G.*

For if $G = HG_1$ and $G_1 = KG$, then $G = HKG$, $G(i - HK) = z$. Since $\mathfrak{D}[\lambda]$ has no proper divisors of zero, $HK = i$ so that H and K are units.

Theorem 74.7. *If $G = (A, B)$, there exist polynomials P and Q and a number $q \neq z$ of $\mathfrak{D}$ such that*

$$qG = PA + QB.$$

By the equations of Theorem 74.5,

$$R_{k+2} = PA + QB,$$

where $G \mid R_{k+2}$. Also, the primitive part of G is associated with the primitive part of R_{k+2}, but the content of G may be only a divisor of the content of R_{k+2}.

Theorem 74.8. *If $A \mid BC$ and is prime to B, then $A \mid C$.*

Let $A = aA'$, $B = bB'$, $C = cC'$, where A', B', C' are primitive. Then, by Corollary 74.3, $A' \mid B'C'$ and $a \mid bc$. If A is prime to B, a is prime to b, and so $a \mid c$ because factorization into primes is unique in $\mathfrak{D}$. Since A is prime to B, G is a unit, and so by Theorem 74.7

$$q = PA + QB, \quad qC = PAC + QBC.$$

Then $A \mid qC$ so that $A' \mid C'$. Then $A \mid C$.

Theorem 74.9. *Factorization into primes is unique up to unit factors in $\mathfrak{D}[\lambda]$.*

This follows as in the proof of Theorem 4.2.

EXERCISES

1. Prove that, if $\mathfrak{D}$ is a field, $\mathfrak{D}[\lambda]$ is a principal ideal ring.
2. Prove that, if $\mathfrak{D}$ is a field, factorization into primes is unique up to unit factors in $\mathfrak{D}[\lambda_1, \lambda_2, \cdots, \lambda_n]$.
3. If a polynomial with coefficients in $[Ra]$ is irreducible in $[Ra]$, then it is irreducible in Ra. Compare with Theorem 45.3.
4. If A is of degree t and B is of degree s, the P and Q of Theorem 74.7 can be so chosen that P is of degree $< s$ and Q is of degree $< t$.

HINT: Set $q_1P = Q_1B + R_1$, $q_2Q = Q_2A + R_2$, so that $qq_1q_2G = (q_1Q_2 + q_2Q_1)AB +$ a polynomial of degree $< s + t$.

75. Modules and ideals. Let $\mathfrak{R}$ be a ring. A subset $\mathfrak{M}$ of $\mathfrak{R}$ is called a *module* if the sum and difference of every two numbers of $\mathfrak{M}$ is in $\mathfrak{M}$. Two numbers a and b of $\mathfrak{R}$ are *congruent modulo* $\mathfrak{M}$,

$$a \equiv b \quad \mod \mathfrak{M},$$

if there exists a number m of $\mathfrak{M}$ such that $a = b + m$, that is, if the difference $a - b$ is in $\mathfrak{M}$.

Theorem 75.1. *The relation of congruence modulo $\mathfrak{M}$ is an equals relation.*

Obviously the relation is determinative, for the difference $a - b$ is in $\mathfrak{R}$, and either is in $\mathfrak{M}$ or is not in $\mathfrak{M}$.

Since $\mathfrak{M}$ is closed under subtraction, it contains $a - a = 0$. Hence $a \equiv a \mod \mathfrak{M}$.

Since $\mathfrak{M}$ contains $0 - m = -m$, and since $a = b + m$ implies that $b = a - m$, the relation is symmetric.

Let $a = b + m_1$, $b = c + m_2$. Since $\mathfrak{M}$ contains $m_1 + m_2$, $a \equiv c \mod \mathfrak{M}$. Thus the relation is transitive.

Theorem 75.2. *Addition in $\Re$ is well defined modulo $\mathfrak{M}$.*

For, if $a = b + m_1$ and $c = d + m_2$, then

$$a + c = b + d + m_1 + m_2,$$

and, since $m_1 + m_2$ is in $\mathfrak{M}$,

$$a + c \equiv b + d \qquad \text{mod } \mathfrak{M}.$$

The corresponding theorem for multiplication cannot be proved for all modules. A module $\mathfrak{M}$ is called a *right ideal* if the product mr is in $\mathfrak{M}$ for every number m of $\mathfrak{M}$ and every number r of $\Re$—in notation,

$$\mathfrak{M}\Re \subseteq \mathfrak{M}.$$

Similarly $\mathfrak{M}$ is a *left ideal* if $\Re\mathfrak{M} \subseteq \mathfrak{M}$. A module $\mathfrak{M}$ which is both a right and a left ideal of $\Re$ is called a *two-sided ideal*. If $\Re$ is commutative, every ideal is two sided.

Theorem 75.3. *If $\mathfrak{J}$ is a two-sided ideal of $\Re$, multiplication in $\Re$ is well defined modulo $\mathfrak{J}$.*

For, if $a = b + m_1$ and $c = d + m_2$, then

$$ac = bd + bm_2 + m_1 d + m_1 m_2.$$

Now bm_2 is in $\mathfrak{J}$ since $\mathfrak{J}$ is a left ideal, $m_1 d$ is in $\mathfrak{J}$ since $\mathfrak{J}$ is a right ideal, and $m_1 m_2$ is in $\mathfrak{J}$ for either reason. Then $bm_2 + m_1 d + m_1 m_2$ is in $\mathfrak{J}$ since $\mathfrak{J}$ is a module.

Let $\Re/\mathfrak{J}$ denote the mathematical system composed of the elements of $\Re$ taken modulo $\mathfrak{J}$ where $\mathfrak{J}$ is a two-sided ideal of $\Re$, addition and multiplication being defined as in $\Re$.

Theorem 75.4. *The system $\Re/\mathfrak{J}$ is a ring.*

Since the associative and distributive laws hold in $\Re$, they hold in $\Re/\mathfrak{J}$. The other properties are obvious.

Corollary 75.41. *If $\Re$ is a commutative ring, so is $\Re/\mathfrak{J}$.*

Corollary 75.42. *If $\Re$ is a ring with unit element, so is $\Re/\mathfrak{J}$.*

Two rings $\Re$ and $\Re'$ are called *homomorphic*, and we write $\Re \sim \Re'$, if there exists a correspondence $r \to r'$ which is a homomorphism with respect to both addition and multiplication (see § 24). Every element r of $\Re$ determines a unique element r' of $\Re'$, but more than one element of $\Re$ may determine the same r'. If the correspondence is biunique, the homomorphism is an *isomorphism*, written $\Re \cong \Re'$.

Let r_i denote the elements of $\Re$. Select from among the r_i a set of elements r_i' which are incongruent modulo $\Im$ and are such that every r_i is congruent to one of them. These r_i' will be called a *complete set of residues* modulo $\Im$, or a *system of representatives* of $\Re/\Im$. The ring $\Re/\Im$ is called a *residue class ring* of $\Re$.

The ring $\Re/\Im$ may be considered as consisting of the representatives r_i', the equality relation being congruence modulo $\Im$. Addition is accomplished by adding the representatives as if they were elements of $\Re$, and then replacing the sum by its representative. Multiplication is handled similarly.

Theorem 75.5.　The rings $\Re$ and $\Re/\Im$ are homomorphic.

Let r_i be the elements of $\Re$, and let r_i' be a system of representatives of $\Re/\Im$. If $r_i \equiv r_i' \bmod \Im$, consider the correspondences

$$r_1 \to r_1', \quad r_2 \to r_2', \quad \cdots.$$

By Theorem 75.2,

$$r_1 + r_2 \to r_1' + r_2',$$

so the addition groups of $\Re$ and $\Re/\Im$ are homomorphic. By Theorem 75.3,

$$r_1 r_2 \to r_1' r_2',$$

so that the same correspondence is also a homomorphism with respect to multiplication. Thus

$$\Re \sim \frac{\Re}{\Im}.$$

Theorem 75.6.　Let $\Re$ and $\mathfrak{S}$ be any two rings such that $\Re \sim \mathfrak{S}$. The set of all elements of $\Re$ which correspond to the 0-element of $\mathfrak{S}$ constitute an ideal $\Im$ such that $\Re/\Im \cong \mathfrak{S}$.

Let $\Im$ denote the set of all numbers z_i of $\Re$ such that $z_i \to 0$. If $z_1 \to 0$ and $z_2 \to 0$, then clearly

$$z_1 \pm z_2 \to 0 \pm 0 = 0,$$

so that the set is a module. Moreover, if r is any element of $\Re$, and if $r \to s$, then

$$r z_i \to s \cdot 0 = 0, \quad z_i r \to 0 \cdot s = 0,$$

so that both $r z_i$ and $z_i r$ are in the set $\Im$. Thus $\Im$ is an ideal.

We shall next show that two numbers of $\Re$ are congruent modulo $\Im$ if and only if they correspond to the same number s of $\mathfrak{S}$. Suppose that

$$r_1 \to s, \quad r_2 \to s.$$

Then

$$r_1 - r_2 \to 0, \quad r_1 - r_2 = z, \qquad\qquad z \in \mathfrak{J}.$$

That is,

(75.1) $$r_1 \equiv r_2 \quad \mod \mathfrak{J}.$$

Conversely, if (75.1) holds, there exists a z in $\mathfrak{J}$ such that

$$r_1 - r_2 = z, \quad r_1 - r_2 \to 0.$$

Let $r_2 \to s$. Then $r_1 \to 0 + s = s$.

It follows immediately that if the r_i' form a system of representatives of $\mathfrak{R}/\mathfrak{J}$, where

$$r_i \equiv r_i' \quad \mod \mathfrak{J},$$

then the correspondence

$$r_i' \leftrightarrow s_i$$

is biunique.

Let

$$r_1' \leftrightarrow s_1, \quad r_2' \leftrightarrow s_2.$$

Then, since r_1' and r_2' are elements of $\mathfrak{R}$, and $\mathfrak{R} \sim \mathfrak{S}$,

$$r_1' + r_2' \to s_1 + s_2.$$

But the correspondence is biunique, so

$$r_1' + r_2' \leftrightarrow s_1 + s_2,$$

where $r_1' + r_2'$ denotes the representative of $r_1' + r_2'$ in $\mathfrak{R}$, i.e., the sum $r_1' + r_2'$ in $\mathfrak{R}/\mathfrak{J}$. Similarly

$$r_1' r_2' \leftrightarrow s_1 s_2.$$

Therefore $\mathfrak{R}/\mathfrak{J} \cong \mathfrak{S}$.

EXERCISES

1. Let $\mathfrak{R}[\rho]$ be a maximal integral domain of an algebraic field, and let the ideal $\mathfrak{A}$ have the minimal basis

$$\omega_1, \omega_2, \cdots, \omega_n, \quad \omega_i = a_{i1}\epsilon_1 + \cdots + a_{ii}\epsilon_i, \qquad a_{ii} > 0.$$

Prove that every number of $\mathfrak{R}[\rho]$ is congruent modulo $\mathfrak{A}$ to one and only one of the numbers

$$r_1 \epsilon_1 + r_2 \epsilon_2 + \cdots + r_n \epsilon_n, \qquad 0 \leqq r_i < a_{ii}.$$

2. Solve the congruence in $Ra[\sqrt{-5}]$,

$$(1 + 2\sqrt{-5})X \equiv 2 + 3\sqrt{-5} \quad \mod (3, 1 + \sqrt{-5}).$$

3. Solve in $Ra[\sqrt{-5}]$,

$$(5 + \sqrt{-5})X^2 + (1 + \sqrt{-5})X + 8 + 3\sqrt{-5} \equiv 0 \quad \mod (3, 1 + \sqrt{-5}).$$

4. Let $\mathfrak{A}$ be an ideal in $\mathfrak{R}[\rho]$. Let

$$\mu\alpha \equiv \mu\beta \qquad \mathrm{mod}\ \mathfrak{A}.$$

Prove that

$$\alpha \equiv \beta \qquad \mathrm{mod}\ \frac{\mathfrak{A}}{\mathfrak{D}}, \qquad\qquad \mathfrak{D} = ((\mu), \mathfrak{A}).$$

HINT: Let $(\mu) = \mathfrak{D}\mathfrak{M}$, $\mathfrak{A} = \mathfrak{D}\mathfrak{B}$ where $(\mathfrak{M}, \mathfrak{B}) = (1)$.

5. If $\mathfrak{A}_1, \mathfrak{A}_2, \cdots, \mathfrak{A}_k$ are ideals of $\mathfrak{R}[\rho]$, relatively prime in pairs, and if $\alpha_1,$ $\alpha_2, \cdots, \alpha_k$ are any numbers of $\mathfrak{R}[\rho]$, prove that there exists a number ω, unique mod $\mathfrak{A}_1\mathfrak{A}_2 \cdots \mathfrak{A}_k$, such that

$$\omega \equiv \alpha_i \qquad \mathrm{mod}\ \mathfrak{A}_i \qquad\qquad (i = 1, 2, \cdots, k).$$

HINT: Set $\mathfrak{B}_i = \mathfrak{A}_1 \cdots \mathfrak{A}_k/\mathfrak{A}_i$. There exist numbers $\beta_i \in \mathfrak{B}_i$ such that

$$\beta_1 + \beta_2 + \cdots + \beta_n = 1.$$

76. Principal ideal rings. If $\mathfrak{J}_1$ and $\mathfrak{J}_2$ are two ideals of a domain of integrity $\mathfrak{D}$, the set of numbers common to $\mathfrak{J}_1$ and $\mathfrak{J}_2$ is clearly an ideal, called the *intersection* of $\mathfrak{J}_1$ and $\mathfrak{J}_2$, written $\mathfrak{J}_1 \wedge \mathfrak{J}_2$ or $[\mathfrak{J}_1, \mathfrak{J}_2]$. The intersection of *all* ideals of $\mathfrak{D}$ is the null ideal $\{0\}$.

If $\mathfrak{J}_1$ and $\mathfrak{J}_2$ are two ideals, the set of numbers which belong to either one of $\mathfrak{J}_1$ and $\mathfrak{J}_2$ do not necessarily constitute an ideal. But if to these numbers we adjoin all numbers of $\mathfrak{D}$ which can be written $a_1 \pm a_2$ where a_1 is in $\mathfrak{J}_1$ and a_2 in $\mathfrak{J}_2$, this set is an ideal, called the *union* of $\mathfrak{J}_1$ and $\mathfrak{J}_2$, written $\mathfrak{J}_1 \vee \mathfrak{J}_2$ or $(\mathfrak{J}_1, \mathfrak{J}_2)$. The union of *all* ideals of $\mathfrak{D}$ is the unit ideal $\{1\}$.

If $\mathfrak{D}$ is a domain of integrity and m is any number of $\mathfrak{D}$, the set of all numbers km where k varies over $\mathfrak{D}$ constitutes an ideal $\{m\}$. An ideal of this type, all of whose elements are multiples of a given one, is called a *principal ideal*. Evidently every number m of $\mathfrak{D}$ defines a principal ideal. If ϵ is a unit of $\mathfrak{D}$, evidently $\{\epsilon\} = \mathfrak{D}$; and $\{m_1\} = \{m_2\}$ if and only if m_1 and m_2 are associated.

In § 69 it was found convenient to define a principal ideal ring by means of three postulates. The terminology is now justified by

Theorem 76.1. A domain of integrity $\mathfrak{D}$ is a principal ideal ring if and only if every ideal of $\mathfrak{D}$ is principal.

First, let $\mathfrak{P}$ be a principal ideal ring according to the definition of § 69. Let $\mathfrak{J}$ be any ideal of $\mathfrak{P}$ with elements a_i. Take any two of these elements, a_1 and a_2, and let d_1 be a greatest common divisor. If d_1 divides every number of $\mathfrak{J}$, then $\mathfrak{J} = \{d_1\}$; for every linear combination of numbers of $\mathfrak{J}$ is a multiple of d_1, and every multiple of $d_1 = ra_1 + sa_2$ is a linear combination of a_1 and a_2. If d_1 does not divide every number of

$\Im$, suppose that a_3 is one which it does not divide. Then $d_2 = (d_1, a_3)$ is a proper divisor of d_1. If d_2 divides every number of $\Im$, then $\Im = \{d_2\}$. If it does not, we obtain a number d_3 which is a proper divisor of d_2. The process terminates in a finite number of steps with a d_n which does divide every number of $\Im$, for the sequence

$$d_1, d_2, d_3, \cdots$$

can contain but a finite number of elements. Thus $\Im = \{d_n\}$.

Second, let $\mathfrak{D}$ be any domain of integrity in which every ideal is principal. Let a and b be any two numbers of $\mathfrak{D}$. The set of numbers

$$ra + sb,$$

where r and s range independently over $\mathfrak{D}$, is clearly an ideal. Since this is principal, there exists a d such that

$$ra + sb = td$$

in the sense that for every pair (r, s) in $\mathfrak{D}$ there exists a t, and for every t there exists a pair (r, s). Denote by t_1 the t corresponding to $r = 1$, $s = 0$, and by t_2 the t corresponding to $r = 0$, $s = 1$. Then

$$a = t_1 d, \quad b = t_2 d,$$

so that d is a common divisor of a and b. Denote by (r_1, s_1) the pair corresponding to $t = 1$. Then

$$d = r_1 a + s_1 b$$

so that every common divisor of a and b divides d. Thus P_1 and P_2 of § 69 are proved.

Now let

$$a_1, a_2, a_3, \cdots$$

be a sequence of numbers of $\mathfrak{D}$ each of which is a divisor of the preceding. Consider the union of the ideals

$$\{a_1\}, \quad \{a_2\}, \quad \{a_3\}, \cdots.$$

It consists of all those numbers of $\mathfrak{D}$ which are in one of these ideals and those numbers which are obtainable from these by a finite number of additions and subtractions. Thus for every number of the union, there exists a finite integer j such that

$$\alpha = k_1 a_1 + \cdots + k_j a_j, \qquad k_i \in \mathfrak{D}.$$

But a_j divides each of $a_1, a_2, \cdots, a_{j-1}$, so $a_j \mid \alpha$, and $\alpha \in \{a_j\}$. Now by hypothesis the union is principal, say equal to $\{d\}$, so d belongs to some

$\{a_j\}$. Let $\{a_n\}$ be the first of these ideals which contains d. For every $k \geqq n$, $a_k \mid a_n \mid d$. But, on the other hand, $a_k \in \{d\}$, so that $d \mid a_k$. Thus

$$a_n, a_{n+1},\ a_{n+2},\ \cdots$$

are all associated. This proves P_3 of § 69.

By § 75, the ring $\mathfrak{P}/\{m\}$ where $\mathfrak{P}$ is a principal ideal ring, $m \in \mathfrak{P}$, is a commutative ring with unit element.

Theorem 76.2. If $m = 0$, $\mathfrak{P}/\{m\} = \mathfrak{P}$. If m is a unit of $\mathfrak{P}$, $\mathfrak{P}/\{m\} = 0$. If m is a prime, $\mathfrak{P}/\{m\}$ is a field. If m is composite, $\mathfrak{P}/\{m\}$ has proper divisors of zero.

If $m = 0$, the congruence

$$a \equiv b \qquad \text{mod } \{m\}$$

becomes $a = b$, so that $\mathfrak{P}/\{m\} = \mathfrak{P}$.

If m is a unit, $\{m\} = \mathfrak{P}$, so that $a \equiv 0$ mod $\{m\}$ for every a.

If m is composite, let $m = m_1 m_2$, where neither m_1 nor m_2 is 0 or a unit. But

$$m_1 m_2 \equiv 0 \qquad \text{mod } \{m\},$$

so m_1 and m_2 are proper divisors of zero.

Consider $\mathfrak{P}/\{p\}$ where p is a prime of $\mathfrak{P}$. Every element a of $\mathfrak{P}$ is either divisible by p or is prime to p. If $p \mid a$,

$$a \equiv 0 \qquad \text{mod } \{p\}.$$

If $p \nmid a$, there exist numbers of $\mathfrak{P}$, by P_2 of § 69, such that

$$ra + sp = 1;$$

that is, such that

$$ra \equiv 1 \qquad \text{mod } \{p\}.$$

Hence every a not in $\{p\}$ has an inverse r in $\mathfrak{P}/\{p\}$. Thus $\mathfrak{P}/\{p\}$ is a field.

EXERCISES

1. Let $\mathfrak{P}$ be a principal ideal ring, $m \in \mathfrak{P}$. The congruence

$$ax \equiv b \qquad \text{mod } m$$

has a solution if and only if $(a, m) \mid b$. If it does, there is a unique solution modulo $m/(a, m)$.

2. Show that every number of $\mathfrak{P}/\{m\}$ where $m \neq 0$ is either a divisor of zero or else has an inverse, but never both.

3. Let $\mathfrak{P}$ be the principal ideal ring $Ra[x]$. Solve the congruence

$$(x^3 + x^2 - \tfrac{1}{2}x - \tfrac{1}{2})X \equiv x^2 - 1 \qquad \text{mod } (x^3 + 1).$$

77. Solution of equations with coefficients in a field. If $\mathfrak{F}$ is any field, all the theorems of elementary algebra which are purely rational in character hold for $\mathfrak{F}[x]$. Thus the theorems of Chapter I for a prime modulus—that is, for $\mathfrak{F} = GF(p)$—correspond to well-known theorems concerning polynomials with rational or real coefficients. Where the proofs of these theorems depend only upon properties shared by all fields, the extension to all fields is immediate.

Theorem 77.1. *If $f(x)$ and $g(x)$ belong to $\mathfrak{F}[x]$, then two polynomials $q(x)$ and $r(x)$ exist in $\mathfrak{F}[x]$ such that*

$$f(x) = q(x) \cdot g(x) + r(x) \qquad \qquad in \ \mathfrak{F}[x],$$

where either $r(x) = 0$ or else the degree of $r(x)$ is less than the degree of $g(x)$.

The proof is like the proof of Theorem 13.1. This proof depends upon the fact that every non-zero number of $\mathfrak{F}$ has an inverse—a property of all fields.

The definition of derivative is exactly as in § 12, and part of Theorem 12.3 can be generalized. Thus we have

Theorem 77.2. *If x_1 is in $\mathfrak{F}$, and if $(x - x_1)^h$ divides $f(x)$ in $\mathfrak{F}[x]$, then $(x - x_1)^{h-1}$ divides $f'(x)$.*

The analogue of Theorem 13.3 is

Theorem 77.3. *If the equation $f(x) = 0$ with coefficients in $\mathfrak{F}$ has the distinct solutions $x_1, x_2, \cdots, x_k$ in $\mathfrak{F}$, where x_i is of multiplicity h_i, then*

$$f(x) = g(x) \cdot (x - x_1)^{h_1}(x - x_2)^{h_2} \cdots (x - x_k)^{h_k},$$

where $g(x) = 0$ has no solution.

This follows from Theorem 77.1 and the fact that $\mathfrak{F}[x]$ contains no proper divisors of zero.

Corollary 77.3. *An equation with coefficients in a field $\mathfrak{F}$ can have no more solutions than its degree.*

The next theorem is an extension of Theorem 38.1.

Theorem 77.4. *If $f(x)$ and $h(x)$ are two polynomials with coefficients in a field $\mathfrak{F}$, $h(x)$ being irreducible in $\mathfrak{F}[x]$, and if in the polynomial domain $\mathfrak{F}'[x]$ of some extended field $\mathfrak{F}' \supset \mathfrak{F}$ they have a factor of degree ≥ 1 in common, then $h(x) \mid f(x)$ in $\mathfrak{F}[x]$.*

Since $h(x)$ is irreducible in the principal ideal ring $\mathfrak{F}[x]$, either $h(x) \mid f(x)$ or else $h(x)$ is prime to $f(x)$. This latter alternative leads to an absurdity, for, by P_2 of § 69, there would exist polynomials $r(x)$ and $s(x)$ such that

$$r(x) \cdot h(x) + s(x) \cdot f(x) = 1 \qquad \text{in } \mathfrak{F}[x].$$

Since $\mathfrak{F}'[x] \supset \mathfrak{F}[x]$, this continues to hold in $\mathfrak{F}'[x]$. If $a(x)$ were a common divisor in $\mathfrak{F}'[x]$ of $h(x)$ and $f(x)$, it would be a divisor of 1, which is not possible if $a(x)$ is of degree $\geqq 1$.

Corollary 77.4. If $f(x)$ and $h(x)$ are two polynomials with coefficients in a field $\mathfrak{F}$, $h(x)$ being irreducible in $\mathfrak{F}[x]$, and if in some extended field $\mathfrak{F}' \supset \mathfrak{F}$, $h(x) = 0$ and $f(x) = 0$ have a root in common, then $h(x) \mid f(x)$ in $\mathfrak{F}[x]$.

This is the special case of the above theorem where $a(x)$ is linear.

EXERCISES

1. Let $\mathfrak{R}$ be the ring of polynomials in x with coefficients in $GF(5)$. Find a g.c.d. of $4x^3 + 2x^2 + 4x + 2$ and $2x^3 + 2x^2 + 1$, and express it linearly in terms of the given polynomials.

2. Let $\mathfrak{F}$ be any field of characteristic p, and $f(x)$ a polynomial with coefficients in $\mathfrak{F}$. If $f'(x)$ is identically 0, $f(x)$ is a polynomial in x^p, and conversely.

3. Let $f(x)$ be a polynomial with coefficients in $GF(p)$. Then $f'(x) = 0$ if and only if $f(x)$ is the pth power of a polynomial. Does any similar result hold for the real field?

78. Algebraic extensions. A field $\mathfrak{F}$ is called *algebraically closed* if every polynomial in $\mathfrak{F}[x]$ of degree exceeding 1 is reducible. That is to say, $\mathfrak{F}$ is algebraically closed if the linear polynomials are the primes of $\mathfrak{F}[x]$. Still another equivalent definition is that $\mathfrak{F}$ is algebraically closed if every equation with coefficients in $\mathfrak{F}$ has a solution in $\mathfrak{F}$.

In Chapter III we talked about algebraic fields, always making the assumption that an equation with rational coefficients has a root of some kind. Usually appeal is made to the Fundamental Theorem of Algebra to justify this assumption. Actually, no assumption of this sort is necessary for the introduction of algebraic fields, as we shall now see.

Let $\mathfrak{F}$ be any field, and $\mathfrak{F}[\lambda]$ its polynomial domain. If $\mathfrak{F}$ is not algebraically closed, there exists a polynomial $m(\lambda)$ of degree $n > 1$ which is irreducible. By Theorem 76.2 the system $\mathfrak{F}[\lambda]/\{m(\lambda)\}$, which we shall denote more briefly by $\mathfrak{F}/\{m\}$, is a field, called the *stem field* of $m(\lambda)$. The elements of this field are the polynomials

$$\alpha(\lambda) = a_0 + a_1\lambda + a_2\lambda^2 + \cdots + a_{n-1}\lambda^{n-1}.$$

The polynomial λ is a root of the equation $m(x) = 0$. If $\alpha(\lambda)$ and $\beta(\lambda)$ are two polynomials, each of degree $< n$, we may write

$$\alpha(\lambda) \cdot \beta(\lambda) = \gamma(\lambda) + q(\lambda) \cdot m(\lambda),$$

by Theorem 77.1, where $\gamma(\lambda)$, of degree $< n$, is uniquely determined. Then, by definition of $\mathfrak{F}/\{m\}$, $\gamma(\lambda)$ is the product of $\alpha(\lambda)$ and $\beta(\lambda)$.

If $\mathfrak{F}$ is the rational field, it is now evident from Theorem 38.3 that $\mathfrak{F}/\{m\}$ is isomorphic with $\mathfrak{F}(\rho)$, and likewise with each of the conjugate fields of $\mathfrak{F}(\rho)$, where ρ is a root of $m(x) = 0$.

In the modular field $GF(p)$, an equation (congruence) may have no solution. Thus

$$x^2 - x - 1 = 0$$

has no solution in $GF(3)$. Galois simply assumed the existence of a solution j, and from it developed what are now called *Galois fields*. This approach was logically unsatisfactory, but it led Cauchy to the wholly satisfactory approach developed in this chapter. Indeed, by this method any field which is not algebraically closed can be algebraically extended.

If

$$f(x) = a_0 + a_1 x + \cdots + a_n x^n = 0$$

is an equation with coefficients in $\mathfrak{F}$, either it is completely reducible in $\mathfrak{F}[x]$ into linear factors, or it has an irreducible factor, say $m_1(x)$. In the latter case let $\mathfrak{F}' = \mathfrak{F}[\lambda_1]/\{m_1(\lambda_1)\}$. Then, in $\mathfrak{F}'[x]$, $m_1(x)$ has the factor $x - \lambda_1$. Now $f(x)$ is either completely reducible into linear factors in $\mathfrak{F}'[x]$, or it has an irreducible factor $m_2(x)$. In the latter case, let $\mathfrak{F}'' = \mathfrak{F}'/\{m_2(\lambda_2)\}$. Then, in $\mathfrak{F}''[x]$, $m_2(x)$ has the linear factor $x - \lambda_2$. Since $f(x)$ is of finite degree, a field $\mathfrak{F}_r$ must be reached after a finite number of steps in which $f(x)$ is completely reducible into linear factors. This field $\mathfrak{F}_r$ is called the *root field* of $f(x) = 0$.

If $f(x)$ is irreducible in $\mathfrak{F}[x]$, but is completely reducible in $\mathfrak{F}'[x]$, the equation $f(x) = 0$ is called *normal* over $\mathfrak{F}$. We have proved

Theorem 78.1. For every polynomial $f(x)$ in $\mathfrak{F}[x]$, the root field exists. For every irreducible polynomial, the stem field exists.

EXERCISES

1. Show that the system $Re[\lambda]/\{\lambda^2 + 1\}$, where Re is the real field, is isomorphic with the complex field C.

2. If, in any principal ideal ring $\mathfrak{P}$, $d = (a, b)$, and if $\mathfrak{R}$ is an integral domain such that $\mathfrak{R} \supset \mathfrak{P}$, then it is also true that $d = (a, b)$ in $\mathfrak{R}$.

3. A polynomial is separable (§ 41) if it has no multiple zero. A polynomial

$f(x)$ with coefficients in a field $\mathfrak{F}$ which is irreducible over $\mathfrak{F}$ is separable over its root field unless $\mathfrak{F}$ is of characteristic p and f is a polynomial in x^p. In the latter case it is inseparable.

4. Show that $\mathfrak{F}[\lambda]/\{\lambda\} = \mathfrak{F}$.

79. Galois fields. Let p be any positive prime integer, and let $m(\lambda)$ be any polynomial of degree n with coefficients in $GF(p)$ which is irreducible in $GF[p, \lambda]$. The existence of such irreducible polynomials for every prime p and integer n will be shown later (Corollary 81.3). By Theorem 76.2, the ring $GF[p, \lambda]/\{m(\lambda)\}$ is a field which we shall denote by $GF(p, m(\lambda))$. This field consists of just p^n elements, namely, the polynomials

$$\alpha(\lambda) = a_0 + a_1\lambda + a_2\lambda^2 + \cdots + a_{n-1}\lambda^{n-1},$$

where each coefficient lies in $GF(p)$. The product of two such elements $\alpha(\lambda)$ and $\beta(\lambda)$ is the unique polynomial $\rho(\lambda)$ of degree $< n$ defined by the division transformation

$$\alpha(\lambda) \cdot \beta(\lambda) = \sigma(\lambda) \cdot m(\lambda) + \rho(\lambda).$$

Theorem 79.1. The generalized Fermat theorem. If α is not 0 in $GF(p, m(\lambda))$, then

$$\alpha^{p^n - 1} = 1.$$

Set $p^n - 1 = k$, and let $\alpha_1, \alpha_2, \cdots, \alpha_k$ be the elements of $GF(p, m(\lambda))$ different from 0. Let α be any one of these elements. Then

(79.1) $$\alpha\alpha_1, \alpha\alpha_2, \cdots, \alpha\alpha_k$$

are each different from 0 (Theorem 33.1). They are distinct, for $\alpha\alpha_i = \alpha\alpha_j$ would imply that

$$\alpha(\alpha_i - \alpha_j) = 0, \qquad \alpha_i = \alpha_j,$$

by the same theorem. Thus the numbers (79.1) are the numbers $\alpha_1, \alpha_2, \cdots, \alpha_k$ in some order, and

$$\prod \alpha\alpha_i = \alpha^k \prod \alpha_i = \prod \alpha_i,$$

$$(\alpha^k - 1) \prod \alpha_i = 0.$$

By Theorem 33.1 again, $\alpha^k = 1$.

Corollary 79.1. If α is any number of $GF(p, m(\lambda))$,

$$\alpha^{p^n} = \alpha.$$

Theorem 79.2. *If* $0, \alpha_1, \alpha_2, \cdots, \alpha_\kappa$ *are the elements of* $GF(p, m(\lambda))$, *then*

$$x^{p^n} - x = x(x - \alpha_1)(x - \alpha_2) \cdots (x - \alpha_k) \qquad in \; GF(p, m(\lambda)).$$

This follows directly from Theorem 77.3 and the fact that the co-efficient of the highest power of x is the same on both sides of the equation.

That is to say, the elements of $GF(p, m(\lambda))$ are the zeros of the function $x^{p^n} - x = 0$ in its root field. Therefore the field $GF(p, m(\lambda))$ depends only upon the prime p and the integer n, and not upon the particular irreducible function $m(\lambda)$ of degree n which was selected as modulus. Hence we have

Corollary 79.2. *If* $m_1(\lambda)$ *and* $m_2(\lambda)$ *are two irreducible functions of degree* n *in* $GF[p, \lambda]$, *the fields* $GF(p, m_1(\lambda))$ *and* $GF(p, m_2(\lambda))$ *are isomorphic.*

We shall denote the Galois field by $GF(p^n)$ when it is not necessary to bring the irreducible function $m(\lambda)$ into evidence.

Theorem 79.3. *If* $m_1(x), m_2(x), \cdots, m_h(x)$ *are the distinct irreducible polynomials of degree* n *in the polynomial domain* $GF[p, x]$, *then*

$$x^{p^n-1} - 1 = m_1(x) \cdot m_2(x) \cdots m_h(x) \cdot g(x).$$

Since the non-zero elements of $GF(p, m_1(\lambda))$ are the zeros of $x^{p^n-1} - 1$, $m_1(x)$ and $x^{p^n-1} - 1$ have a zero α_1 in common. Hence, by Corollary 77.4,

$$x^{p^n-1} - 1 = m_1(x) \cdot g_1(x).$$

Similarly $m_2(x)$ and $x^{p^n-1} - 1$ have a zero α_2 in common. But α_2 is not a zero of $m_1(x)$, or $m_1(x)$ would be associated with $m_2(x)$. Hence α_2 is a zero of $g_1(x)$, and

$$x^{p^n-1} - 1 = m_1(x) \cdot m_2(x) \cdot g_2(x).$$

After h steps we have the theorem.

EXERCISES

1. Show that $x^2 - x - 1$ is irreducible over $GF(3)$. Use it to construct the multiplication table of the field $GF(3^2)$. Show that $(2\lambda + 1)^8 = 1$.

2. Solve the equation

$$x^2 + 2x + 2 = 0 \qquad\qquad in \; GF(3^2).$$

3. What are the units of $GF[p, \lambda]$? Show that every polynomial is associated with one whose leading coefficient is 1.

4. Find all the polynomials of degree 2 and leading coefficient 1 which are irreducible over $GF(3)$. Show that their product divides $x^8 - 1$.

5. If $m_1(x)$, $m_2(x)$, $\cdots$, $m_k(x)$ are the distinct irreducible polynomials of degree n in $GF[p, x]$, show that each equation $m_i(x) = 0$ has in $GF(p^n)$ as many solutions as its degree.

6. Show that $x^2 + x - 1$ is irreducible over $GF(3)$. Exhibit an isomorphism between $GF(3, \lambda^2 - \lambda - 1)$ and $GF(3, \lambda^2 + \lambda - 1)$.

HINT: Find a root u of $x^2 + x - 1 = 0$ in $GF(3, \lambda^2 - \lambda - 1)$, and let $x \leftrightarrow u$.

80. Automorphisms of a Galois field.

Theorem 80.1. *In the Galois field $GF(p, m(\lambda))$,*

$$m(\lambda) = c(x - \lambda)(x - \lambda^p)(x - \lambda^{p^2}) \cdots (x - \lambda^{p^{n-1}}).$$

By Theorem 11.3,

$$m(x^{p^m}) = [m(x)]^{p^m}$$

in $GF[p, x]$ for every integer m. Since $m(\lambda) = 0$ in $GF(p, m(\lambda))$, λ^{p^m} is a root of $m(x) = 0$ for every integer m. We need to show that for $m = 0$, $1, \cdots, n - 1$, these powers are distinct. Let

$$\lambda^{p^m} = \lambda^{p^l}, \qquad\qquad l < m < n.$$

Raise each side to the positive power p^{n-l}. Then

$$\lambda^{p^{m-l+n}} = \lambda^{p^n} = \lambda.$$

Hence

$$(\lambda^{p^{m-l}})^{p^n} = \lambda^{p^{m-l}} = \lambda.$$

Let $\beta(\lambda)$ be any number of $GF(p, m(\lambda))$. Then

$$\beta(\lambda) = \beta(\lambda^{p^{m-l}}) = [\beta(\lambda)]^{p^{m-l}},$$

and so $\beta(\lambda)$ satisfies the equation

$$x^{p^{m-l}} - x = 0.$$

Since this equation has p^n roots, it must vanish identically. That is, $m = l$.

Corollary 80.1. *The Galois field $GF(p^n)$ is cyclic, its automorphisms being*

$$\lambda \leftrightarrow \lambda^{p^m} \qquad\qquad (m = 0, 1, \cdots n - 1).$$

Theorem 80.2. *The multiplication group of $GF(p^n)$ is the cyclic group of order $p^n - 1$.*

The multiplication group $\mathfrak{G}$ of $GF(p^n)$ consists of the elements of the field with 0 omitted. By Theorem 79.2, these numbers are the zeros of

$$x^{p^n-1} - 1.$$

Let $p^n - 1 = p_1^{n_1} p_2^{n_2} \cdots p_k^{n_k}$, where the p_i are distinct primes. Then the multiplication group $\mathfrak{G}$ is abelian and by Corollary 31.3 can be written

$$\mathfrak{G} = \mathfrak{H}_1 \times \mathfrak{H}_2 \times \cdots \times \mathfrak{H}_k,$$

where $\mathfrak{H}_i$ is an abelian group of order $p_i^{n_i}$ consisting of all elements of $\mathfrak{G}$ whose periods are powers of p_i. To prove that $\mathfrak{G}$ is cyclic, it is sufficient according to Ex. 6, § 31, to prove each $\mathfrak{H}_i$ cyclic. But by Corollary 77.3 the equation

$$x^{p_i^{n_i-1}} - 1 = 0$$

has at most $p_i^{n_i-1}$ roots, so the remaining $p_i^{n_i} - p_i^{n_i-1} = \varphi(p_i^{n_i})$ elements of $\mathfrak{H}_i$ are primitive, and $\mathfrak{H}_i$ is cyclic.

EXERCISES

1. Factor $x^2 + x - 1$ in $GF(3, \lambda^2 - \lambda - 1)$, and show that the result agrees with Theorem 80.1.

2. In $GF(3, \lambda^2 - \lambda - 1)$, $x^2 - x - 1 = 0$ has another root u besides λ. Show that $u \leftrightarrow \lambda$ is an automorphism. Show that $\lambda \leftrightarrow \lambda^2$ is the same automorphism.

3. Find the automorphisms of

$$GF(3, \lambda^3 - \lambda - 1).$$

4. If $m \mid p^n - 1$, the equation $x^m = 1$ has exactly m solutions in $GF(p^n)$.

5. By considering the multiplication group of $GF(p, m(\lambda))$, prove Theorem 79.1 by group theory.

6. Show that every Galois field is normal. (See §36.)

81. Existence of Galois fields. Let p be any prime, and n any integer > 1.

Theorem 81.1.   The zeros of $x^{p^n} - x$ in its root field over $GF(p)$ form a field $\mathfrak{F}$.

Let $\mathfrak{F}_r$ denote the root field of $f(x) = x^{p^n} - x = 0$ over $GF(p)$. In $\mathfrak{F}_r$ this polynomial $f(x)$ has exactly p^n zeros,

$$\alpha_0 = 0, \quad \alpha_1 = 1, \quad \alpha_2, \quad \alpha_3, \quad \cdots, \quad \alpha_k, \quad k = p^n - 1.$$

The derivative of $f(x)$ is

$$f'(x) = p^n x^{p^n-1} - 1 = -1 \qquad \text{in } GF[p, x].$$

Since $f'(x)$ has no zeros, the zeros of $f(x)$ are distinct by Theorem 77.2.

Let α_i and α_j be two zeros of $f(x)$. Since $\mathfrak{F}_r$ is of characteristic p, it follows from Ex. 2, § 72, that

$$(\alpha_i \pm \alpha_j)^{p^n} = \alpha_i^{p^n} \pm \alpha_j^{p^n} = \alpha_i \pm \alpha_j.$$

Thus the set of zeros of $f(x)$ is closed under addition and subtraction. Also

$$(\alpha_i\alpha_j)^{p^n} = \alpha_i^{p^n}\alpha_j^{p^n} = \alpha_i\alpha_j.$$

And, if $\alpha_i \neq 0$, it has an inverse α_i^{-1} in $\mathfrak{F}_r$. Then

$$1 = (\alpha_i\alpha_i^{-1})^{p^n} = \alpha_i^{p^n}(\alpha_i^{-1})^{p^n} = \alpha_i(\alpha_i^{-1})^{p^n},$$

so that

$$(\alpha_i^{-1})^{p^n} = \alpha_i^{-1}$$

by Theorem 33.5. Hence α_i^{-1} is in $\mathfrak{F}$. Thus $\mathfrak{F}$ is a field.

It is not yet clear, however, that $\mathfrak{F}$ is a Galois field for every n. That is, it is not evident that the converse of Theorem 79.2 holds.

We first note the following fact:

Theorem 81.2. The multiplication group of $\mathfrak{F}$ is the cyclic group of order $p^n - 1$.

The proof is exactly like that of Theorem 80.2.

Thus there exists a generator α of this multiplication group such that $\mathfrak{F}$ consists of 0 and the powers α, α^2, $\cdots$, $\alpha^k = 1$.

Theorem 81.3. If α is a generator of the multiplication group of $\mathfrak{F}$, then α satisfies an irreducible equation $m(x) = 0$ with coefficients in $GF(p)$ of degree n.

There are p^{n+1} numbers represented in the form

$$x_0 + x_1\alpha + x_2\alpha^2 + \cdots + x_n\alpha^n$$

where the x's range over $GF(p)$. Since there are but p^n numbers in $\mathfrak{F}$, two of these numbers are equal. Their difference gives a dependence relation $m(\alpha) = 0$ among the powers of α. Thus $m(x) = 0$ is an equation of degree at most n satisfied by α.

Now suppose that there were a dependence relation

$$\alpha^h = c_0 + c_1\alpha + c_2\alpha^2 + \cdots + c_{h-1}\alpha^{h-1} \qquad h < n,$$

with coefficients in $GF(p)$. Then each of the $p^n - 1$ powers of α could be written in the form

$$x_0 + x_1\alpha + x_2\alpha^2 + \cdots + x_{h-1}\alpha^{h-1}.$$

But there are only p^h numbers so representable. Hence α satisfies no equation of degree $< n$. That is, $m(x)$ is irreducible of degree n.

Corollary 81.3. *For every positive integer n, there exists an irreducible polynomial with coefficients in $GF(p)$ of degree n.*

Theorem 81.4. *The zeros of $x^{p^n} - x$ in its root field over $GF(p)$ form a Galois field for every prime p and every positive integer n.*

If α is a generator of the multiplication group of the root field $\mathfrak{F}$, the numbers

$$x_0 + x_1\alpha + x_2\alpha^2 + \cdots + x_{n-1}\alpha^{n-1}$$

are all in $\mathfrak{F}$, and are distinct, since, if two of them were equal, their difference would give a dependence relation, contrary to Theorem 81.3. Since they are p^n in number, they are the numbers of $\mathfrak{F}$. But α satisfies an irreducible equation $m(x) = 0$ of degree n over $GF(p)$, and so $\mathfrak{F} \cong GF(p, m(x))$.

Corollary 81.4. *For every prime p and every positive integer n, the Galois field $GF(p^n)$ exists.*

Suppose now that $\mathfrak{F}_1$ is a field composed of a finite number of elements. By Theorem 72.3, it is of characteristic p, and contains $GF(p)$ as its prime subfield.

Theorem 81.5. *The number of numbers in $\mathfrak{F}_1$ is a power of p.*

Let β_1 be any number of $\mathfrak{F}_1$ not in $GF(p)$. Then $\mathfrak{F}_1$ contains the p^2 numbers

$$a_0 + a_1\beta_1.$$

These are all distinct, for, if two of them were equal, we should have a relation

$$c_0 + c_1\beta_1 = 0 \qquad (c_0, c_1) \neq (0, 0) \text{ in } GF(p).$$

If $c_1 = 0$, so does c_0, and therefore $c_1 \neq 0$. Hence we should have $\beta_1 = - c_0 c_1^{-1}$, which is in $GF(p)$.

Either p^2 is the number of elements in $\mathfrak{F}_1$, or else there is a number β_2 of $\mathfrak{F}_1$ which is not of the form $a_0 + a_1\beta_1$. Then $\mathfrak{F}_1$ contains all the p^3 numbers

$$a_0 + a_1\beta_1 + a_2\beta_2.$$

These are all distinct, for, if they were not, we should have a relation

$$c_0 + c_1\beta_1 + c_2\beta_2 = 0, \qquad (c_0, c_1, c_2) \neq (0, 0, 0).$$

We cannot have $c_2 = 0$, as we have seen. Then

$$\beta_2 = - c_2^{-1}c_0 - c_2^{-1}c_1\beta_1,$$

contrary to the selection of β_2.

Since $\mathfrak{F}_1$ is finite, the number of such β's is finite, and a point is finally reached where every number of $\mathfrak{F}_1$ is given without repetition by the form

$$a_0 + a_1\beta_1 + a_2\beta_2 + \cdots + a_{n-1}\beta_{n-1},$$

so that $\mathfrak{F}_1$ contains exactly p^n numbers.

Theorem 81.6. *Every finite field is isomorphic with a Galois field.*

If $\mathfrak{F}_1$ is of order p^n, each of its numbers β_i different from 0 is an element of the multiplication group of order $p^n - 1$, and hence by Ex. 2, § 23, its period divides $p^n - 1$. Thus β_i satisfies the equation

(81.1) $$x^{p^n-1} - 1 = 0$$

with coefficients in the prime field $GF(p)$. Since $\mathfrak{F}_1$ is a field, no equation in $\mathfrak{F}_1$ can have more solutions than its degree. Then the elements of $\mathfrak{F}_1$ are the zeros of (81.1) in its root field over $GF(p)$. By Theorem 81.4, $\mathfrak{F}_1$ is a Galois field.

EXERCISES

1. A polynomial $g(x)$ which is irreducible in $GF[p, x]$ of degree n divides $x^{p^m} - x$ if and only if $n \mid m$.

2. The product of the irreducible polynomials in $GF[p, x]$ of prime degree n is

$$\frac{x^{p^n} - x}{x^p - x},$$

and they are $(p^n - p)/n$ in number. (Why is this number always an integer?) Illustrate these statements with Ex. 4, § 79.

3. Show that in $GF(3, \lambda^2 + 2\lambda + 2)$, $\lambda + 1$ is a zero of the irreducible function $x^2 + 1$, yet is not a generator of the multiplication group.

4. It is not true that every root of an irreducible polynomial $m(x)$ of degree n is a generator of the multiplication group of $GF(p^n)$. For $p = 3$ and $n = 2$, find the number of generators and also the number of such roots.

82. Transcendental extensions. There are two very simple ways of extending a field $\mathfrak{F}$ to a field $\mathfrak{F}^*$ which contains $\mathfrak{F}$ properly. In each case, the field $\mathfrak{F}$ is first extended to its polynomial domain $\mathfrak{F}[\lambda]$ by the method of § 73. If there exists a polynomial $m(\lambda)$ which is irreducible in $\mathfrak{F}[\lambda]$ of degree > 1, the polynomials of $\mathfrak{F}[\lambda]$ taken modulo $m(\lambda)$ constitute a *finite algebraic extension* $\mathfrak{F}(\lambda, m(\lambda))$ which contains $\mathfrak{F}$ as a proper subfield. All fields except those which are algebraically closed can be so extended. The number λ satisfies the equation $m(\lambda) = 0$ with coefficients in $\mathfrak{F}$, and so it is algebraic relative to $\mathfrak{F}$.

A second method of extension is to pass from $\mathfrak{F}$ to $\mathfrak{F}[\lambda]$ as before, and from $\mathfrak{F}[\lambda]$ to its quotient field $\mathfrak{F}(\lambda)$ by the method of § 71. This quotient field consists of all rational functions of λ with coefficients in $\mathfrak{F}$. Since λ does not satisfy any polynomial equation with coefficients in $\mathfrak{F}$, it is called *transcendental* over $\mathfrak{F}$, and $\mathfrak{F}(\lambda)$ is called a *transcendental extension* of $\mathfrak{F}$.

Theorem 82.1. *Two transcendental extensions of $\mathfrak{F}$ are isomorphic.*

For, clearly, $\mathfrak{F}(\lambda)$ and $\mathfrak{F}(\mu)$ are isomorphic under the correspondence $\lambda \leftrightarrow \mu$.

Theorem 82.2. *All automorphisms of $\mathfrak{F}(\lambda)$ are given by*

$$(82.1) \qquad \lambda \leftrightarrow \lambda' = \frac{a\lambda + b}{c\lambda + d}, \qquad ad - bc \neq 0.$$

Suppose that, under some automorphism of $\mathfrak{F}(\lambda)$,

$$\lambda \leftrightarrow h(\lambda) = \frac{p(\lambda)}{q(\lambda)},$$

where $p(\lambda)$ and $q(\lambda)$ are relatively prime polynomials. Then every rational function of h is a rational function of λ. It must be true, conversely, that every rational function of λ is a rational function of h, and so in particular there must exist a rational function f such that

$$f(h(\lambda)) = \lambda.$$

Suppose that

$$f(\mu) = \frac{r(\mu)}{s(\mu)}, \quad r(\mu) = \sum_{i=0}^{k} r_i \mu^i, \quad s(\mu) = \sum_{i=0}^{k} s_i \mu^i,$$

where $r(\mu)$ and $s(\mu)$ are relatively prime polynomials, and either r_k or s_k is not zero. Then

$$f(h(\lambda)) = \frac{\displaystyle\sum_{i=0}^{k} r_i \left(\frac{p(\lambda)}{q(\lambda)}\right)^i}{\displaystyle\sum_{i=0}^{k} s_i \left(\frac{p(\lambda)}{q(\lambda)}\right)^i} = \lambda,$$

which immediately reduces to

$$(82.2) \qquad \sum_{i=0}^{k} r_i [p(\lambda)]^i [q(\lambda)]^{k-i} = \lambda \sum_{i=0}^{k} s_i [p(\lambda)]^i [q(\lambda)]^{k-i}.$$

In particular it is true that

$$r_0 [q(\lambda)]^k \equiv \lambda s_0 [q(\lambda)]^k \qquad \mod p(\lambda).$$

Since $p(\lambda)$ is prime to $q(\lambda)$, this implies that

$$r_0 - \lambda s_0 \equiv 0 \qquad \text{mod } p(\lambda).$$

If $p(\lambda)$ were of degree > 1, the last congruence would imply $r_0 = s_0 = 0$, so that $r(\mu)$ and $s(\mu)$ would have the common factor μ and not be relatively prime. Since $p(\lambda)$ cannot vanish identically, it is linear.

It also follows from (82.2) that

$$r_k[p(\lambda)]^k \equiv \lambda s_k[p(\lambda)]^k \qquad \text{mod } q(\lambda),$$

and in an exactly similar manner it can be shown that $q(\lambda)$ is linear.

Now assume that

$$h(\lambda) = \frac{p(\lambda)}{q(\lambda)} = \frac{a\lambda + b}{c\lambda + d} = \lambda'.$$

Since we must have $p(\lambda)$ prime to $q(\lambda)$, it must be true that $ad - bc \neq 0$. Then

$$\lambda = \frac{-d\lambda' + b}{c\lambda' - a}, \qquad (-d)(-a) - bc \neq 0.$$

Thus the correspondences described in the theorem are biunique, and are the only ones which are biunique.

EXERCISES

1. Show that every biunique correspondence $h(\lambda) = \lambda' \leftrightarrow \lambda = f(\lambda')$ of $\mathfrak{F}(\lambda)$ with itself is necessarily an automorphism with respect to both addition and multiplication.

2. Call

$$\begin{bmatrix} a & b \\ c & d \end{bmatrix}$$

the matrix of the transformation (82.1), and show that the matrix of the product (iterate) of two transformations is equal to the product of the matrices of the factors.

3. Show that the "birational transformations" (82.1) form a group under iteration.

4. Show that the only rational functions $h(\lambda)$ such that $f(h(\lambda)) = \lambda^2$ for some rational function f are of the form

$$h(\lambda) = \frac{a\lambda^2 + b}{c\lambda^2 + d}.$$

Suggested Readings

Steinitz, E. *Algebraische Theorie der Körper.* de Gruyter, Leipzig, 1930.

Haupt, O. *Einführung in die Algebra*, Vol. I. Akad. Verlag., Leipzig, 1929.

Ore, Oystein. *L'algèbre abstraite.* Hermann, Paris, 1936.

Dickson, L. E. *Linear Groups with an Exposition of the Galois Field Theory*, Part I. Teubner, Leipzig, 1901.

Serret, J. A. *Cours d'algèbre supérieure*, Vol. II, Section III. Gauthier-Villars, Paris, 1885.

Albert, A. A. *Modern Higher Algebra*, Chapters I, II. University of Chicago Press, 1937.

van der Waerden, B. L. *Moderne Algebra*, Vol. I, Chapters III, IV, V. Springer, Berlin, 1937.

CHAPTER VI

PERFECT FIELDS

83. Regular sequences of rational numbers. If a and b are elements of a field $\mathfrak{F}$, the function $\varphi(a)$ is called a *valuation* for $\mathfrak{F}$ if:

1. $\varphi(a)$ is a positive number or 0 of some ordered field.
2. $\varphi(a) > 0$ for $a \neq 0$, $\quad \varphi(0) = 0$.
3. $\varphi(ab) = \varphi(a) \cdot \varphi(b)$.
4. $\varphi(a + b) \leqq \varphi(a) + \varphi(b)$.

If $\mathfrak{F}$ is the rational field Ra, the ordinary absolute value $\mid a \mid$ is a valuation. The only properties of $\mid a \mid$ which we shall use are those listed above.

A set or sequence of rational numbers

$$\{a_p\} = (a_1, a_2, \cdots) \qquad (p = 1, 2, \cdots)$$

is called a *regular* (or *fundamental*, or *Cauchy*) sequence if, for every positive rational number ϵ, there is a positive integer n_ϵ such that

$$\mid a_p - a_q \mid < \epsilon \qquad \text{for every } p > n_\epsilon, q > n_\epsilon.$$

Two regular sequences

$$\{a_p\} = (a_1, a_2, \cdots), \quad \{b_p\} = (b_1, b_2, \cdots)$$

are defined to be *equal* if, for every positive rational number ϵ, there is a positive integer n_ϵ such that

$$\mid a_p - b_p \mid < \epsilon, \qquad p > n_\epsilon.$$

Theorem 83.1. Every regular sequence is bounded in absolute value.

Choose ϵ, and determine the corresponding n_ϵ for which

$$\mid a_p - a_q \mid < \epsilon, \qquad p, q > n_\epsilon.$$

Take $n = n_\epsilon$. Then

$$\mid a_p - a_{n+1} \mid < \epsilon, \qquad p > n,$$

so that

$$\mid a_p \mid \leqq \mid a_{n+1} \mid + \mid a_p - a_{n+1} \mid < \mid a_{n+1} \mid + \epsilon.$$

Thus for every ϵ there is a bound $M_\epsilon = \mid a_{n+1} \mid + \epsilon$ such that, for $p > n_\epsilon$, $\mid a_p \mid < M_\epsilon$.

Addition of regular sequences is defined by the equation

$$\{a_p\} + \{b_p\} = \{a_p + b_p\}.$$

Theorem 83.2. The sum of two regular sequences is regular.

Suppose that $\{a_p\}$ and $\{b_p\}$ are regular, so that

$$\left| a_p - a_q \right| < \frac{\epsilon}{2}, \qquad\qquad p, q > n_1,$$

$$\left| b_p - b_q \right| < \frac{\epsilon}{2}, \qquad\qquad p, q > n_2.$$

Denote by n the larger of n_1, n_2. Then

$$\left|(a_p + b_p) - (a_q + b_q)\right| \leq \left| a_p - a_q \right| + \left| b_p - b_q \right| < \epsilon, \qquad p, q > n.$$

Theorem 83.3. The regular sequences form an abelian group relative to addition.

Closure was proved in Theorem 83.2. The associative law is obvious. The identity of addition, $\{0\}$, is evidently regular, as is the inverse $\{-a_p\}$ of $\{a_p\}$. The commutative law holds.

EXERCISES

1. Prove that equality of regular sequences fulfills the postulates of § 21.
2. Prove that addition and multiplication of regular sequences are well defined.
3. Let $(a_1, a_2, \cdots)$ be any sequence of rational numbers which are bounded in absolute value. Prove that $\{a_p/2^p\}$ is regular, and find an n_ϵ.
4. Prove that $\varphi(\pm 1) = 1$, $\varphi(-a) = \varphi(a)$.

84. The real field. The sequence $\{0\}$ is clearly equal to the identity element of addition which we shall, as usual, call *zero*.

Theorem 84.1. A sequence $\{a_p\}$ is equal to zero if and only if for every positive ϵ there exists an integer n_ϵ such that

$$\left| a_p \right| < \epsilon, \qquad\qquad p > n_\epsilon.$$

This comes immediately from the definition of equality of two sequences.

Theorem 84.2. If $\{a_p\}$ is not equal to zero, there is an $\eta > 0$ and an integer n such that

$$\left| a_p \right| \geq \eta, \qquad\qquad p > n.$$

Let $\{a_p\}$ be a sequence for which the conclusion of the theorem does not hold. That is, for every $\eta > 0$ and every integer n, there is at least one $q > n$ such that

$$| a_q | < \eta.$$

But there is an n such that, for $p > n$ and $q > n$,

$$| a_p - a_q | < \eta.$$

Then

$$| a_p | \leq | a_q | + | a_p - a_q | < 2\eta$$

for every η if $p > n$, so that $\{a_p\}$ is equal to zero, contrary to assumption.

Multiplication of regular sequences is defined by the equation

$$\{a_p\} \times \{b_p\} = \{a_p b_p\}.$$

Theorem 84.3. *The product of two regular sequences is regular.*

By Theorem 83.1, $\{a_p\}$ and $\{b_p\}$ are bounded. That is,

$$| a_p | < M_1, \quad | b_q | < M_2, \qquad p > n_1, q > n_2.$$

Then for every ϵ, n' and n'' exist so that

$$| a_p - a_q | < \frac{\epsilon}{2M_2}, \qquad\qquad p, q > n',$$

$$| b_p - b_q | < \frac{\epsilon}{2M_1}, \qquad\qquad p, q > n''.$$

Let n be the greatest of n_1, n_2, n', n''. Then, multiplying the above inequalities by $| b_p |$ and $| a_q |$, respectively, we have

$$| a_p b_p - a_q b_p | < \frac{\epsilon}{2}, \quad | a_q b_p - a_q b_q | < \frac{\epsilon}{2}, \qquad p, q > n,$$

$$| a_p b_p - a_q b_q | < \epsilon, \qquad\qquad p, q > n.$$

Theorem 84.4. *The regular sequences which are not equal to zero form an abelian group relative to multiplication.*

It was proved in the last theorem that, if $\{a_p\}$ and $\{b_p\}$ are regular, $\{a_p b_p\}$ is regular. If $\{a_p\}$ and $\{b_p\}$ are not equal to zero, numbers $\eta_1 > 0$ and $\eta_2 > 0$ exist, by Theorem 84.2, such that for $p > n$

$$| a_p | \geq \eta_1, \quad | b_p | \geq \eta_2.$$

Then

$$| a_p b_p | \geq \eta_1 \eta_2 > 0, \qquad\qquad p > n,$$

so that $\{a_p b_p\}$ is not equal to zero.

The associative and commutative laws are evident.   The identity is $\{1\} = (1, 1, \cdots)$, which is not equal to zero.

An inverse can be defined.   Suppose that

$$| a_p | \geqq \eta_1 > 0, \qquad\qquad p > n.$$

Define $b_p = 0$ for $p \leqq n$, $b_p = 1/a_p$ for $p > n$.   Then

$$\{a_p\}\{b_p\} = (0, \cdots, 0, 1, 1, \cdots) = \{1\}.$$

It remains to be shown that $\{b_p\}$ is regular and not equal to zero. Suppose that

$$\left| a_q - a_p \right| = \left| a_p a_q \left(\frac{1}{a_p} - \frac{1}{a_q} \right) \right| \leqq \epsilon \eta_1^2, \quad p, q > n_1 \geqq n.$$

Then, dividing by $| a_p a_q | \geqq \eta_1^2$, we have

$$\left| \frac{1}{a_p} - \frac{1}{a_q} \right| \leqq \epsilon \qquad\qquad p, q > n_1.$$

If $\{b_p\}$ were equal to zero, we should have $\{a_p\}\{b_p\} = \{0\}$, whereas this product is equal to $\{1\}$.

We shall denote by Re the mathematical system composed of all regular sequences of rational numbers with equality, addition, and multiplication as defined above.

Theorem 84.5.   The system Re is a field.

In addition to the results of Theorems 83.3 and 84.4, only the distributive law is needed.

$$[\{a_p\} + \{b_p\}]\{c_p\} = \{a_p c_p + b_p c_p\} = \{a_p\}\{c_p\} + \{b_p\}\{c_p\}.$$

This field is called the *real field,* and its numbers are called *real numbers.*

Theorem 84.6.   The real field is of characteristic 0.

For the sequences $(a, a, a, \cdots)$ are isomorphic with the numbers a of the rational field.   Hence Re contains Ra as its prime subfield.

EXERCISE

1. Prove that a subsequence of a given regular sequence is equal to the given sequence.

85. Properties of the real field.   A regular sequence is called *positive* if there exists an $\eta > 0$ and an n such that, for $p > n$, $a_p \geqq \eta$.   A regular sequence is called *negative* if there exists an $\eta > 0$ and an n such that, for $p > n$, $-a_p \geqq \eta$.

Theorem 85.1.   Every regular sequence is of just one of the following three types: (1) *zero,* (2) *positive,* (3) *negative.*

If $\{a_p\}$ is not zero, it follows from Theorem 84.2 that there is an $\eta > 0$ and an n such that

$$|\,a_p\,| \geqq \eta, \quad |\,a_p - a_q\,| < \eta, \qquad\qquad p, q > n.$$

Thus a_p and a_q have the same sign for p, $q > n$, and either $a_p \geqq \eta$ or $-a_p \geqq \eta$ for every $p > n$. That these three types are mutually exclusive follows immediately from their definitions.

An order relation is now readily established for real numbers. We say that $\{a_p\} > \{b_p\}$ if $\{a_p\} - \{b_p\}$ is positive, and $\{a_p\} < \{b_p\}$ if $\{a_p\} - \{b_p\}$ is negative. Thus $\{a_p\}$ is positive if $\{a_p\} > 0$.

Theorem 85.2.   Given any two distinct real numbers, there is a rational number between them.

If $\{a_p\}$ and $\{b_p\}$ are distinct, we can assume without loss of generality that $\{a_p - b_p\}$ is positive. Then

$$a_p - b_p \geqq \eta > 0 \qquad\qquad p > n_1.$$

Also we can make

$$|\,b_p - b_q\,| < \frac{\eta}{4}, \qquad\qquad p, q > n_2.$$

Take n the larger of n_1 and n_2, and define

$$c_p = b_{n+1} + \tfrac{1}{2}\eta$$

so that $\{c_p\}$ is rational. Also

$$
\begin{aligned}
a_p - c_p &= a_p - b_{n+1} - \tfrac{1}{2}\eta \\
&= a_p - b_p + b_p - b_{n+1} - \tfrac{1}{2}\eta \\
&> \eta - \tfrac{1}{4}\eta - \tfrac{1}{2}\eta = \tfrac{1}{4}\eta, \qquad\qquad p > n,
\end{aligned}
$$

so that $\{a_p - c_p\}$ is positive. Furthermore,

$$
\begin{aligned}
c_p - b_p &= b_{n+1} + \tfrac{1}{2}\eta - b_p \\
&> \tfrac{1}{2}\eta - \tfrac{1}{4}\eta = \tfrac{1}{4}\eta, \qquad\qquad p > n,
\end{aligned}
$$

so that $\{c_p - b_p\}$ is also positive.

The real field is also a field with a valuation, namely, the absolute value. We can therefore define regular sequences of real numbers and repeat all the results of the last three paragraphs for such sequences. The result of all this, however, is to obtain the real field over again. A field which is incapable of extension by means of regular sequences with respect to a given valuation is called *perfect* with respect to this valuation.

Two sequences $\{\alpha_p\}$ and $\{\beta_p\}$ of real numbers are called equal if, for every positive real number κ, there is a positive integer n_κ such that

$$|\, \alpha_p - \beta_p \,| < \kappa, \qquad\qquad p > n_\kappa.$$

If this holds for every real positive κ, then surely it holds for every rational positive ϵ, so that equality with respect to real absolute value implies equality according to the definition of § 83.

Theorem 85.3.   The real field is perfect with respect to absolute value.

Let $\{\alpha_p\}$ be a sequence of real numbers.   For every $p \geqq 1$, select a rational number a_p so that (Theorem 85.2)

$$\alpha_p < a_p < \alpha_p + \frac{1}{p}.$$

Let ϵ be any positive real number.   Then

$$|\, a_p - \alpha_p \,| < \frac{1}{p} < \epsilon, \qquad\qquad p > 1/\epsilon,$$

so that $\{\alpha_p\} = \{a_p\}$.

EXERCISES

1. If for every positive integer n there is a $p > n$ and a $q > n$ such that a_p and a_q have opposite signs, then $\{a_p\} = 0$.

2. Prove that the square of every non-zero regular sequence is positive.

3. Prove that the product of a positive sequence and a negative sequence is negative.

86. Polynomials over the real field.   A real function is a correspondence such that, to every real number x of a certain range, there corresponds exactly one real number y.   This correspondence is written $y = f(x)$.   If $f(x)$ is a polynomial, there is a y corresponding to every real number x.

Let $a = \{\alpha_p\}$ be a regular sequence of real numbers, and let $\beta_p = f(\alpha_p)$.   If for *every* regular sequence $\{\alpha_p\}$ equal to a it is true that $\{\beta_p\}$ is regular and equal to $f(a)$, then $y = f(x)$ is said to be *continuous* at $x = a$.

Theorem 86.1.   The polynomial

$$y = a_0 x^n + \cdots + a_{n-1}\, x + a_n,$$

where the a's are real, is continuous for every x.

The product and sum of regular sequences are regular (Theorems 84.3 and 83.2).

Theorem 86.2. Let the real polynomial

$$y = a_0 x^n + \cdots + a_{n-1} x + a_n$$

be positive for $x = \xi_2$ *and negative for* $x = \xi_1$. *Then there is a real x between* ξ_1 *and* ξ_2 *whose corresponding y is zero.*

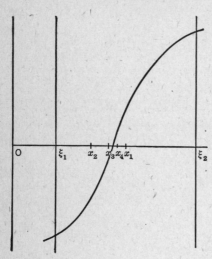

In the interval (ξ_1, ξ_2) there are some positive y's and some negative y's. Let $x_1 = \frac{1}{2}(\xi_1 + \xi_2)$. Unless $f(x_1) = 0$, there are both positive and negative y's in at least one of the intervals (ξ_1, x_1) or (x_1, ξ_2). If this is true of the first interval, define $x_2 = \frac{1}{2}(\xi_1 + x_1)$. Unless $f(x_2) = 0$, one of the intervals (ξ_1, x_2) or (x_2, x_1) contains both positive and negative y's. Continue in this way, obtaining a sequence $\{x_p\}$. Denote by $\{y_p\}$ the sequence of corresponding y's.

The sequence $\{x_p\}$ is regular. Clearly

$$| x_p - x_{p+k} | \leqq 2 | x_p - x_{p+1} | \leqq | \xi_1 - \xi_2 | \frac{1}{2^p}.$$

Hence we can make

$$| x_p - x_q | < \epsilon$$

by taking p and q sufficiently large.

The sequence $\{y_p\}$ is now seen to be regular, since $f(x)$ is continuous (Theorem 86.1).

If $y_i > 0$, there is a $j > i$ such that $y_j < 0$, and vice versa. For suppose that there were a last negative y, say y_{p-1}, and therefore $y_{p+i} > 0$ for every i. Then, according to the law of formation agreed upon,

$$x_{p+1} = \frac{x_{p-1} + x_p}{2},$$

$$x_{p+2} = \frac{x_{p-1} + x_{p+1}}{2} = \frac{3x_{p-1} + x_p}{4},$$

$$\cdots \cdots \cdots \cdots \cdots \cdots \cdots$$

$$x_{p+i} = \frac{(2^i - 1)x_{p-1} + x_p}{2^i} = x_{p-1} + \frac{x_p - x_{p-1}}{2^i}.$$

That is,

$$\left| x_{p-1} - x_{p+i} \right| = \left| \frac{x_p - x_{p-1}}{2^i} \right|.$$

This can be made $< \epsilon$ for i sufficiently large. Hence $\{x_p\} = x_{p-1}$. Since f is continuous, $\{y_p\} = y_{p-1}$. That is,

$$\left| y_{p-1} - y_{p+q} \right| < \epsilon, \qquad\qquad q > n_\epsilon.$$

Since $y_{p-1} < 0$, it is true that $y_{p+q} < 0$ for q sufficiently large, contrary to assumption.

It is now evident from Problem 1, § 85, that $\{y_p\} = 0$.

Theorem 86.3. *Every equation of odd degree with real coefficients has a real root.*

Let

$$y = a_0 x^n + \cdots + a_{n-1}x + a_n, \qquad\qquad a_0 \neq 0.$$

Choose

$$x > \frac{|a_1| + |a_2| + \cdots + |a_n|}{|a_0|}, \qquad\qquad x > 1.$$

Then

$$|a_0| \, x^n > |a_1| \, x^{n-1} + |a_2| \, x^{n-1} + \cdots + |a_n| \, x^{n-1}$$
$$> |a_1| \, x^{n-1} + |a_2| \, x^{n-2} + \cdots + |a_n| \,.$$

When x has this value, y has the sign of a_0, and for $-x$ and n odd, it has the sign of $-a_0$. Hence, by Theorem 86.2, $y = 0$ has a root.

EXERCISES

1. Show that every positive real number has a positive square root.
2. Show that every complex number $a + ib$ has a complex square root.
HINT: Square $\sqrt{(\sqrt{a^2 + b^2} + a)/2} + i\sqrt{(\sqrt{a^2 + b^2} - a)/2}$.
3. Show that every quadratic equation with complex coefficients has a complex root.

87. The complex field. The polynomial $x^2 + 1$ is irreducible in the real field Re, since the square of every real number is ≥ 0 (Ex. 2, § 85). The algebraic extension of the real field by means of the irreducible polynomial $x^2 + 1$ is called the *complex field*, and is denoted by C.

Theorem 87.1. *Every equation with real coefficients has a complex root.*

Let the polynomial $g(x)$ have real coefficients, and be of degree n, where

$$n = 2^\nu q, \qquad\qquad q \text{ odd.}$$

The theorem is known to be true for $\nu = 0$ (Theorem 86.3). The proof is by induction on ν.

Let Re^* be an algebraic extension of the real field in which $g(x) = 0$ has n roots

$$\alpha_1, \alpha_2, \cdots, \alpha_n.$$

Let h be a rational integer, as yet undefined, and form the function

$$G(x, h) = \prod_{i<j} (x - \alpha_i - \alpha_j - h\alpha_i\alpha_j).$$

Then $G(x, h)$ is of degree

$$\frac{2^\nu q(2^\nu q - 1)}{2} = 2^{\nu-1}q', \qquad\qquad q' \text{ odd.}$$

Now $G(x, h)$ is symmetric in the roots α_i and α_j, and so has real coefficients. By the assumption of induction, it has a complex root which must be one of the numbers

$$\alpha_i + \alpha_j + h\alpha_i\alpha_j.$$

Now let h take on the values $1, 2, \cdots, 2^{\nu-1}q' + 1$. Since there are but $2^{\nu-1}q'$ distinct pairs (i, j) there must exist two different integers h_1 and h_2 yielding the same pair (i, j) such that

$$\alpha_i + \alpha_j + h_1\alpha_i\alpha_j, \quad \alpha_i + \alpha_j + h_2\alpha_i\alpha_j$$

are both complex. Then

$$\alpha_i + \alpha_j, \quad \alpha_i\alpha_j$$

are both complex. But α_i and α_j are the roots of the quadratic equation

$$x^2 - (\alpha_i + \alpha_j)x + \alpha_i\alpha_j = 0$$

with complex coefficients. These are complex, by Ex. 3, § 86.

Theorem 87.2.† *Every equation with complex coefficients has a complex root.*

Let $f(x)$ be a polynomial with complex coefficients. Let $\bar{f}(x)$ be the conjugate polynomial, obtained by replacing every coefficient in $f(x)$ by its complex conjugate. Then

$$g(x) = f(x) \cdot \bar{f}(x)$$

has real coefficients, since the substitution of $-i$ for i leaves it invariant. Hence every solution of $g(x) = 0$ is a solution of $f(x) = 0$ or of $\bar{f}(x) = 0$.

† Theorem 87.2 has been called the "Fundamental Theorem of Algebra." Modern algebra does not attach quite this importance to it.

If x is a solution of $f(x) = 0$, then $\bar{x}$ is a solution of $\bar{f}(x) = 0$. By Theorem 87.1, $g(x) = 0$ has a complex solution. So then does $f(x) = 0$.

Corollary 87.2. The complex field is algebraically closed.

EXERCISES

1. Prove that, in $C[x]$, every polynomial is reducible into linear factors.
2. What are the primes of the integral ring $Re[x]$?
3. Find the complex roots of $28z^3 + 9z^2 - 1 = 0$.

88. The p-adic numbers of Hensel. Let p be a fixed rational prime. If a is a rational number $\neq 0$, it is uniquely expressible in the form

$$a = \frac{r}{s} p^n,$$

where r and s are prime to p. We define

$$\varphi(a) = p^{-n}, \quad a \neq 0, \quad \varphi(0) = 0.$$

Theorem 88.1. The function $\varphi(a)$ is a valuation for the rational field.

It is clear that $\varphi(a) > 0$ for $a \neq 0$, while $\varphi(0) = 0$. Also, if

$$a = \frac{r_1}{s_1} p^m, \quad b = \frac{r_2}{s_2} p^n, \qquad r_1, r_2, s_1, s_2 \text{ prime to } p,$$

then

$$ab = \frac{r_1 r_2}{s_1 s_2} p^{m+n} \qquad r_1 r_2, s_1 s_2 \text{ prime to } p,$$

so that

$$\varphi(ab) = p^{-m-n} = \varphi(a) \cdot \varphi(b).$$

Without loss of generality, assume that $m \leq n$. Then

$$a + b = \frac{r_1 s_2 + r_2 s_1 p^{n-m}}{s_1 s_2} p^m,$$

where $s_1 s_2$ is prime to p, so that

$$\varphi(a + b) \leq p^{-m} = \varphi(a),$$

$$\varphi(a + b) \leq \varphi(a) + \varphi(b).$$

Consider the set of all sequences

$$\{a_i\} = (a_1, a_2, \cdots, a_i, \cdots)$$

of rational numbers. The sequence is *regular* if for every positive rational number ϵ there is an integer n_ϵ such that

$$\varphi(a_i - a_j) < \epsilon, \qquad\qquad i, j > n_\epsilon.$$

The definitions of equality, addition, and multiplication of regular sequences is the same as in § 83. Since the only properties of absolute value which we used in §§ 83 and 84 are properties of our valuation φ, it follows that all these properties of the real field are shared by the sequences defined above. For every prime p, then, we have a field, called the *p-adic field* Ωp. Every p-adic field is of characteristic 0.

We shall see later that Ωp is isomorphic with Ωq only if $p = q$.

EXERCISE

1. Carry through the proofs of the theorems of §§ 83 and 84 with absolute value replaced by the valuation φ.

89. Development of the p-adic numbers.

Theorem 89.1. Every p-adic number can be represented by a sequence $\{c_i p^{n_i}\}$, *where the c_i are rational integers* ≥ 0.

Let

$$\alpha = \{a_i\}, \quad a_i = \frac{h_i}{k_i} p^{n_i},$$

where h_i and k_i are integers prime to p, $k_i \neq 0$. If $i < n_i$, set $c_i = 1$. If $i \geq n_i$, define c_i as a root of the congruence

$$k_i x_i \equiv h_i \mod p^{i-n_i}$$

which, by Theorem 6.2, has a solution ≥ 0. In either case there is an l_i such that $k_i c_i - h_i = l_i p^{i-n_i}$.

Then

$$\varphi\left(c_i p^{n_i} - \frac{h_i}{k_i} p^{n_i}\right) = \varphi\left(p^{n_i} \frac{k_i c_i - h_i}{k_i}\right)$$

$$= \varphi\left(p^{n_i} \frac{l_i p^{i-n_i}}{k_i}\right) = \varphi\left(\frac{l_i}{k_i} p^i\right) \leq p^{-i},$$

which is $< \epsilon$ for i sufficiently large. Thus

$$\{a_i\} = \{c_i p^{n_i}\}, \qquad\qquad c_i \geq 0.$$

Theorem 89.2. If $\{c_i p^{n_i}\}$ *is a p-adic number where the c_i are rational integers* ≥ 0 *and prime to p, there is a smallest n_i.*

Take $\epsilon = 1$ so that there is an N_1,

$$\varphi(c_i p^{n_i} - c_j p^{n_j}) < 1 \qquad\qquad i, j > N_1.$$

Suppose, for some i and j, that $n_j < n_i$, $n_j < 0$.   Then

$$c_i p^{n_i} - c_j p^{n_j} = p^{n_j}(c_i p^{n_i - n_j} - c_j),$$

where $n_i - n_j \geqq 1$.   Since $p \nmid c_j$, $p \nmid c_i p^{n_i - n_j} - c_j$, so that

$$\varphi(c_i p^{n_i} - c_j p^{n_j}) = p^{-n_j},$$

which contradicts the convergence condition if $n_j < 0$.   In the finite interval $0, \cdots, N_1$ there is of course a smallest n_i.

This result means, then, that every p-adic sequence can be written

$$\alpha = p^{\mu}\{c_i p^{n_i}\} = p^{\mu}\{d_i\},$$

where μ is a positive or negative integer or 0 and the d_i are positive integers, for 0's can be omitted.

$\dashv$ *Theorem 89.3.   Every regular p-adic sequence $\{d_i\}$ of positive integers is equal to a power series*

$$a_0 + a_1 p + a_2 p^2 + \cdots, \qquad 0 \leqq a_i < p.$$

Each positive integer d_i can be uniquely expressed

$$d_i = d_{i0} + d_{i1}p + d_{i2}p^2 + \cdots + d_{in_i}p^{n_i}, \quad 0 \leqq d_{ik} < p.$$

Since $\{d_i\}$ is regular, there is an N_1 such that

$$\varphi(d_i - d_j) \leqq p^{-1}, \qquad\qquad i, j \geqq N_1.$$

That is,

$$d_i \equiv d_j \qquad \mathrm{mod}\ p \qquad\qquad i, j \geqq N_1.$$

Hence all but a finite number of the d_i have the same d_{i0}.   Delete from the sequence $\{d_i\}$ that finite number of d_i which do not conform, and relabel the remaining d_i.   By Ex. 1, §84, the new sequence is equal to the old.

There is an N_2 such that

$$\varphi(d_i - d_j) \leqq p^{-2}, \qquad\qquad i, j \geqq N_2.$$

Hence all but a finite number of the d_i have the same d_{i1}.   Delete from the sequence $d_1, d_2, \cdots, d_{N_2}$ those which do not conform, and relabel the d_i.

It is clear that there exists a sequence $\{d_i\}$, equal to the original sequence, such that the d_{i0} are all alike (equal to a_0), the d_{i1} are all alike (equal to a_1) except possibly for $d_{01}, \cdots$, the d_{ij} are all alike (equal to a_j) for every $i \geqq j$.   Set

$$e_1 = a_0, \quad e_2 = a_0 + a_1 p, \quad e_3 = a_0 + a_1 p + a_2 p^2, \cdots$$

Then
$$\varphi(d_i - e_i) \leqq p^{-n}, \qquad\qquad i > n,$$

so that $\{d_i\} = \{e_i\}$. But, by definition, the series

$$a_0 + a_1 p + a_2 p^2 + \cdots$$

means the sequence

$$\{a_0, \ a_0 + a_1 p, \ a_0 + a_1 p + a_2 p^2, \cdots\}.$$

Now by Theorem 89.2 it is clear that every p-adic number can be written

$$\alpha = p^\mu (a_0 + a_1 p + a_2 p^2 + \cdots),$$

where the a_i are rational integers, $0 \leqq a_i < p$, and μ is maximal, that is, $a_0 \neq 0$. The integer μ is called the *order* of α. If $\mu \geqq 0$, α is a p-adic *integer*, and (for reasons to appear later) α is a *unit* if $\mu = 0$.

The above representation of the p-adic numbers as a series corresponds to the representation of the positive real numbers by infinite decimals,

$$10^\mu \left[a_0 + a_1 \tfrac{1}{10} + a_2 \left(\tfrac{1}{10}\right)^2 + \cdots\right].$$

Both are automatically convergent.

EXERCISES

1. Let $10^i b_i$ be the integral part of $10^i a_i$. Show that
$$|a_i - b_i| < \epsilon, \qquad\qquad i > \log_{10} 1/\epsilon.$$

2. Let $\alpha = \{a_i\}$ be a Cauchy sequence. Show that $\alpha = \{d_i\}$, where d_i is a finite decimal.

3. Prove that every Cauchy sequence is equal to an infinite decimal. (Parallel of Theorem 89.3.)

90. The rational numbers in Ωp. It is clear from Theorem 89.1 that every finite p-adic series is equal to a positive integer divided by a power of p, and the converse is evident. A finite series is periodic of period zero.

Theorem 90.1. A p-adic series is periodic if and only if it is equal to a rational number.

Every periodic series is equal to the sum of a rational number and a series

$$\alpha = A + p^k B + p^{k+l} B + p^{k+2l} B + \cdots,$$

where k is a positive integer and

$$A = a_0 + a_1 p + \cdots + a_{k-1} p^{k-1}, \qquad 0 \leqq a_i < p,$$
$$B = b_0 + b_1 p + \cdots + b_{l-1} p^{l-1}, \qquad 0 \leqq b_i < p.$$

We shall call B the *period* of α. Then

$$\alpha - A = p^k B + p^l[p^k B + p^{k+l}B + \cdots]$$
$$= p^k B + p^l[\alpha - A].$$

That is,

$$\alpha = A + \frac{p^k B}{1 - p^l},$$

which is clearly rational.

To prove the converse, first suppose that $\alpha = r/s$ is a negative proper rational fraction, $(r, s) = 1$, s prime to p and positive. Let l be the exponent to which p belongs modulo s (§ 15), so that

$$p^l \equiv 1 \quad \bmod s.$$

Then there exists an $m < 0$ such that

$$1 - p^l = ms,$$

$$\alpha = \frac{r}{s} = \frac{mr}{1 - p^l}, \qquad\qquad mr > 0.$$

Since α is proper, mr is expressible in the form

$$mr = B = b_0 + b_1 p + \cdots + b_{l-1}p^{l-1}, \qquad 0 \leqq b_i < p.$$

Then

$$\alpha = B + p^l B + p^{2l}B + \cdots,$$

and α is periodic.

If α is positive, it can be written as the sum of a polynomial in p and a negative proper fraction. The development of $-\alpha$ can be obtained by subtracting the development of α from

$$0 = p \cdot 1 + (p - 1) \cdot p + (p - 1) \cdot p^2 + (p - 1) \cdot p^3 + \cdots.$$

Neither of these steps will destroy the periodicity of the series.

EXERCISES

1. Develop -1 and $2/3$ in $\Omega 5$.
2. What rational number is defined by

$$\alpha = 1 + 1 \cdot 3 + 2 \cdot 3^2 + 1 \cdot 3^3 + 2 \cdot 3^4 + 1 \cdot 3^5 + \cdots,$$

where the coefficients after the first are alternately 1 and 2?
3. What rational number is defined by

$$\beta = 3 \cdot 1 + 1 \cdot 5 + 2 \cdot 5^2 + 1 \cdot 5^3 + 2 \cdot 5^4 + \cdots ?$$

4. For what value of p will it be true that

$$3/8 = 1 + 3p + 3p^3 + 3p^5 + 3p^7 + \cdots ?$$

5. Let the rational number α be represented as an infinite repeating decimal in the scale of p, namely,

$$\alpha = \left(\frac{a_1}{p} + \frac{a_2}{p^2} + \cdots + \frac{a_n}{p^n} \right) + \left(\frac{a_1}{p^{n+1}} + \cdots + \frac{a_n}{p^{2n}} \right) + \cdots.$$

Show that, in Ωp,

$$\alpha = (b_0 + b_1 p + \cdots + b_n p^n) + (b_1 p^{n+1} + \cdots + b_n p^{2n}) + \cdots,$$

where

$$b_0 = p - a_n, \; b_n = p - 1 - a_n, \; b_i = p - 1 - a_{n-i}, \; i = 1, 2, \cdots, n-1.$$

91. Solution of equations in Ωp. If $f(x) = 0$ is an equation of degree n with coefficients in Ωp, and α is a p-adic number, then $f(\alpha)$ is also a p-adic number, of some order μ, and can be written $f(\alpha) = p^{\mu} g(\alpha)$, where g is integral. Then α is a solution of $f(x) = 0$ if and only if every coefficient of $g(\alpha)$ is zero, i.e., if and only if

$$g(\alpha) \equiv 0 \qquad \mod p^n, \qquad\qquad (n = 1, 2, \cdots).$$

If $f(x) = 0$ has an integral p-adic solution α, the actual determination of a reasonable number of terms of α is quite simple. We solve the congruence

$$f(x) \equiv 0 \qquad \mod p^n$$

by the method of Theorem 14.2, which gives a solution in the form

$$\alpha = a_0 + a_1 p + \cdots + a_{n-1} p^{n-1}, \qquad\qquad 0 \le a_i < p.$$

In case the leading coefficient of $f(x)$ is divisible by p, it may happen that $f(x) = 0$ has a p-adic solution which is not integral. A substitution $x = y/p^\nu$ may be made where ν is sufficiently large so that the leading coefficient of the transformed equation is prime to p. If the new equation has an integral p-adic solution, then the original equation has a solution

$$\alpha = p^{-\nu}(a_0 + a_1 p + a_2 p^2 + \cdots).$$

Theorem 91.1.   If p is an odd prime, the equation

$$x^2 = c \qquad \Omega p, \qquad\qquad p^2 \nmid c,$$

has just two solutions or no solution according as c is a quadratic residue of p or not.

The condition $p^2 \nmid c$ is no real restriction, for it can always be achieved by a substitution of the type $x = y p^\mu$.

If $(c/p) = 1$, the congruence

$$x^2 \equiv c \qquad \mod p$$

has a solution x_1 prime to p. (See § 18.) Let $x_1^2 - c = h_1 p$. Then $2x_1$ is prime to p, so that

$$2x_1y_1 + h_1 \equiv 0 \qquad \mod p$$

has a solution y_1. Let $x_2 = x_1 + y_1 p$, $x_2^2 - c = h_2 p^2$. Then

$$2x_1y_2 + h_2 \equiv 0 \qquad \mod p$$

has a solution y_2. Let $x_3 = x_1 + y_1 p + y_2 p^2$. Clearly the process can be continued indefinitely.

If $(c/p) = -1$, the congruence

$$x^2 \equiv c \qquad \mod p$$

has no solution, so the equation

$$x^2 = c \qquad \Omega p$$

clearly has no solution.

If $p \mid c$ but $p^2 \nmid c$, then $c = pc'$ where c' is prime to p. Then

$$x^2 \equiv c \qquad \mod p$$

has the unique solution $x_1 = 0$, and $h_1 = -c'$. But the congruence

$$2x_1y_1 - h_1 \equiv 0 \qquad \mod p$$

reduces to $c' \equiv 0 \mod p$, whereas $p \nmid c'$. Thus there is no solution in this case.

Theorem 91.2. *If p and q are distinct odd primes, the fields Ωp and Ωq are not isomorphic.*

Any isomorphism between Ωp and Ωq would make the 0 and 1 elements of the two fields correspond to each other, so the rational subfields of Ωp and Ωq would correspond element for element.

Suppose $p > q$ and $(p/q) = 1$. Then the equation

$$x^2 = p$$

is solvable in Ωq and not solvable in Ωp, by Theorem 91.1. But p is self-corresponding in the two fields, and, if α were a solution in Ωq, its correspondent under any isomorphism would be a solution of the same equation in Ωp.

Suppose $p > q$ and $(p/q) = -1$. Let $n < q$ be a non-residue of q. This exists, since the interval $1, 2, \cdots, q - 1$ contains $(q - 1)/2$ non-residues modulo q (Theorem 17.3). Then np is a residue modulo q (Theorem 17.2) so that

$$x^2 \equiv np$$

is solvable in Ωq. Since $n < q < p$, $p^2 \nmid np$ and $x^2 = np$ has no solution in Ωp.

Theorem 91.3.   The equation

$$x^2 + x + c = 0$$

has a solution in $\Omega 2$ if and only if c is even.

If c is odd,

$$f(x) = x^2 + x + c \equiv 0 \qquad \text{mod } 2$$

has no solution.

If c is even, the above congruence has a solution.   Since

$$f'(x) = 2x + 1 \equiv 1 \qquad \text{mod } 2,$$

the successive coefficients a_i are always determinable from the equation

$$f'(x_{i-1})a_i + h_{i-1} \equiv a_i + h_{i-1} \equiv 0 \qquad \text{mod } 2.$$

Theorem 91.4.   If p is an odd prime, the fields $\Omega 2$ and Ωp are non-isomorphic.

In the congruence

$$x^2 + x + c \equiv 0 \qquad \text{mod } p,$$

set $x = y + k$.   Then

$$x^2 + x + c \equiv y^2 + y(2k + 1) + k^2 + k + c \qquad \text{mod } p.$$

Let c' be an even quadratic non-residue of p, which exists, since, if n is an odd quadratic non-residue, $n + p$ is even.   Let k be a solution of

$$2k + 1 \equiv 0 \qquad \text{mod } p,$$

and define

$$c = - c' - k^2 - k.$$

Thus c is even.   Then

$$x^2 + x + c \equiv 0 \qquad \text{mod } p$$

has no solution, for if x_1 were a solution, then $y_1 = x_1 - k$ would be a solution of

$$y^2 \equiv c' \qquad \text{mod } p,$$

whereas c' is a non-residue of p.

By Theorem 91.3,

$$x^2 + x + c = 0$$

has a solution in $\Omega 2$, and we have just shown that it has no solution in Ωp.   Thus $\Omega 2$ and Ωp are non-isomorphic.

Corollary 91.4.   If p and q are distinct primes, Ωp and Ωq are non-isomorphic.

EXERCISES

1. Solve the equation $x^2 = 7$ in $\Omega 3$.   Also the equation $x^2 = 4$ in $\Omega 5$.
2. Solve the equation $x^2 + x + 1 = 0$ in $\Omega 7$.   If α and β are the solutions, show that $\alpha^2 = \beta$ and $\beta^2 = \alpha$.
3. Solve the equation $9x^2 = 7$ in $\Omega 3$.
4. Solve the equation $x^2 + x + 4 = 0$ in $\Omega 2$.

92. The p-adic extensions of algebraic fields.   Let α be any number $\neq 0$ of the algebraic field $\mathfrak{F}$, and let p be a prime ideal of $[\mathfrak{F}]$.   Then

$$\alpha = \frac{r}{s},$$

where r and s are in $[\mathfrak{F}]$, and neither is 0.   Let p^ρ be the highest power of p which divides r—in notation, $p^\rho \| r$.   Also let $p^\sigma \| s$, where we shall write r and s for the principal ideals (r) and (s).   Define

$$\varphi(\alpha) = e^{\sigma - \rho}, \quad \alpha \neq 0, \quad \varphi(0) = 0.$$

The base may be taken as any convenient real number > 1, and the base of the natural system of logarithms is as convenient as any.

Theorem 92.1.   The function $\varphi(\alpha)$ is a valuation for $\mathfrak{F}$.

The first two properties of a valuation as given in § 83 are obvious, and the third is proved as in Theorem 88.1, using ideals instead of numbers.

The fourth property is somewhat more troublesome.   Let

$$\alpha = \frac{r_1}{s_1}, \quad \beta = \frac{r_2}{s_2},$$

$$p^{\rho_1} \| r_1, \quad p^{\sigma_1} \| s_1, \quad p^{\rho_2} \| r_2, \quad p^{\sigma_2} \| s_2$$

so that

$$\varphi(\alpha) = e^{\sigma_1 - \rho_1}, \quad \varphi(\beta) = e^{\sigma_2 - \rho_2},$$

and

$$\alpha + \beta = \frac{r_1 s_2 + r_2 s_1}{s_1 s_2}.$$

Clearly, $p^{\sigma_1 + \sigma_2} \| s_1 s_2$.   Let $\kappa = \min(\rho_1 + \sigma_2, \rho_2 + \sigma_1)$, so that

$$p^\kappa \mid (r_1 s_2, r_2 s_1).$$

But, by Theorem 67.2,

$$(r_1 s_2, r_2 s_1) \mid (r_1 s_2 + r_2 s_1),$$

so that p divides the numerator of $\alpha + \beta$ to at least the κth power. If $\varphi(\alpha + \beta) = e^{-\tau}$, then

$$\tau \geqq \kappa - \sigma_1 - \sigma_2 \geqq \min(\rho_1 - \sigma_1, \rho_2 - \sigma_2),$$

$$-\tau \leqq \max(\sigma_1 - \rho_1, \sigma_2 - \rho_2),$$

$$\varphi(\alpha + \beta) \leqq \max[\varphi(\alpha), \varphi(\beta)] \leqq \varphi(\alpha) + \varphi(\beta).$$

Theorem 92.2. *For every prime ideal p of $\mathfrak{F}$, the p-adic extension field $\mathfrak{F}$ exists.*

The treatment is similar to the derivation of the real numbers from the rational numbers in § 83.

EXERCISE

1. Write out a simplified proof of Theorem 92.1 for the case that $[\mathfrak{F}]$ is a principal ideal ring.

SUGGESTED READINGS

HENSEL, K. *Theorie der algebraischen Zahlen.* Teubner, Leipzig, 1908.

HENSEL, K. *Zahlentheorie.* Göschen, Berlin, 1913.

VAN DER WAERDEN, *Moderne Algebra*, Vol. I, Chapters IX, X. Springer, Berlin, 1937.

CHAPTER VII

MATRICES

93. Groups with operators. Let $\mathfrak{G}$ be a group with elements $a, b,$ $c, \cdots$. Suppose that there exists a correspondence

$$a \to a', \quad b \to b', \quad c \to c', \cdots,$$

where $a', b', c', \cdots$ are in $\mathfrak{G}$, but are not necessarily distinct. Such a correspondence is called an *endomorphism* if

$$a \to a', \quad b \to b' \quad \text{imply that} \quad ab \to a'b'.$$

An endomorphism may be thought of as being accomplished by means of an *operator*. We define α to be the operator such that

$$\alpha a = a', \quad \alpha b = b', \quad \alpha c = c', \cdots$$

with the distributive property

(93.1)
$$\alpha(ab) = \alpha a \cdot \alpha b.$$

Every group $\mathfrak{G}$ has at least two operators, namely, the *unit operator* ι such that $\iota a = a$ for every $a \in \mathfrak{G}$, and the *zero operator* o such that $oa = i$ for every $a \in \mathfrak{G}$, where i is the identity of $\mathfrak{G}$.

Theorem 93.1. Every operator α carries every subgroup $\mathfrak{H}$ of $\mathfrak{G}$ into a subgroup $\alpha\mathfrak{H}$ of $\mathfrak{G}$.

Denote by $\alpha\mathfrak{H}$ the set of elements into which the elements of $\mathfrak{H}$ are carried by α. From (93.1),

$$\alpha a \cdot \alpha b = \alpha(ab),$$

so that $\alpha\mathfrak{H}$ is closed under multiplication. Let i be the identity of $\mathfrak{G}$. For every $a \in \mathfrak{H}$,

$$\alpha a = \alpha(ia) = \alpha i \cdot \alpha a,$$

so that $\alpha i = i$. Hence $i \in \alpha\mathfrak{H}$. Also

$$i = \alpha i = \alpha(aa^{-1}) = \alpha a \cdot \alpha(a^{-1})$$

for every $a \in \mathfrak{G}$, so $\alpha(a^{-1}) = (\alpha a)^{-1}$. Therefore $\alpha\mathfrak{H}$ is a group.

If α and β are two operators, then

$$\beta(\alpha a) = \beta a' = a''.$$

If we define $\beta(\alpha a) = (\beta\alpha)a$, then $\beta\alpha$ is an operator carrying a into a''. The operator $\beta\alpha$ we shall call the *product* of the operators β and α.

Theorem 93.2. Multiplication of operators is associative.

For, if $\gamma a = a'$,

$$[(\alpha\beta)\gamma]a = (\alpha\beta)a', \quad [\alpha(\beta\gamma)]a = \alpha[(\beta\gamma)a] = \alpha(\beta a') = (\alpha\beta)a'.$$

Since this is true for every $a \in \mathfrak{G}$, the operators $(\alpha\beta)\gamma$ and $\alpha(\beta\gamma)$ are equal.

A set of operators containing the unit operator and the product of every two operators of the set is called an *operator domain*. Clearly the set of all operators on $\mathfrak{G}$ is an operator domain. A subgroup $\mathfrak{H} \subseteq \mathfrak{G}$ is called *admissible* relative to the operator domain Ω if $\Omega\mathfrak{H} \subseteq \mathfrak{H}$—that is, for every $\alpha \in \Omega$ and every $a \in \mathfrak{H}$, $\alpha a \in \mathfrak{H}$.

Suppose that $\mathfrak{G}$ is an abelian group of finite or infinite order. For convenience we shall denote the group operation by $+$. Let Ω be the domain of all its endomorphisms. Since $\alpha a + \beta a \in \mathfrak{G}$, there is a correspondence carrying a into $\alpha a + \beta a$. Now

$$\alpha(a + b) + \beta(a + b) = \alpha a + \alpha b + \beta a + \beta b = (\alpha a + \beta a) + (\alpha b + \beta b).$$

Hence (93.1) is satisfied, and the correspondence defines an operator which we shall denote by $\alpha + \beta$, and call the *sum* of the operators α and β. That is,

(93.2) $$(\alpha + \beta)a = \alpha a + \beta a.$$

Since $\mathfrak{G}$ is abelian, $\alpha + \beta = \beta + \alpha$.

Theorem 93.3. The domain Ω of all endomorphisms of an abelian group $\mathfrak{G}$ is a ring with unit element.

The zero operator o is the zero element of Ω, and the unit operator ι is the unit element.

EXERCISES

1. Let $\mathfrak{G}$ be a finite group, Ω the domain of its inner automorphisms. Show that Ω is an operator domain. What are the admissible subgroups?

2. Show that every abelian group has an operator domain composed of the operators $\alpha(\ ) = (\ )^m$, where m is a rational integer. Let $\mathfrak{G}$ be the four-group. Find Ω, and the subgroups described in Theorem 93.1.

3. Let $\mathfrak{G}$ be the addition group of the integral algebraic numbers of some

algebraic field. Define Ω to be the domain of all multiplications by the numbers of $\mathfrak{G}$. What are the admissible subgroups?

4. Let $\mathfrak{G}$ be the cyclic group of order 5. Show that its endomorphism ring is $GF(5)$. (See Ex. 2, § 24.) Generalize to the cyclic group of prime order p.

5. Find the endomorphism ring of the four-group. Is it commutative? Does it have divisors of zero?

6. Check through all the postulates for a ring given in § 68 for the endomorphism ring of an abelian group.

94. Vectors and linear systems. Let $\mathfrak{R}$ be a ring. Consider the n-uples of numbers of $\mathfrak{R}$,

$$v_1 = (a_1, a_2, \cdots, a_n), \quad v_2 = (b_1, b_2, \cdots, b_n), \cdots,$$

where $v_1 = v_2$ if and only if

$$a_i = b_i \qquad\qquad (i = 1, 2, \cdots, n).$$

One operation, called *addition*, is defined:

$$v_1 + v_2 = (a_1 + b_1, a_2 + b_2, \cdots, a_n + b_n).$$

Such n-uples are called *vectors* of *order n*, and $a_1, a_2, \cdots, a_n$ are called the *components* of v.

It is clear that the set of all vectors of order n over $\mathfrak{R}$ is an abelian group with respect to addition, the identity being the zero-vector $(0, 0, \cdots, 0)$.

We now define an operator domain, and call the operation *scalar multiplication*. Let c be any number of $\mathfrak{R}$. Then

$$cv_1 = (ca_1, ca_2, \cdots, ca_n).$$

If $\mathfrak{R}$ is a ring with unit element, we may define

$$(1, 0, \cdots, 0) = \epsilon_1, \quad (0, 1, \cdots, 0) = \epsilon_2, \cdots, \quad (0, 0, \cdots, 1) = \epsilon_n$$

and write

$$(a_1, a_2, \cdots, a_n) = a_1\epsilon_1 + a_2\epsilon_2 + \cdots + a_n\epsilon_n.$$

Now let $\mathfrak{R}$ be a field $\mathfrak{F}$. A set of nth order vectors over $\mathfrak{F}$ which is closed under addition and scalar multiplication is called a *linear system* of *order n*. If

$$v_1, v_2, \cdots, v_m$$

are any nth order vectors, the set of vectors

$$c_1v_1 + c_2v_2 + \cdots + c_mv_m,$$

where $c_1, c_2, \cdots, c_m$ range over $\mathfrak{F}$, constitutes such a linear system.

The vectors $v_1, v_2, \cdots, v_m$ are said to be *linearly dependent* with respect to $\mathfrak{F}$ if there exists a relation

$$(94.1) \qquad\qquad c_1 v_1 + c_2 v_2 + \cdots + c_m v_m = 0, \qquad\qquad c_i \in \mathfrak{F},$$

where the c's are not all 0. On the other hand, $v_1, v_2, \cdots, v_m$ are *linearly independent* if every relation (94.1) implies $c_1 = c_2 = \cdots = c_m = 0$.

Theorem 94.1. *In every linear system S over a field $\mathfrak{F}$, there exists a set*

$$v_1, v_2, \cdots, v_r, \qquad\qquad r \leqq n,$$

which are linearly independent, and are such that every vector of S is a linear combination of them.

If there exists in S a vector of the type

$$(a_{11}, 0, \cdots, 0), \qquad\qquad a_{11} \neq 0,$$

call it v_1. If there is a vector of the type

$$(a_{21}, a_{22}, 0, \cdots, 0), \qquad\qquad a_{22} \neq 0,$$

call it v_2, etc. If there is a vector of the type

$$(a_{n1}, a_{n2}, \cdots, a_{nn}), \qquad\qquad a_{nn} \neq 0,$$

call it v_n.

The v's which exist are linearly independent. For, consider a relation

$$c_1(a_{11}, 0, \cdots, 0) + c_2(a_{21}, a_{22}, \cdots, 0) + \cdots + c_n(a_{n1}, a_{n2}, \cdots, a_{nn}) = 0,$$

where some of the terms may not actually be present. If c_n is present, then v_n exists and $a_{nn} \neq 0$, so that $c_n = 0$. If c_{n-1} is present, v_{n-1} exists and $a_{n-1,n-1} \neq 0$, so that $c_{n-1} = 0$, etc.

Let $v = (b_{n1}, b_{n2}, \cdots, b_{nn})$ be any vector of S. If $b_{nn} \neq 0$, then v_n exists, and the vector

$$v - \frac{b_{nn}v_n}{a_{nn}}$$

has 0 for its last component, and is in S. Let

$$v' = (b_{n-1,1}, b_{n-1,2}, \cdots, b_{n-1,n-1}, 0)$$

denote v or $v - b_{nn}v_n/a_{nn}$ according as $b_{nn} = 0$ or $b_{nn} \neq 0$. If $b_{n-1,n-1} \neq 0$, then v_{n-1} exists and

$$v' - \frac{b_{n-1,n-1}v_{n-1}}{a_{n-1,n-1}}$$

has 0's for its last two components, and is in S. Finally we have

$$v - \frac{b_{nn}v_n}{a_{nn}} - \cdots - \frac{b_{11}v_1}{a_{11}} = 0,$$

$$v = \frac{b_{11}v_1}{a_{11}} + \frac{b_{22}v_2}{a_{22}} + \cdots + \frac{b_{nn}v_n}{a_{nn}},$$

with the understanding that, if v_i does not exist, the ith term simply is not present.

Relabel the v_i's which exist $v_1, v_2, \cdots, v_r$. The theorem is now proved.

A set of vectors having the properties described in the theorem constitutes a *basis* for S.

Two sets of vectors $u_1, u_2, \cdots, u_r$ and $v_1, v_2, \cdots, v_s$ are called *linearly equivalent* if the linear systems which they define are the same.

Theorem 94.2. (*The Replacement Theorem of Steinitz.*) *Let $v_1, v_2, \cdots, v_s$ be linearly independent vectors, each linearly dependent upon $u_1, u_2, \cdots, u_r$. There exists among the $u_1, u_2, \cdots, u_r$ a subset of s vectors (which we may take to be $u_1, u_2, \cdots, u_s$) such that $u_1, u_2, \cdots, u_r$ are linearly equivalent to $v_1, v_2, \cdots, v_s, u_{s+1}, \cdots, u_r$.*

The proof is by induction. For $s = 0$, it is trivial. Suppose that it holds for $v_1, v_2, \cdots, v_{s-1}$. Then v_s is a linear combination of $u_1, u_2, \cdots, u_r$, and so by the induction hypothesis v_s has the form

$$v_s = a_1v_1 + \cdots + a_{s-1}v_{s-1} + a_su_s + \cdots + a_ru_r.$$

Not all of $a_s, a_{s+1}, \cdots, a_r$ are 0, for $v_1, v_2, \cdots, v_s$ are linearly independent. Suppose that $a_s \neq 0$. Then we can write

$$u_s = b_1v_1 + \cdots + b_sv_s + b_{s+1}u_{s+1} + \cdots + b_ru_r.$$

Thus the sets $(v_1, v_2, \cdots, v_{s-1}, u_s, \cdots, u_r)$ and $(v_1, v_2, \cdots, v_s, u_{s+1}, \cdots, u_r)$ are linearly equivalent.

Corollary 94.2. *If $u_1, u_2, \cdots, u_r$ and $v_1, v_2, \cdots, v_s$ each consist of linearly independent vectors, and if the sets are linearly equivalent, then $r = s$.*

A linear system S may have many bases, but by this corollary the number of vectors in a basis is always the same. This number r we shall call the *rank* of the linear system.

EXERCISES

1. Show that scalar multiplication has the properties

$$c(v_1 + v_2) = cv_1 + cv_2,$$

$$c(dv) = (cd)v, \quad (c + d)v = cv + dv.$$

2. Find a basis for the linear system formed by

$$v_1 = (2, 1, 3, 5), \quad v_2 = (4, -1, 0, 4),$$

$$v_3 = (6, 2, 2, 1), \quad v_4 = (14, 3, 8, 15).$$

What is the rank of this system?

3. Let u_1, u_2, u_3, u_4 be linearly independent vectors,

$$v_1 = u_1 + u_2 + u_3 + u_4,$$

$$v_2 = u_1 \qquad - u_3 - u_4,$$

$$v_3 = \qquad 2u_2 + u_3.$$

Carry through the proof of Theorem 94.2 with this example, and note in particular that it is legitimate to start the induction with $s = 0$.

4. If v_1, v_2, $\cdots$, v_m are linearly dependent vectors, it is always possible to express some one of them as a linear combination of the others. Prove this statement.

5. If among the vectors v_1, v_2, $\cdots$, v_m there exists a subset of linearly dependent vectors, then the given vectors are linearly dependent. Prove.

95. Orthogonal systems. Two vectors

$$u = (a_1, a_2, \cdots, a_n), \quad v = (x_1, x_2, \cdots, x_n)$$

over a field $\mathfrak{F}$ are said to be *orthogonal* if

$$a_1 x_1 + a_2 x_2 + \cdots + a_n x_n = 0.$$

It is clear that, if v is orthogonal to one or more vectors, it is orthogonal to the linear system which they define. It is also clear that all the vectors orthogonal to a linear system constitute a linear system, called the *orthogonal complement* of the first linear system.

Theorem 95.1. *If the linear system S' of rank r' is the orthogonal complement of the linear system S of rank r, then $r + r' = n$.*

Let S have a basis of the type obtained in Theorem 94.1, namely,

$$u_1 = (a_{11}, 0, \cdots, 0), \quad u_2 = (a_{21}, a_{22}, \cdots, 0), \cdots, \quad u_n = (a_{n1}, a_{n2}, \cdots, a_{nn}),$$

where it is understood that $a_{ii} \neq 0$ or else u_i is not present. If $v = (x_1, x_2, \cdots, x_n)$ is a vector of S', then

$$
\begin{aligned}
a_{11} x_1 &= 0, \\
a_{21} x_1 + a_{22} x_2 &= 0, \\
a_{31} x_1 + a_{32} x_2 + a_{33} x_3 &= 0, \\
\cdots \cdots \cdots \cdots \cdots \cdots & \\
a_{n1} x_1 + a_{n2} x_2 + \cdots + a_{nn} x_n &= 0.
\end{aligned}
$$

(95.1)

If $a_{11} \neq 0$, then $x_1 = 0$. If $a_{22} \neq 0$, x_2 is a multiple of x_1. In general, if $a_{ii} \neq 0$, x_i is a definite linear combination of $x_1, x_2, \cdots, x_{i-1}$. On the other hand, if $a_{ii} = 0$, x_i is entirely arbitrary. If S is of rank r, exactly $n - r$ equations are missing, $n - r$ of the x_i are arbitrary, and the other x_i's are definite linear combinations of these. Thus the linear system S' can be written

$$x_{i_1} v_1 + x_{i_2} v_2 + \cdots + x_{i_{n-r}} v_{n-r},$$

where the v's are vectors whose components are definite numbers of $\mathfrak{F}$, while the x's are arbitrary numbers of $\mathfrak{F}$. Moreover, the v's are linearly independent, since each v has a 1 in the ith position and 0's in each preceding position.

The theory of systems of homogeneous linear equations has now been completely treated. If

$$\begin{aligned} a_{11}x_1 + a_{12}x_2 + \cdots + a_{1n}x_n &= 0, \\ a_{21}x_1 + a_{22}x_2 + \cdots + a_{2n}x_n &= 0, \\ \cdots \quad \cdots \quad \cdots \quad \cdots \quad \cdots \\ a_{k1}x_1 + a_{k2}x_2 + \cdots + a_{kn}x_n &= 0 \end{aligned}$$

(95.2)

is such a system, the coefficients of each equation determine a vector

$$u_i = (a_{i1}, a_{i2}, \cdots, a_{in}).$$

All the vectors $u_1, u_2, \cdots, u_k$ determine a linear system S. The problem of solving equations (95.2) is the problem of determining the orthogonal complement S' of S. We have

Theorem 95.2. If the coefficients of a system of linear equations in n unknowns form a linear system of rank r, there exist just $n - r$ linearly independent solutions and every solution is a linear combination of these.

A basis of the linear system of solution vectors is called a *fundamental system of solutions* of the equations. By the Steinitz Replacement Theorem we have

Theorem 95.3. Any set of solutions of system (95.2) is a fundamental system provided that they are linearly independent and $n - r$ in number.

EXERCISES

1. In solid analytic geometry, the direction of a line is determined by its direction cosines. Suppose that l_1 has the direction cosines $\alpha_1, \alpha_2, \alpha_3$, and l_2 the direction cosines $\beta_1, \beta_2, \beta_3$. What is the geometric interpretation of the statement that the vectors $(\alpha_1, \alpha_2, \alpha_3)$ and $(\beta_1, \beta_2, \beta_3)$ are orthogonal?

2. What is the orthogonal complement of a line through the origin in three-space? of a plane through the origin?

3. Let S have a basis

$$u_1 = (3, 0, 0, 0), \quad u_2 = (2, -1, 2, 0).$$

Carry through the proof of Theorem 95.1 to find a basis of the orthogonal complement.

4. Solve the system of equations

$$4x + 8y + 18z + 7w = 0,$$
$$4y + 10z + w = 0,$$
$$10x + 18y + 40z + 17w = 0,$$
$$x + 7y + 17z + 3w = 0$$

by first obtaining an equivalent system of form (95.1).

5. Prove that, if S' is the orthogonal complement of S, then S is the orthogonal complement of S'.

96. Arrays and determinants. A linear system composed of all linear combinations of the vectors

$$v_i = (a_{i1}, a_{i2}, \cdots, a_{in}) \qquad (i = 1, 2, \cdots, k)$$

with components in a ring $\Re$ is completely determined by the $k \times n$ array

$$A = \begin{bmatrix} a_{11} & a_{12} & \cdots & a_{1n} \\ a_{21} & a_{22} & \cdots & a_{2n} \\ \cdot & \cdot & \cdots & \cdot \\ a_{k1} & a_{k2} & \cdots & a_{kn} \end{bmatrix} = (a_{rs}),$$

where r is the row index and s the column index. The vectors v_i are called the *row vectors* of A.

By changing rows to columns, we obtain an $n \times k$ array

$$A^{\mathsf{T}} = \begin{bmatrix} a_{11} & a_{21} & \cdots & a_{k1} \\ a_{12} & a_{22} & \cdots & a_{k2} \\ \cdot & \cdot & \cdots & \cdot \\ a_{1n} & a_{2n} & \cdots & a_{kn} \end{bmatrix} = (a_{sr})$$

called the *transpose* of A. The vectors v_i are the *column vectors* of A^{T}.

There is no reason why the components of a vector have to be written in a line. If the number of components is nk, the vector may be written in the form of the array A, or of the array A^{T}. So that arrays may be considered as instances of vectors, we define equality, sum, and scalar product as in § 94. Thus, for two $k \times n$ arrays $A = (a_{rs})$ and $B = (b_{rs})$, $A = B$ means that $a_{rs} = b_{rs}$ for every r and s. Also

$$A + B = (a_{rs} + b_{rs}), \quad cA = (ca_{rs}).$$

If $k = n$, A is called a *square array* of *order n*. If A is a square array with elements in a ring $\mathfrak{R}$, every function of the components or *elements* a_{rs} whose functional value is a number of $\mathfrak{R}$ is called a *scalar function* of A. Some of these functions are of great importance, e.g., the *trace*

$$t(A) = a_{11} + a_{22} + \cdots + a_{nn},$$

and the *determinant*, $d(A)$, which we shall discuss briefly.

By definition

$$d(A) = \begin{vmatrix} a_{11} & a_{12} & \cdots & a_{1n} \\ a_{21} & a_{22} & \cdots & a_{2n} \\ \cdots & \cdots & \cdots & \cdots \\ a_{n1} & a_{n2} & \cdots & a_{nn} \end{vmatrix} = \sum (-1)^{i} a_{1i_1} a_{2i_2} \cdots a_{ni_n}$$

where the summation extends over all substitutions of the symmetric group of order $n!$ with the understanding that $i \equiv 0$ or 1 mod 2 according as the substitution

$$\begin{pmatrix} 1 & 2 & \cdots & n \\ i_1 & i_2 & \cdots & i_n \end{pmatrix}$$

is even or odd. By Theorem 30.3, $d(A)$ is uniquely defined.

It will be assumed that the reader is familiar with the ordinary theorems concerning determinants, all of which are valid when $\mathfrak{R}$ is a commutative ring.

EXERCISES

1. Prove from the definition of determinant that $d(A^\mathsf{T}) = d(A)$.

2. Prove that, if B is obtained from the square array A by multiplying all the elements of any row (or column) by k, then $d(B) = kd(A)$.

3. Prove that, if A is a square array each element of whose kth row is a sum $b_s + c_s$, then the two arrays B and C which differ from A only in that the kth row of B consists of the b_s and the kth row of C consists of the c_s are such that

$$d(A) = d(B) + d(C).$$

Prove the similar theorem for columns.

4. Prove that, if B is obtained from the square array A by the interchange of two rows or of two columns, then $d(B) = -d(A)$.

5. If the elements of A lie in a field $\mathfrak{F}$ of characteristic $\neq 2$, use Ex. 4 to prove that an array with two equal rows (or columns) is of determinant 0. Make a special proof of this theorem which is valid when $\mathfrak{F}$ is of characteristic 2.

97. Rank of an array. A square array with elements in a ring $\Re$ is called *singular* if its determinant is zero. The *rank* of a rectangular array is the order of a square subarray of maximum order which is non-singular. Though rank can thus be defined for a matrix with elements in a ring, the concept is most useful when the ring becomes a field.

Theorem 97.1. The rank of a rectangular array with elements in a field is equal to the rank of the linear system of its column vectors, and also equal to the rank of the linear system of its row vectors.

Let

$$A = \begin{bmatrix} a_{11} & a_{12} & \cdots & a_{1n} \\ a_{21} & a_{22} & \cdots & a_{2n} \\ \cdot & \cdot & \cdot & \cdot \\ a_{k1} & a_{k2} & \cdots & a_{kn} \end{bmatrix},$$

whose column vectors are

$$v_i = (a_{1i}, a_{2i}, \cdots, a_{ki}) \qquad (i = 1, 2, \cdots, n).$$

These form a linear system S whose rank (§ 94) we denote by r. If the array A is of rank ρ (in the sense of this paragraph), we may suppose the notation so chosen that

$$B = \begin{bmatrix} a_{11} & a_{12} & \cdots & a_{1\rho} \\ a_{21} & a_{22} & \cdots & a_{2\rho} \\ \cdot & \cdot & \cdot & \cdot \\ a_{\rho 1} & a_{\rho 2} & \cdots & a_{\rho\rho} \end{bmatrix}, \qquad b = d(B) \neq 0.$$

Now $v_1, v_2, \cdots, v_\rho$ are linearly independent, for a linear relation among these v's would imply a linear relation among the columns of B, whereas $b \neq 0$. Thus $r \geqq \rho$.

Suppose that $\rho < n$. For every h and l,

$$B_{lh} = \begin{bmatrix} a_{11} & \cdots & a_{1\rho} & a_{1h} \\ \cdot & \cdot & \cdot & \cdot \\ a_{\rho 1} & \cdots & a_{\rho\rho} & a_{\rho h} \\ a_{l1} & \cdots & a_{l\rho} & a_{lh} \end{bmatrix}, \quad d(B_{lh}) = b_{lh} = 0 \qquad \begin{array}{l} (h = \rho + 1, \cdots n; \\ l = 1, 2, \cdots, k). \end{array}$$

The cofactors of the elements of the last row are independent of l, and we denote them by A^h_s. Note that $A^h_h = b$. Then by the Laplace development,

$$A^h_1 a_{l1} + A^h_2 a_{l2} + \cdots + A^h_\rho a_{l\rho} + b a_{lh} = 0.$$

Since this holds for every l,

$$A^h_1 v_1 + A^h_2 v_2 + \cdots + A^h_\rho v_\rho + b v_h = 0 \qquad (h = \rho + 1, \cdots, n).$$

Since $b \neq 0$, every v_h is linearly dependent upon $v_1, v_2, \cdots, v_\rho$, so that $r \leqq \rho$. If $\rho = n$, obviously $r \leqq \rho$.

EXERCISES

1. Prove that the rows of the array

$$\begin{bmatrix} A_1^{\rho+1} & A_2^{\rho+1} & \cdots & A_\rho^{\rho+1} & b & 0 & \cdots & 0 \\ A_1^{\rho+2} & A_2^{\rho+2} & \cdots & A_\rho^{\rho+2} & 0 & b & \cdots & 0 \\ \cdot & \cdot & & \cdot & \cdot & \cdot & & \cdot \\ A_1^n & A_2^n & \cdots & A_\rho^n & 0 & 0 & \cdots & b \end{bmatrix}$$

furnish a basis for the linear system S' complementary to S. Thus they form a fundamental system of solutions of the system of homogeneous equations

$$\sum_{j=1}^{n} a_{ij}x_j = 0 \qquad\qquad (i = 1, 2, \cdots, k).$$

2. Prove that, if in a $k \times n$ array there is one ρ-rowed non-singular minor, while every $(\rho + 1)$-rowed minor obtained from it by adding one row and one column is singular, the rank of the array is ρ.

3. Find, by means of Ex. 2 above, the rank of the linear system given in Ex. 2, § 94.

4. Determine the rank of the array

$$\begin{bmatrix} 2 & 1 & 3 & 4 & 2 \\ -1 & 5 & 0 & 3 & 8 \\ 4 & 1 & 4 & 2 & 2 \\ 9 & -2 & 10 & 7 & -2 \end{bmatrix}.$$

5. If A is a rectangular array with elements in a field, show that the rank of the linear system defined by its row vectors is equal to the rank of the linear system defined by its column vectors.

98. Total matric algebra. Let $\mathfrak{R}$ be a ring. Consider the set of all $n \times n$ arrays with elements in $\mathfrak{R}$. It is understood that an array is an instance of a vector, so that addition and scalar multiplication are already defined as in § 96.

If $A = (a_{rs})$ and $B = (b_{rs})$ are two such arrays, we define their *product* to be the array

$$(98.1) \qquad\qquad AB = \left(\sum_{i=1}^{n} a_{ri}b_{is} \right).$$

Thus the element in row r and column s of the product AB is

$$a_{r1}b_{1s} + a_{r2}b_{2s} + \cdots + a_{rn}b_{ns}.$$

Theorem 98.1. Multiplication as defined by (98.1) is associative, and distributive with respect to addition.

For, if A and B are defined as above, and $C = (c_{rs})$, then

$$(AB)C = \left(\sum_i a_{ri}b_{is}\right)(c_{rs}) = \left(\sum_{i,j}(a_{ri}b_{ij})c_{js}\right).$$

Since multiplication in $\Re$ is associative, this is equal to

$$\left(\sum_{i,j} a_{ri}(b_{ij}c_{js})\right) = A(BC).$$

Also,

$$A(B+C) = (a_{rs})(b_{rs} + c_{rs}) = \left(\sum_i a_{ri}(b_{is} + c_{is})\right).$$

Since multiplication in $\Re$ is distributive, this is equal to

$$\left(\sum_i a_{ri}b_{is} + \sum_i a_{ri}c_{is}\right) = AB + AC.$$

A mathematical system $\mathfrak{M}$ whose elements are $n \times n$ arrays which are subject to the additional operation of multiplication as defined by (98.1) is called a *total matric algebra* over $\Re$ of *order* n^2. A *matrix* is an element of a total matric algebra.

Although a matrix, a square array, and a mere set of n^2 numbers arranged in the form of a square look alike, they are mathematically different because of their membership in mathematical systems in which different operations have been defined. A matrix is a square array, but not every square array is a matrix.

We have proved

Theorem 98.2. A total matric algebra over a ring is a ring.

The matrices of the type

$$S_k = \begin{bmatrix} k & 0 & \cdots & 0 \\ 0 & k & \cdots & 0 \\ \cdot & \cdot & \cdot & \cdot \\ 0 & 0 & \cdots & k \end{bmatrix}$$

are called *scalar matrices*. From the definitions of addition and multiplication of matrices, it follows that

$$S_a + S_b = S_{a+b}, \quad S_a S_b = S_{ab}.$$

It is also evident that $S_a = S_b$ if and only if $a = b$. Hence we have

Theorem 98.3. The scalar matrices of $\mathfrak{M}$ constitute a subring of $\mathfrak{M}$ isomorphic with $\Re$.

It is also clear that
$$S_k A = (ka_{rs}) = kA,$$
so that the operation of scalar multiplication, defined for vectors and arrays, is an instance of matric multiplication. This is the justification of the term " scalar matrix."

If $\Re$ is a ring with unit element 1, we define Kronecker's delta, δ_{rs}, to be this unit element or 0 according as $r = s$ or $r \neq s$. The scalar matrices can then be written $S_k = (k\delta_{rs})$. Then $S_1 = I = (\delta_{rs})$ is a unit element for $\mathfrak{M}$, so that we have

Theorem 98.4. A total matric algebra over a ring with unit element is a ring with unit element.

EXERCISES

1. Form the products
$$\begin{bmatrix} 2 & 4 \\ 3 & 6 \end{bmatrix} \begin{bmatrix} 2 & -4 \\ -1 & 2 \end{bmatrix}, \quad \begin{bmatrix} 0 & 1 & 0 \\ 0 & 0 & 1 \\ 0 & 0 & 0 \end{bmatrix}^3.$$

2. Show that the matrix
$$X = \begin{bmatrix} 1 & 3 \\ 2 & 1 \end{bmatrix}$$
satisfies the quadratic equation $X^2 - 2X - 5I = 0$.

3. Exhibit an example to disprove the following statement: A total matric algebra over a commutative ring is a commutative ring.

4. Let $\mathfrak{M}$ be a total matric algebra with elements in a ring $\Re$ with unit element. Prove that, if $AX = XA$ for every matrix X of $\mathfrak{M}$, then A is scalar and its elements are commutative with every element of $\Re$.

5. Show that the correspondence
$$x + iy \longleftrightarrow \begin{bmatrix} x & -y \\ y & x \end{bmatrix}$$
is an isomorphism between the field $Ra(\sqrt{-1})$ and a matric subalgebra of order 2 of the total matric algebra of order 4 over Ra.

99. The determinant of a matrix. If A is an $n \times n$ array (or matrix) with elements in a commutative ring $\Re$, we denote by

(99.1) $$A_{s_1 s_2 \cdots s_m}^{r_1 r_2 \cdots r_m}$$

the subarray obtained from A by striking out all the rows except those numbered $r_1, r_2, \cdots, r_m$, and all the columns except those numbered $s_1, s_2, \cdots, s_m$, and then rearranging the rows and columns until the indices are in the orders $r_1, r_2, \cdots, r_m$ and $s_1, s_2, \cdots, s_m$. We call it a *minor array* (or *minor matrix*) of A, and its determinant a *minor determinant* of $d(A)$.

Theorem 99.1. *Let A and B be $n \times n$ matrices, and let*

$$M^{r_1 r_2 \cdots r_m}_{s_1 s_2 \cdots s_m}$$

be any m-rowed minor matrix of the product matrix $M = AB$. Then

$$d(M^{r_1 r_2 \cdots r_m}_{s_1 s_2 \cdots s_m}) = \sum_{[k_1, \cdots, k_m]} d(A^{r_1 r_2 \cdots r_m}_{k_1 k_2 \cdots k_m}) \, d(B^{k_1 k_2 \cdots k_m}_{s_1 s_2 \cdots s_m}),$$

where the summation is over all $\binom{n}{m}$ selections of $k_1, k_2, \cdots, k_m$ from $1, 2, \cdots, n$ without regard for order.

By definition

$$AB = \left(\sum_i a_{ri} b_{is} \right)$$

so that

$$d(M^{r_1 \cdots r_m}_{s_1 \cdots s_m}) = \sum_{h_1, \cdots, h_m} (-1)^h \sum_{i_1} a_{r_1 i_1} b_{i_1 h_1} \cdots \sum_{i_m} a_{r_m i_m} b_{i_m h_m}$$

where h is 0 or 1 according as the substitution

$$\begin{pmatrix} s_1 & s_2 & \cdots & s_m \\ h_1 & h_2 & \cdots & h_m \end{pmatrix}$$

is even or odd. This can be written as a sum of n^m determinants,

$$\sum_{i_1, \cdots, i_m = 1}^{n} \sum_{h_1, \cdots, h_m} (-1)^h a_{r_1 i_1} b_{i_1 h_1}, \cdots a_{r_m i_m} b_{i_m h_m}.$$

Since only the inner summation involves the h's, this is equal to

$$\sum_{i_1, \cdots, i_m = 1}^{n} a_{r_1 i_1} \cdots a_{r_m i_m} \sum_{h_1, \cdots, h_m} (-1)^h b_{i_1 h_1} \cdots b_{i_m h_m}$$

$$= \sum_{i_1, \cdots, i_m = 1}^{n} a_{r_1 i_1} \cdots a_{r_m i_m} d(B^{i_1 \cdots i_m}_{s_1 \cdots s_m}).$$

But each of these determinants $d(B)$ is 0 unless $i_1, i_2, \cdots, i_m$ are distinct, so that the summation can be restricted to the $n!/(n-m)!$ permutations of $i_1, i_2, \cdots, i_m$ selected from among $1, 2, \cdots, n$. These permutations may be grouped into $\binom{n}{m}$ sets of $m!$ permutations each, a set being determined by a selection without regard to order of m

numbers $k_1, k_2, \cdots, k_m$ from among $1, 2, \cdots, n$, and the permutations of the set being the permutations

$$\begin{pmatrix} k_1 & k_2 & \cdots & k_m \\ i_1 & i_2 & \cdots & i_m \end{pmatrix}.$$

Thus

$$d(M^{r_1\cdots r_m}_{s_1\cdots s_m}) = \sum_{[k_1,\cdots,k_m]} \sum_{(i_1,\cdots,i_m)} a_{r_1i_1} \cdots a_{r_mi_m} d(B^{i_1\cdots i_m}_{s_1\cdots s_m})$$

where $[k_1, \cdots, k_m]$ stands for a combination and $(i_1, \cdots, i_m)$ a permutation.

Let $k_1 < k_2 < \cdots < k_m$, and let i be 0 or 1 according as

$$\begin{pmatrix} k_1 & k_2 & \cdots & k_m \\ i_1 & i_2 & \cdots & i_m \end{pmatrix}$$

is even or odd. Then

$$d(B^{i_1\cdots i_m}_{s_1\cdots s_m}) = (-1)^i d(B^{k_1\cdots k_m}_{s_1\cdots s_m})$$

so that

$$d(M^{r_1\cdots r_m}_{s_1\cdots s_m}) = \sum_{[k_1,\cdots,k_m]} \sum_{(i_1,\cdots,i_m)} (-1)^i a_{r_1i_1} \cdots a_{r_mi_m} d(B^{k_1\cdots k_m}_{s_1\cdots s_m}).$$

Since $d(B^{k_1\cdots k_m}_{s_1\cdots s_m})$ does not involve the i's, it is a common factor of every term, and

$$d(M^{r_1\cdots r_m}_{s_1\cdots s_m}) = \sum_{[k_1,\cdots,k_m]} \left[\sum_{(i_1,\cdots,i_m)} (-1)^i a_{r_1i_1} \cdots a_{r_mi_m} \right] d(B^{k_1\cdots k_m}_{s_1\cdots s_m})$$

$$= \sum_{[k_1,\cdots,k_m]} d(A^{r_1\cdots r_m}_{k_1\cdots k_m}) d(B^{k_1\cdots k_m}_{s_1\cdots s_m}).$$

which is the theorem.

This theorem has many applications in matric theory. One of the most important is given by

Corollary 99.1. The determinant of the product of two matrices is equal to the product of their determinants.

This is the special case of the theorem when $m = n$ and $r_i = s_i = i$. This result indicates that the correspondence

$$A \rightarrow d(A)$$

defines a homomorphism of the matric algebra $\mathfrak{M}$ onto the ring $\mathfrak{R}$.

EXERCISES

1. Carry through the proof of Theorem 99.1 for M_{13}^{32} where $n = 3$.

2. Use Theorem 99.1 to prove that the rank of a product of two matrices is $\leqq$ the rank of either factor.

3. Show that the rank of a matrix is not changed if it is multiplied on either side by a non-singular matrix. (See § 100.)

4. Let A be a matrix of order n, and let $C_r(A)$ be the matrix of order $m = \binom{n}{r}$ whose elements are the r-rowed minor determinants of A numbered in any convenient order. We call $C_r(A)$ the rth adjugate of A. Prove that

$$C_r(AB) = C_r(A)C_r(B).$$

5. Show that, if A has only 0's below the main diagonal, the same is true for $C_r(A)$, for a proper ordering of the indices.

100. Transposes and Adjoints. The transpose of a matrix was defined in § 96. A matrix S such that $S^\mathsf{T} = S$ is *symmetric*. A matrix Q such that $Q^\mathsf{T} = -Q$ is called *skew*.

Theorem 100.1. The operation T *defines an anti-automorphism of the matric algebra M.*

That is, the correspondence $A \leftrightarrow A^\mathsf{T}$ is biunique and

$$(A + B)^\mathsf{T} = A^\mathsf{T} + B^\mathsf{T}, \quad (AB)^\mathsf{T} = B^\mathsf{T}A^\mathsf{T}.$$

For

$$A + B = (a_{rs}) + (b_{rs}) = (a_{rs} + b_{rs}),$$

$$(A + B)^\mathsf{T} = (a_{sr} + b_{sr}) = (a_{sr}) + (b_{sr}) = A^\mathsf{T} + B^\mathsf{T}.$$

Also

$$AB = \left(\sum_i a_{ri}b_{is}\right),$$

$$(AB)^\mathsf{T} = \left(\sum_i a_{si}b_{ir}\right) = \left(\sum_i b_{ir}a_{si}\right) = B^\mathsf{T}A^\mathsf{T}.$$

Theorem 100.2. If $\mathfrak{M}$ is a matric algebra over a field $\mathfrak{F}$ of characteristic $\neq 2$, every matrix is uniquely expressible as the sum of a symmetric matrix and a skew matrix.

First, assume that such a representation exists, i.e.,

$$A = S + Q, \quad S^\mathsf{T} = S, \quad Q^\mathsf{T} = -Q.$$

Then

$$A^\mathsf{T} = S^\mathsf{T} + Q^\mathsf{T} = S - Q,$$

so that

(100.1) $$S = \frac{A + A^\mathsf{T}}{2}, \quad Q = \frac{A - A^\mathsf{T}}{2}.$$

Hence, if the representation exists, it is unique.

If $\mathfrak{F}$ is of characteristic not 2, form the matrices

$$S = \frac{A + A^\mathsf{T}}{2}, \quad Q = \frac{A - A^\mathsf{T}}{2}.$$

Evidently S is symmetric and Q is skew, and $S + Q = A$.

The matrix obtained from $A = (a_{rs})$ by replacing each element a_{rs} by the cofactor A_{sr} of a_{sr} is called the *adjoint* of A, written $A^\wedge$ or adj A. Every matrix has an adjoint, but, if the order of A is n and its rank is $< n - 1$, $A^\wedge = 0$.

It is a well-known theorem of determinant theory that the sum of the products of the elements of a row (or column) of a matrix by the cofactors of these elements is equal to the determinant, while the sum of the products of the elements of a row (or column) by the cofactors of the elements of a different row (or column) is zero. In notation,

(100.2) $$\sum_{i=1}^{n} A_{ir} a_{is} = \sum_{i=1}^{n} a_{ri} A_{si} = \delta_{rs} d(A).$$

In the notation of adjoints, this becomes

Theorem 100.3. *If $\mathfrak{R}$ is a commutative ring with unit element,* $A^\wedge A = A A^\wedge = Id(A)$.

If $d(A) \neq 0$, A is called *non-singular*. If A is non-singular, the matrix $A^\wedge/d(A)$ exists and is such that its product in either order with A is the identity matrix $I = (\delta_{rs})$. Hence we call

$$\frac{A^\wedge}{d(A)} = A^{-1}$$

the *inverse* of A.

Theorem 100.4. $(AB)^\wedge = B^\wedge A^\wedge$, *and, if A and B are non-singular,* $(AB)^{-1} = B^{-1}A^{-1}$.

Let $AB = M$. Then, by Theorem 99.1,

$$M^\wedge = (M_{sr}) = \left(\sum_{i=1}^{n} A_{si} B_{ir} \right)$$

$$= (B_{sr})(A_{sr}) = B^\wedge A^\wedge.$$

The second part of the theorem follows from the first part and from the fact that $d(AB) = d(B)d(A)$.

EXERCISES

1. Represent A as a sum of a symmetric and a skew matrix:

$$A = \begin{bmatrix} 2 & -1 & 3 \\ 0 & 4 & -3 \\ 7 & -2 & 5 \end{bmatrix}.$$

2. Prove that, if A is non-singular and $XA = I$, then $X = A^{-1}$.

3. Prove the second part of Theorem 100.4 by showing that

$$(B^{-1}A^{-1})(AB) = I.$$

Why cannot this method be used to prove the first part of Theorem 100.4?

4. Show that $C_r(I_n) = I_m$ and that $C_r(A)$ is non-singular if and only if A is non-singular. I_n means the unit matrix of order n. (Cf. Ex. 4, § 99.)

5. Prove that, if A is of rank r, $C_r(A)$ is of rank 1.

101. The characteristic equation. Let $\mathfrak{R}$ be a ring with unit element, and $\mathfrak{M}$ a total matric algebra of order n^2 over $\mathfrak{R}$. Then $\mathfrak{M}$ is also a ring with unit element. It was shown in § 73 that the polynomial domain $\mathfrak{M}[\Lambda]$ is again a ring with unit element, and that the elements of $\mathfrak{M}[\Lambda]$ are the polynomials

$$\mathbf{A} = A_0 + A_1\Lambda + A_2\Lambda^2 + \cdots + A_m\Lambda^m \quad (m = 0, 1, 2, \cdots),$$

$$A_i = (a_{irs}) \qquad (i = 0, 1, \cdots, m).$$

Now let $\mathfrak{R}[\lambda]$ be the polynomial domain of $\mathfrak{R}$, and let $\mathfrak{M}_{\mathfrak{R}[\lambda]}$ be a total matric algebra of order n^2 over $\mathfrak{R}[\lambda]$. The elements of $\mathfrak{M}_{\mathfrak{R}[\lambda]}$ are the matrices

$$A = \left(\sum_{i=0}^{m} a_{irs}\lambda^i \right) \qquad (m = 0, 1, 2, \cdots).$$

But, by the definitions of addition and scalar multiplication for $\mathfrak{M}_{\mathfrak{R}[\lambda]}$, we can write

$$A = A_0 + A_1\lambda + A_2\lambda^2 + \cdots + A_m\lambda^m, \quad A_i = (a_{irs}) \quad (i = 0, 1, \cdots, m).$$

Theorem 101.1. A matric algebra $\mathfrak{M}_{\mathfrak{R}[\lambda]}$ of order n^2 over the polynomial ring $\mathfrak{R}[\lambda]$ of a ring $\mathfrak{R}$ with unit element is isomorphic with the polynomial ring $\mathfrak{M}[\Lambda]$ of a matric algebra $\mathfrak{M}$ of order n^2 over $\mathfrak{R}$.

The correspondence $A \leftrightarrow \mathbf{A}$ is clearly biunique.   If also $B \leftrightarrow \mathbf{B}$, then

$$AB = \left(\sum_{k=1}^{n} \sum_{i=1}^{m} a_{irk}\lambda^i \sum_{j=1}^{l} b_{jks}\lambda^j \right)$$

$$= \left(\sum_{i,j} \left[\sum_k a_{irk}b_{jks} \right] \lambda^{i+j} \right)$$

$$= \sum_{i,j} A_i B_j \lambda^{i+j},$$

while

$$\mathbf{AB} = \sum_{i,j} A_i B_j \Lambda^{i+j}.$$

Thus $AB \leftrightarrow \mathbf{AB}$.

Under this isomorphism $\lambda \leftrightarrow \Lambda$.

If $\Re$ is a commutative ring with identity element, the polynomial ring $\Re[\lambda]$ is also a commutative ring with identity element.   If we take two numbers of $\Re[\lambda]$,

$$A(\lambda) = \sum a_i \lambda^i, \quad B(\lambda) = \sum b_j \lambda^j,$$

the operation of replacing λ by a number λ_0 of $\Re$ is a well-defined operation.   That is,

$$[A(\lambda) + B(\lambda)]_{\lambda=\lambda_0} = A(\lambda_0) + B(\lambda_0),$$

$$[A(\lambda) \cdot B(\lambda)]_{\lambda=\lambda_0} = A(\lambda_0) \cdot B(\lambda_0).$$

Consequently if $f(\lambda)$ and $g(\lambda)$ are any polynomials in numbers of $\Re[\lambda]$, and if $f(\lambda) = g(\lambda)$ in $R[\lambda]$, then it follows that $f(\lambda_0) = g(\lambda_0)$ in $\Re$ for every λ_0 in $\Re$.

If $\Re$ is a non-commutative ring with unit element, the situation is very different.   Even the substitution of λ_0 for λ in $A(\lambda)$ is not well defined, for

$$A(\lambda) = \sum a_i \lambda^i = \sum \lambda^i a_i \qquad\qquad \text{in } \Re[\lambda],$$

while it is not usually true that

$$\sum a_i \lambda_0^i = \sum \lambda_0^i a_i.$$

This difficulty may be met by defining $A_L(\lambda_0)$ to mean $\Sigma a_i \lambda_0^i$ where all the coefficients a_i are on the left.

There are further difficulties, however.   Let

$$A(\lambda) = \sum a_i \lambda^i, \quad B(\lambda) = \sum b_j \lambda^j.$$

By definition

$$C(\lambda) = A(\lambda) \cdot B(\lambda) = \sum c_k \lambda^k,$$

where

$$c_k = \sum_{i+j=k} a_i b_j.$$

Thus

$$C_L(\lambda_0) = \sum_k \sum_{i+j=k} a_i b_j \lambda_0^k,$$

while

$$A_L(\lambda_0) \cdot B_L(\lambda_0) = \sum a_i \lambda_0^i \sum b_j \lambda_0^j$$

is usually a different number of $\mathfrak{R}$.

The following theorem, then, is not trivial.

Theorem 101.2. If $F(\Lambda)$ is a polynomial in $\mathfrak{M}[\Lambda]$, and if A is a matrix of $\mathfrak{M}$ such that $F_L(A) = 0$, and if $G(\Lambda) \cdot F(\Lambda) = H(\Lambda)$, where $G(\Lambda)$ is any polynomial, then

$$H_L(A) = 0.$$

Let

$$F(\Lambda) = \sum_{i=0}^m B_i \Lambda^i, \quad G(\Lambda) = \sum_{j=0}^l C_j \Lambda^j, \quad H(\Lambda) = G(\Lambda) \cdot F(\Lambda) = \sum_{k=0}^{l+m} D_k \Lambda^k.$$

Then

$$\sum_{k=0}^{l+m} D_k \Lambda^k = \sum_{j=0}^l C_j \Lambda^j \sum_{i=0}^m B_i \Lambda^i = \sum_{k=0}^{l+m} \left[\sum_{i+j=k} C_j B_i \right] \Lambda^k,$$

so that

$$D_k = \sum_{i+j=k} C_j B_i \qquad (k = 0, 1, \cdots, l + m).$$

Hence

$$H_L(A) = \sum_{k=0}^{l+m} \sum_{i+j=k} C_j B_i A^k = \sum_{j=0}^l C_j \left[\sum_{i=0}^m B_i A^i \right] A^j$$

$$= \sum_{j=0}^l C_j \cdot F_L(A) \cdot A^j = 0.$$

Let $\mathfrak{R}$ now become a field, and let $\mathfrak{M}_{\mathfrak{R}}$ be a matric ring of order n^2. Let $F(\Lambda) \leftrightarrow F(\lambda)$ under the isomorphism of Theorem 101.1, where F is of degree m. Let $dF(\lambda) = f(\lambda) \leftrightarrow f(\Lambda)$. Then $f(\Lambda)$ has coefficients which are scalar matrices, and is of degree $\leqq mn$ in Λ. Then we have

Theorem 101.3. If $F_L(A) = 0$, then A satisfies the matric equation $f(\Lambda) = 0$ with scalar coefficients.

By (100.2) we have
$$\text{adj } F(\lambda) \cdot F(\lambda) = f(\lambda) \cdot I.$$

If adj $F(\lambda) \leftrightarrow G(\Lambda)$, $F(\lambda) \leftrightarrow F(\Lambda)$ and $f(\lambda) \cdot I \leftrightarrow f(\Lambda)$ under the isomorphism of Theorem 101.1,

$$G(\Lambda) \cdot F(\Lambda) = f(\Lambda).$$

But $F_L(A) = 0$, so by Theorem 101.2,

$$f(A) = G_L(A) \cdot F_L(A) = 0.$$

The linear instance of this theorem is of great importance. Let $F(\Lambda) = \Lambda - A$. Then

$$f(\lambda) = \begin{vmatrix} \lambda - a_{11} & - a_{12} \cdots & - a_{1n} \\ - a_{21} & \lambda - a_{22} \cdots & - a_{2n} \\ \cdot & \cdot \quad \cdot \quad \cdot & \cdot \\ - a_{n1} & - a_{n2} \cdots & \lambda - a_{nn} \end{vmatrix}.$$

The equation $f(\lambda) = 0$, which is of degree n, is known as the *characteristic equation* of A.

Corollary 101.3. (*Hamilton-Cayley Theorem.*) *Every matrix satisfies its characteristic equation.*

EXERCISES

1. The equation

$$\begin{bmatrix} 0 & 1 \\ 2 & 1 \end{bmatrix} \Lambda^2 + \begin{bmatrix} 1 & -1 \\ 2 & 0 \end{bmatrix} \Lambda + \begin{bmatrix} 7 & -1 \\ -42 & -18 \end{bmatrix} = 0$$

is satisfied by

$$A = \begin{bmatrix} 5 & 1 \\ -2 & 2 \end{bmatrix}.$$

Find a scalar equation satisfied by A.

2. Show that the matrix

$$A = \begin{bmatrix} 2 & 1 & 3 \\ 1 & 0 & 2 \\ 3 & 1 & -1 \end{bmatrix}$$

satisfies its characteristic equation.

3. If A is any $n \times n$ matrix with elements in a field,

$$I, A, A^2, \cdots, A^{n^2}$$

are linearly dependent. Hence A satisfies an equation with scalar coefficients of degree at most n^2. Fill in the details of this proof.

4. The characteristic function $| \lambda I - A | = f(\lambda)$ of the matrix

$$A = \begin{bmatrix} 2 & 1 \\ 1 & 2 \end{bmatrix}$$

factors into two rational factors, $f(\lambda) = f_1(\lambda) \cdot f_2(\lambda)$. Show that neither $f_1(A)$ nor $f_2(A)$ is 0, but that their product in either order is 0.

5. For each of the following matrices, the characteristic function is a perfect square, $f(\lambda) = [f_1(\lambda)]^2$. Is it true that $f_1(A) = 0$? $f_1(B) = 0$?

$$A = \begin{bmatrix} 3 & 0 \\ 0 & 3 \end{bmatrix}, \quad B = \begin{bmatrix} 3 & 1 \\ 0 & 3 \end{bmatrix}.$$

102. The minimum equation. We saw in the last paragraph that every $n \times n$ matrix A with elements in a field $\mathfrak{F}$ satisfies an equation with scalar coefficients of degree n. But A may satisfy such an equation of degree $< n$, e.g., a scalar matrix satisfies a linear equation.

The degree μ of a scalar equation of lowest degree which is satisfied by A is called the *index* of A. If $\mu < n$, A is called *derogatory*.

Let

$$m(\lambda) = \lambda^\mu + m_1\lambda^{\mu-1} + \cdots + m_\mu = 0$$

be an equation of lowest degree satisfied by A.

Theorem 102.1. If $f(A) = 0$, then $m(\lambda) \mid f(\lambda)$.

Write

$$f(\lambda) = q(\lambda) \cdot m(\lambda) + r(\lambda),$$

where either $r(\lambda) = 0$ or $r(\lambda)$ is of degree $< \mu$. Since $f(A) = m(A) = 0$, $r(A) = 0$. Since μ was minimal, $r(\lambda) = 0$.

Corollary 102.1. The function $m(\lambda)$ is unique.

For, if there were two of the same degree, each would divide the other, and since each has leading coefficient 1, they would coincide.

The function $m(\lambda)$ is called the *minimum function* of A. Its constant term will be called the *norm* of A, written $N(A)$.

Theorem 102.2. If $f(\lambda)$ is the characteristic function of A, and if $h(\lambda)$ is the greatest common divisor of the $(n - 1)$ rowed minor determinants of $\lambda I - A$, then

$$m(\lambda) = \frac{f(\lambda)}{h(\lambda)}$$

is the minimum function of A.

The elements of the adjoint matrix adj $(\lambda I - A)$ are polynomials in λ of degree $n - 1$ at most. Let $h(\lambda)$ be the greatest common divisor of these elements, that is, the greatest common divisor of the $(n - 1)$ rowed minor determinants of $\lambda I - A$, and let $f(\lambda)/h(\lambda) = g(\lambda)$. Then we can write

$$\operatorname{adj}\,(\lambda I - A) = h(\lambda) \cdot K(\lambda),$$

where $K(\lambda)$ is a matrix whose elements are polynomials in λ without common factor. Since by (100.2)

$$f(\lambda) \cdot I = \operatorname{adj}\,(\lambda I - A) \cdot (\lambda I - A),$$

we have

$$g(\lambda) \cdot h(\lambda) \cdot I = h(\lambda) \cdot K(\lambda) \cdot (\lambda I - A);$$

and, since $h(\lambda) \neq 0$,

(102.1) $$g(\lambda) \cdot I = K(\lambda) \cdot (\lambda I - A).$$

Now $K(\lambda)$ can be written as a polynomial in λ with matric coefficients. Hence, by Theorem 101.2, $g(A) = 0$. Then, by Theorem 102.1, $m(\lambda) \mid g(\lambda)$, where $m(\lambda)$ is the minimum function of A.

Let λ and ν be two indeterminates. From the algebraic identity

$$m(\lambda) - m(\nu) = (\lambda - \nu) \cdot k(\lambda, \nu)$$

we obtain

$$m(\lambda) \cdot I - m(A) = m(\lambda I) - m(A)$$

$$= (\lambda I - A) \cdot k(\lambda I, A),$$

for A is commutative with every coefficient. Note that $m(A) = 0$. Then

$$\operatorname{adj}\,(\lambda I - A) \cdot m(\lambda) = \operatorname{adj}\,(\lambda I - A) \cdot (\lambda I - A) \cdot k(\lambda I, A)$$

$$= f(\lambda) \cdot k(\lambda I, A).$$

That is,

$$h(\lambda) \cdot K(\lambda) \cdot m(\lambda) = h(\lambda) \cdot g(\lambda) \cdot k(\lambda I, A).$$

Since $h(\lambda) \neq 0$, it may be canceled. Since $g(\lambda)$ divides every element of $K(\lambda) \cdot m(\lambda)$ and the elements of $K(\lambda)$ are relatively prime, $g(\lambda) \mid m(\lambda)$. Since $g(\lambda)$ and $m(\lambda)$ have leading coefficients 1, they are equal.

Theorem 102.3. *The distinct factors of the characteristic function $f(\lambda)$ of A which are irreducible in $\mathfrak{F}$ coincide with the distinct irreducible factors of the minimum function $m(\lambda)$.*

By Theorem 102.2,

$$f(\lambda) = m(\lambda) \cdot h(\lambda),$$

where $h(\lambda)$ is the greatest common divisor of the elements of the adjoint of $\lambda I - A$. Then every factor of $m(\lambda)$ divides $f(\lambda)$.

From (102.1),

$$m(\lambda) \cdot I = K(\lambda) \cdot (\lambda I - A).$$

Taking determinants, we have

$$[m(\lambda)]^n = dK(\lambda) \cdot f(\lambda).$$

Hence every irreducible factor of $f(\lambda)$ divides $m(\lambda)$.

EXERCISES

1. Let

$$f(\lambda) = \lambda^n - t_1\lambda^{n-1} + t_2\lambda^{n-2} - \cdots \pm t_n = 0$$

be the characteristic equation of A. Show that t_i is the sum of all the principal i-rowed minor determinants of A.

2. Prove that $N(A) = 0$ if and only if $d(A) = 0$.

3. Prove that every matrix has an inverse or is a divisor of zero according as its norm (or determinant) is not or is zero.

HINT: $m(\lambda) = \lambda(\lambda^{\mu-1} + m_1\lambda^{\mu-2} + \cdots + m_{\mu-1}) + N(A)$. Note that A^{-1} is representable as a polynomial in A.

4. Show that $x^n + a_1 x^{n-1} + a_2 x^{n-2} + \cdots + a_n = 0$ is the minimum equation of the matrix

$$\begin{bmatrix} 0 & 0 & \cdots & 0 - a_n \\ 1 & 0 & \cdots & 0 - a_{n-1} \\ \cdot & \cdot & \cdots & \cdot \\ 0 & 0 & \cdots & 1 - a_1 \end{bmatrix}.$$

This matrix (or its transpose) is called the *companion matrix* of the given equation.

5. Show that $(x - \lambda)^n = 0$ is the minimum equation of the $n \times n$ matrix

$$\begin{bmatrix} \lambda & 1 & 0 & \cdots & 0 \\ 0 & \lambda & 1 & \cdots & 0 \\ \cdot & \cdot & \cdot & \cdots & \cdot \\ 0 & 0 & 0 & \cdots & \lambda \end{bmatrix}.$$

This matrix (or its transpose) is said to be in *Jordan form* or to be a *Jordan matrix*.

103. Associated integral matrices. Let $\mathfrak{P}$ be a principal ideal ring (§ 69). A matric algebra $\mathfrak{M}$ with elements in $\mathfrak{P}$ is a ring with unit element.

A matrix U of $\mathfrak{M}$ is a *unit* if there exists a matrix U' of $\mathfrak{M}$ such that

$$UU' = I.$$

That is, U is a unit if U^{-1} has elements in $\mathfrak{P}$.

Theorem 103.1. *U is a unit of $\mathfrak{M}$ if and only if $d(U)$ is a unit of $\mathfrak{P}$.*

For $UU' = I$ implies that $d(U) \cdot d(U') = 1$, so that $d(U)$ is a unit of $\mathfrak{P}$. Conversely, if $d(U)$ is a unit of $\mathfrak{P}$, U^{-1} has elements in $\mathfrak{P}$.

A unit matrix is called *unimodular.*

Theorem 103.2. *Let a_1, a_2, $\cdots$, a_n be numbers of $\mathfrak{P}$ with greatest common divisor d_n. There exists a matrix of determinant d_n having a_1, a_2, $\cdots$, a_n as its first row.*

The theorem is trivially true for $n = 1$. Suppose it to hold for $n - 1$, and let D_{n-1} be a matrix of order $n - 1$ which has a_1, a_2, $\cdots$, a_{n-1} as its first row, and whose determinant is $d_{n-1} = (a_1, a_2, \cdots, a_{n-1})$. Determine p and q so that

$$pd_{n-1} - qa_n = d_n.$$

Consider the matrix

$$D_n = \begin{bmatrix} & & & & a_n \\ & D_{n-1} & & & 0 \\ & & & & \cdots \\ \dfrac{a_1 q}{d_{n-1}} & \dfrac{a_2 q}{d_{n-1}} & \cdots & \dfrac{a_{n-1} q}{d_{n-1}} & p \end{bmatrix}.$$

Clearly

$$d(D_n) = pd(D_{n-1}) + (-1)^{n-1} a_n d(H_{n-1}),$$

where H_{n-1} is obtained from D_{n-1} by replacing the first row a_1, a_2, $\cdots$, a_{n-1}, by q/d_{n-1} times this row, and then making a cyclic permutation of the rows. That is,

$$d(H_{n-1}) = \frac{q}{d_{n-1}} d_{n-1} (-1)^{n-2} = (-1)^n q.$$

Hence

$$d(D_n) = pd_{n-1} - qa_n = d_n,$$

Corollary 103.2. *If $a_1, a_2, \cdots, a_n$ are relatively prime in $\mathfrak{P}$, there exists a unimodular matrix having $a_1, a_2, \cdots, a_n$ as any prescribed row or column.*

Two matrices A and B are called *left associates* if there exists a unimodular matrix U such that

$$A = UB.$$

The following operations upon the rows of a matrix are called *elementary operations:*

1. The interchange of any two rows.

2. The multiplication of the elements of a row by a unit u of $\mathfrak{P}$.

3. The addition to the elements of any row of k times the corresponding elements of another row, where k is in $\mathfrak{P}$.

Theorem 103.3.   Each elementary operation upon a matrix A can be accomplished by multiplying A on the left by a unimodular matrix E which is obtained by performing the given elementary operation upon the unit matrix I.

Thus, to interchange the first and second rows of A, we have

$$\begin{bmatrix} 0 & 1 & 0 \\ 1 & 0 & 0 \\ 0 & 0 & 1 \end{bmatrix} \begin{bmatrix} a_{11} & a_{12} & a_{13} \\ a_{21} & a_{22} & a_{23} \\ a_{31} & a_{32} & a_{33} \end{bmatrix} = \begin{bmatrix} a_{21} & a_{22} & a_{23} \\ a_{11} & a_{12} & a_{13} \\ a_{31} & a_{32} & a_{33} \end{bmatrix}.$$

To multiply the second row of A by u,

$$\begin{bmatrix} 1 & 0 & 0 \\ 0 & u & 0 \\ 0 & 0 & 1 \end{bmatrix} \begin{bmatrix} a_{11} & a_{12} & a_{13} \\ a_{21} & a_{22} & a_{23} \\ a_{31} & a_{32} & a_{33} \end{bmatrix} = \begin{bmatrix} a_{11} & a_{12} & a_{13} \\ ua_{21} & ua_{22} & ua_{23} \\ a_{31} & a_{32} & a_{33} \end{bmatrix}.$$

To increase the elements of the second row by k times the corresponding elements of the first row,

$$\begin{bmatrix} 1 & 0 & 0 \\ k & 1 & 0 \\ 0 & 0 & 1 \end{bmatrix} \begin{bmatrix} a_{11} & a_{12} & a_{13} \\ a_{21} & a_{22} & a_{23} \\ a_{31} & a_{32} & a_{33} \end{bmatrix} = \begin{bmatrix} a_{11} & a_{12} & a_{13} \\ ka_{11} + a_{21} & ka_{12} + a_{22} & ka_{13} + a_{23} \\ a_{31} & a_{32} & a_{33} \end{bmatrix}.$$

These left factors are called *elementary matrices*.

Theorem 103.4.   Every matrix with elements in $\mathfrak{P}$ is the left associate of a matrix having 0's above the main diagonal, and each element below the main diagonal reduced modulo the diagonal element above it.

This normal form is known as *Hermite's normal form*.

Let $A = (a_{rs})$ have elements in $\mathfrak{P}$. Either every element of the last column is 0, or there is at least one non-zero element, which by a permutation of the rows can be put into the (n, n) position. Let d_n be a g.c.d. of the elements $a_{1n}, a_{2n}, \cdots, a_{nn}$ of the last column, and suppose that

$$b_1 a_{1n} + b_2 a_{2n} + \cdots + b_n a_{nn} = d_n.$$

Then $b_1, b_2, \cdots, b_n$ are relatively prime, and by Corollary 103.2 there exists a unimodular matrix U having $b_1, b_2, \cdots, b_n$ as its last row.

Then $A_1 = UA$ has d_n in the (n, n) position, where d_n divides every element of the last column. Then, by subtracting a proper multiple of the last row from each of the other rows, a matrix A_2 is obtained whose last column has only 0's above the main diagonal. Since these operations can be accomplished by multiplying on the left by a unimodular matrix, A_2 is a left associate of A.

In the $(n - 1)$th column of A_2, either every element of the first $n - 1$ rows is 0 or a permutation of the first $n - 1$ rows will place a non-zero element in the $(n - 1, n - 1)$ position. Let d_{n-1} be a g.c.d. of $a_{1,n-1}$, $a_{2,n-1}$, $\cdots$, $a_{n-1,n-1}$, and let

$$c_1 a_{1,n-1} + c_2 a_{2,n-1} + \cdots + c_{n-1} a_{n-1,n-1} = d_{n-1}.$$

Let

$$U_1 = \begin{bmatrix} u_{11} & u_{12} & \cdots & u_{1,n-1} & 0 \\ \cdots & \cdots & \cdots & \cdots & \cdots \\ c_1 & c_2 & \cdots & c_{n-1} & 0 \\ 0 & 0 & \cdots & 0 & 1 \end{bmatrix}$$

be unimodular (Corollary 103.2). Then $U_1 A_2$ has 0's above the main diagonal in the last column, d_{n-1} in the $(n - 1, n - 1)$ position, and each element above d_{n-1} divisible by d_{n-1}, so that these can be made 0's by elementary transformations. The process can be continued until only 0's lie above the main diagonal.

By subtracting a multiple of the $(n - 1)$th row from the nth row, $a_{n,n-1}$ can be reduced modulo $a_{n-1,n-1}$. Similarly every element can be reduced modulo the diagonal element above it. It is understood that $a \equiv b \bmod 0$ means $a = b$.

The most important case of this theorem is where $\mathfrak{P}$ is the ring $[Ra]$ of rational integers. A ring such as $[Ra]$, or $Ra[i]$ in which a Euclid algorithm exists is called a *euclidean ring*.

Theorem 103.5. If A has elements in a euclidean ring $\mathfrak{E}$, the reduction to normal form can be accomplished by elementary transformations.

Either every element of the last column is 0, or there is one non-zero element with minimum absolute value (or norm) which, by an interchange of the rows, can be put into the (n, n) position. If a_{nn} does not divide some a_{in}, set

$$a_{in} = q a_{nn} + r,$$

where r has absolute value (or norm) less than that of a_{nn}. By an elementary transformation of the third type, a_{in} can be replaced by r. Again interchange rows if necessary so that the element in the (n, n) position is of minimum absolute value (norm), and proceed as before.

Eventually a_{nn} will divide every a_{in}. Now proceed as in the proof of Theorem 103.4.

Theorem 103.6.   Every unimodular matrix with elements in a euclidean ring $\mathfrak{E}$ is a product of a finite number of elementary matrices.

Let U be unimodular. By Theorem 103.5 there exist elementary matrices such that

$$E_1E_2 \cdots E_kU$$

has 0's above the main diagonal. Hence the product of the diagonal elements is a unit of $\mathfrak{E}$, so that each diagonal element is a unit of $\mathfrak{E}$. By elementary transformations of Type 2, each of these can be made 1. Since each element below the main diagonal is reduced modulo 1, it is 0. Hence we may assume that

$$E_1E_2 \cdots E_kU = I, \qquad U = E_k^{-1}E_{k-1}^{-1} \cdots E_2^{-1}E_1^{-1}.$$

Since the inverse of every elementary matrix is elementary (see Ex. 1 to follow), we have U factored into elementary matrices.

EXERCISES

1. Prove that the inverse of every elementary transformation is an elementary transformation of the same type.

2. Show that if A and B are associated non-singular matrices of the third order in the Hermite form with elements in $[Ra]$, with diagonal elements positive and with elements below the diagonal chosen from the same residue system, then $A = B$.

3. Let A be of the third order, in the Hermite form with $a_{11} \neq 0$, $a_{33} \neq 0$, $a_{22} = 0$. Show that every element of the second row can be made 0.

4. Construct a unimodular matrix with elements in $[Ra]$ having 12, -10, 9, 8 as its first row.

5. Reduce to Hermite form

$$\begin{bmatrix} 2 & 6 & 9 \\ -2 & 0 & 4 \\ 2 & 1 & -1 \end{bmatrix}, \text{ also } \begin{bmatrix} 0 & 0 & 2-\lambda \\ 0 & 1+\lambda & 2\lambda \\ 2-\lambda & 0 & 0 \end{bmatrix}.$$

6. Express the unimodular matrix $\begin{bmatrix} 5 & 3 & 4 \\ 3 & 1 & 3 \\ 6 & 3 & 5 \end{bmatrix}$ as a product of elementary matrices.

7. The interchange of two rows can be accomplished by elementary transformations of the other types. Prove.

104. Greatest common divisors. If three matrices A, C, D exist with elements in a principal ideal ring $\mathfrak{P}$ such that $A = CD$, then D is called a *right divisor*, and C a *left divisor*, of A. Also, A is called a *left multiple* of D, and a *right multiple* of C.

If D is a right divisor of two matrices A and B, and if D is a left multiple of every common right divisor of A and B, then D is called a *greatest common right divisor* (g.c.r.d.) of A and B. A common left multiple of two matrices A and B which is a right divisor of every common left multiple is called a *least common left multiple* (l.c.l.m.) of A and B.

Similar definitions hold for greatest common left divisor and least common right multiple, whose properties obviously parallel those of the g.c.r.d. and l.c.l.m.

Theorem 104.1. Every pair of $n \times n$ matrices A and B with elements in $\mathfrak{P}$ have a g.c.r.d. D expressible in the form

$$D = PA + QB.$$

Consider the matrix

$$K = \begin{bmatrix} A & 0 \\ B & 0 \end{bmatrix}$$

of order $2n$. As in Theorem 103.4, a unimodular matrix X of order $2n$ can be found such that the g.c.d. of the elements of the nth column of K is in the (n, n) position in XK. Then elementary transformations will reduce to 0 every element of this column below a_{nn}. This process may be continued to obtain

(104.1)
$$\begin{bmatrix} X_{11} & X_{12} \\ X_{21} & X_{22} \end{bmatrix} \begin{bmatrix} A & 0 \\ B & 0 \end{bmatrix} = \begin{bmatrix} D & 0 \\ 0 & 0 \end{bmatrix}, \qquad X = \begin{bmatrix} X_{11} & X_{12} \\ X_{21} & X_{22} \end{bmatrix}.$$

Hence

(104.2)
$$X_{11}A + X_{12}B = D.$$

Since X is unimodular, it has an inverse Y whose elements belong to $\mathfrak{P}$. Then

$$\begin{bmatrix} A & 0 \\ B & 0 \end{bmatrix} = \begin{bmatrix} Y_{11} & Y_{12} \\ Y_{21} & Y_{22} \end{bmatrix} \begin{bmatrix} D & 0 \\ 0 & 0 \end{bmatrix}, \qquad Y = X^{-1} = \begin{bmatrix} Y_{11} & Y_{12} \\ Y_{21} & Y_{22} \end{bmatrix},$$

so that

(104.3)
$$A = Y_{11}D, \qquad B = Y_{21}D.$$

Equations (104.2) and (104.3) together show that D is a g.c.r.d. of A and B. If $A = B = 0$, then $D = 0$.

Theorem 104.2.   If D is a g.c.r.d. of A and B, so is UD for every uni-modular matrix U.   Conversely, if D is non-singular, every g.c.r.d. of A and B is of the form UD.

For if D satisfies (104.2) and (104.3), and if U is any unimodular matrix,

$$A = Y_{11}U^{-1}UD, \quad B = Y_{21}U^{-1}UD, \quad UD = UX_{11}A + UX_{12}B,$$

so that UD is also a g.c.r.d. of A and B.   If D and D_1 are both g.c.r.d.'s of A and B, and if D is non-singular,

$$D = PD_1, \quad D_1 = QD, \quad D = PQD, \quad PQ = I,$$

so that P is unimodular and D_1 is associated with D.

The algorithm of this paragraph not only proves the existence of the g.c.r.d. but also furnishes a very practical method for its determination. When $\mathfrak{P}$ is a euclidean ring, all operations can be carried out by means of elementary transformations.

Theorem 104.3.   Every pair of non-singular matrices A and B with elements in $\mathfrak{P}$ have a l.c.l.m. which is unique up to a unimodular left factor.

From (104.1), $X_{21}A + X_{22}B = 0$.   Define

$$M = X_{21}A = -X_{22}B.$$

Clearly M is a common left multiple of A and B.   We shall show that M is a l.c.l.m. by showing that, where M_1 is any common left multiple of A and B, M is a right divisor of M_1.

Let M_2 be a g.c.r.d. of M and M_1.   Then

$$M_2 = PM + QM_1, \quad M = HM_2,$$

so that M_2 is a common left multiple of A and B.   Suppose that

$$M_2 = KA = LB.$$

Then

$$M = X_{21}A = HM_2 = HKA, \quad M = -X_{22}B = HM_2 = HLB.$$

Since A and B are non-singular,

$$X_{21} = HK, \quad X_{22} = -HL.$$

Now X and Y are reciprocal unimodular matrices, so that

$$I = X_{21}Y_{12} + X_{22}Y_{22} = HKY_{12} - HLY_{22} = H(KY_{12} - LY_{22}).$$

Since H is a divisor of I, it is unimodular, so that M_2 is associated with M.   This means that M is a right divisor of M_1.   Thus every common left multiple of A and B is a left multiple of M, and M is a l.c.l.m. of A and B.

EXERCISES

1. Find a g.c.r.d. and a l.c.l.m. of

$$A = \begin{bmatrix} 63 & 10 \\ 80 & 73 \end{bmatrix}, \quad B = \begin{bmatrix} 30 & 2 \\ 16 & 32 \end{bmatrix}.$$

Express the former linearly in terms of A and B.

2. Find a g.c.r.d. of

$$A = \begin{bmatrix} -10 & -2 & 14 \\ -56 & -52 & -4 \\ 8 & -22 & -52 \end{bmatrix}, \quad B = \begin{bmatrix} 12 & 11 & -1 \\ 4 & 15 & 22 \\ -44 & -31 & 15 \end{bmatrix}.$$

3. Prove that, if the $2n \times n$ array $\begin{bmatrix} A \\ B \end{bmatrix}$ is of rank n, the matrices A and B have a non-singular g.c.r.d.

4. Show that, if D is a g.c.r.d. of A and B, $d(D)$ is a common divisor of $d(A)$ and $d(B)$. Show by an example that it is not always the g.c.d.

5. Parallel the theory of §104 for columns and right associates.

105. Equivalence of matrices. Let $A = PBQ$ where each matrix has its elements in a principal ideal ring $\mathfrak{P}$. Then A is a *multiple* of B.

Theorem 105.1. If A is a multiple of B, the g.c.d., d_i, of the i-rowed minor determinants of B divides the g.c.d., d_i', of the i-rowed minor determinants of A.

This follows from Theorem 99.1. For, if $A = PBQ$,

$$d(A_{s_1 \cdots s_i}^{r_1 \cdots r_i}) = \sum d(P_{h_1 \cdots h_i}^{r_1 \cdots r_i}) d(B_{k_1 \cdots k_i}^{h_1 \cdots h_i}) d(Q_{s_1 \cdots s_i}^{k_1 \cdots k_i}).$$

Thus every common divisor of all the

$$d(B_{k_1 \cdots k_i}^{h_1 \cdots h_i})$$

is a divisor of every

$$d(A_{s_1 \cdots s_i}^{r_1 \cdots r_i}).$$

Two matrices A and B with elements in $\mathfrak{P}$ are called *equivalent* if there exist two unimodular matrices U and V such that

$$A = UBV.$$

We have directly from the above theorem

Corollary 105.1. If A and B are equivalent, every g.d.c., d_i, of the *i-rowed minor determinants of B is associated with every g.c.d., d_i' of the i-rowed minor determinants of A.*

To save space, we shall use the notation $[a_1, a_2, \cdots, a_n]$ to denote the diagonal matrix

$$\begin{bmatrix} a_1 & 0 & \cdots & 0 \\ 0 & a_2 & \cdots & 0 \\ \cdot & \cdot & \cdot & \cdot \\ 0 & 0 & \cdots & a_n \end{bmatrix}.$$

Theorem 105.2. Every matrix A of rank ρ with elements in $\mathfrak{P}$ is equivalent to a diagonal matrix $[h_1, h_2, \cdots, h_\rho, 0, \cdots 0]$, where $h_i \mid h_{i+1}$.

This is known as *Smith's normal form* (for H. J. S. Smith).

If A is of rank ρ, the rows and columns can be shifted by elementary transformations so that the minor determinant of order ρ in the upper left corner is $\neq 0$. Then as in the proof of Theorem 103.4 the element a_{11} in the (1, 1) position can be made $\neq 0$ and a g.c.d. of the elements of the first column. If a_{11} is not a divisor of all the elements of the first row, it can be replaced by a proper divisor. By the descending chain condition, we ultimately reach an a_{11} which divides every element of the first row and every element of the first column. Then by elementary transformations we can make all these elements except a_{11} equal to 0.

Suppose that there is an element of the matrix, say a_{ij}, not divisible by a_{11}. Add column j to column 1, so that column 1 consists of a_{11} and a_{ij}, $i = 2, \cdots, n$. Then, starting over again, a_{11} can be replaced by a proper divisor of itself. Thus eventually a point is reached where a_{11} is the only non-zero element in the first row or column, and is a divisor of every element of the matrix.

Now we leave the first row and column alone, and work with the $(n-1)$-rowed minor in the lower right corner. We proceed as before to make a_{22} the only non-zero element in the first row and column of this minor (the second row and column of A), and a divisor of every other element of A except a_{11}. Since every element of the minor in its new form is a linear combination of the original elements, it is still true that a_{11} divides a_{22}.

Proceeding in this way, we finally reach a matrix

$$\begin{bmatrix} D & 0 \\ 0 & M \end{bmatrix}, \quad D = [h_1, h_2, \cdots, h_\rho], \qquad h_i \neq 0.$$

Now $M = 0$, for if one element of M were $\neq 0$, it could be shifted into the $(\rho + 1, \rho + 1)$ position, and A would have a non-vanishing minor of order $\rho + 1$, whereas it is of rank ρ.

The numbers $h_1, h_2, \cdots, h_\rho$ in the normal form of A are called its *invariant factors*.

Theorem 105.3. *If A and B are equivalent, the invariant factors of A are (up to unit factors) the same as the invariant factors of B.*

It was shown in Corollary 105.1 that the corresponding d_i's are associated. But

$$d_i = h_1 h_2 \cdots h_i, \quad h_i = \frac{d_i}{d_{i-1}} \qquad (h_1 = d_1, i = 2, 3, \cdots, \rho)$$

so that the d's determine the h's, and conversely.

Theorem 105.4. *Two matrices A and B with elements in $\mathfrak{P}$ are equivalent if and only if they have the same invariant factors.*

If A and B have the same invariant factors, they can be reduced to the same normal form S,

$$S = UAV = U_1 B V_1, \quad U_1^{-1} U A V V_1^{-1} = B,$$

so that A and B are equivalent. And, as we saw in Theorem 105.3, if A and B are equivalent, they have the same invariant factors.

EXERCISES

1. Prove that two matrices A and B with elements in a field are equivalent if and only if they have the same rank.

2. Find the Smith normal form of the matrix

$$\begin{bmatrix} -2 & 0 & 10 \\ 0 & -3 & -4 \\ 1 & 2 & -1 \end{bmatrix},$$

whose elements are rational integers.

3. Find the Smith normal form of the matrix

$$\begin{bmatrix} \lambda(\lambda - 1)^3 & 0 & 0 \\ 0 & \lambda - 1 & 0 \\ 0 & 0 & \lambda \end{bmatrix},$$

whose elements are in $Ra[\lambda]$.

4. Reduce the following matrix with elements in $Ra[i]$ to a Smith normal form:

$$\begin{bmatrix} -1 + 8i & -23 + 2i \\ -5 + i & 13i \end{bmatrix}.$$

See Ex. 1, § 50.

5. Show that, if $h_n(\lambda)$ is the last invariant factor of $I\lambda - A$, then $h_n(\lambda) = 0$ is the minimum equation of A.

6. Let A, B, P, Q have elements in any commutative ring. Show that, if $A = PBQ$, the rank of A cannot exceed the rank of B.

106. Elementary divisors. Suppose that

$$h_i = p_1^{e_{i1}} p_2^{e_{i2}} \cdots p_k^{e_{ik}},$$

where the p's are primes. Since $h_i \mid h_{i+1}$, the exponents of each p_l form a sequence

$$e_{1l} \leqq e_{2l} \leqq \cdots \qquad\qquad (l = 1, 2, \cdots, k).$$

Such of these powers $p_l^{e_{il}}$ as are not units are called the *elementary divisors* of A. Each is defined up to a unit factor.

Theorem 106.1. Two matrices A and B with elements in a principal ideal ring are equivalent if and only if they have the same rank and the same elementary divisors.

It is evident that the invariant factors determine the elementary divisors. The converse is also true, for h_ρ is the product of the highest power of p_1 that occurs by the highest power of p_2 that occurs, etc. Then $h_{\rho-1}$ is formed in the same way from the remaining elementary divisors. When the elementary divisors are exhausted, the remaining h's are 1's.

Theorem 106.2. Suppose that A is equivalent to $[g_1, g_2, \cdots, g_\rho, 0, \cdots, 0]$, where $g_i \neq 0$, but it is not necessarily true that $g_i \mid g_{i+1}$. The prime power factors of the g's are the elementary divisors of A.

Consider any prime p, and arrange the g's according to ascending powers of this prime. That is,

$$g_{i_1} = p^{k_1} f_1, \quad g_{i_2} = p^{k_2} f_2, \cdots, \quad g_{i_\rho} = p^{k_\rho} f_\rho,$$

where the f's are prime to p and

$$k_1 \leqq k_2 \leqq \cdots \leqq k_\rho.$$

Then the highest power of p dividing d_{i-1} has the exponent

$$k_1 + k_2 + \cdots + k_{i-1}.$$

Hence the highest power of p dividing h_i has the exponent k_i. But by definition the elementary divisors are the highest powers of the prime factors of the h's which divide the h's.

Let

$$A = \begin{bmatrix} B & 0 \\ 0 & C \end{bmatrix},$$

where the 0's stand for blocks of 0's, and B and C stand for square arrays of elements not necessarily 0; we say that A is the *direct sum* of B and C, and write $A = B + C$.

Corollary 106.2. *If $A = B + C$, the elementary divisors of A are those of B together with those of C.*

For B and C can be reduced independently to diagonal form.

EXERCISES

1. By Theorem 106.2 write out the normal form of the matrix

$$\begin{bmatrix} 20 & 0 & 0 & 0 \\ 0 & 18 & 0 & 0 \\ 0 & 0 & 75 & 0 \\ 0 & 0 & 0 & 42 \end{bmatrix}$$

with elements in $[Ra]$.

2. Find the invariant factors of the matrix

$$\begin{bmatrix} \lambda^2(\lambda - 1)^2 & 0 & 0 & 0 \\ 0 & \lambda(\lambda - 1)^3 & 0 & 0 \\ 0 & 0 & \lambda - 1 & 0 \\ 0 & 0 & 0 & \lambda \end{bmatrix}$$

with elements in $Ra[\lambda]$.

3. Find the invariant factors of the matrix

$$\begin{bmatrix} 2\lambda & 3 & 0 & 1 & \lambda \\ 4\lambda & 3(\lambda + 2) & 0 & \lambda + 2 & 2\lambda \\ 0 & 6\lambda & \lambda & 2\lambda & 0 \\ \lambda - 1 & 0 & \lambda - 1 & 0 & 0 \\ 3(\lambda - 1) & 1 - \lambda & 2(\lambda - 1) & 0 & 0 \end{bmatrix}$$

with elements in $Ra[\lambda]$.

4. The matrix

$$\begin{bmatrix} 0 & 0 & 7 - 6\lambda \\ 10 & -4 + \lambda & 2\lambda \\ 2 + 4\lambda & 5 & 0 \end{bmatrix}$$

has elements in the polynomial domain of $GF(5)$. Find its invariant factors.

107. Equivalence in polynomial domains. We shall now consider matrices with elements in the polynomial domain $\mathfrak{F}[\lambda]$ of a field. This is a euclidean ring.

By Theorem 101.1, every matrix

$$A = (a_{rs0} + a_{rs1}\lambda + \cdots + a_{rsk}\lambda^k)$$

with elements in $\mathfrak{F}[\lambda]$ can be written

$$A = A_0 + A_1\lambda + \cdots + A_k\lambda^k, \qquad\qquad A_i = (a_{rsi}).$$

where the A_i have elements in $\mathfrak{F}$. The matrix A is of *degree k* if $A_k \neq 0$. It is *proper of degree k* if A_k is non-singular.

Theorem 107.1. If A and B are matrices with elements in $\mathfrak{F}[\lambda]$, and if B is proper of degree l, then there exist matrices Q and R (also Q_1 and R_1) such that

$$A = BQ + R, \quad A = Q_1B + R_1,$$

where either $R = 0$ ($R_1 = 0$) or else R (R_1) is of degree $< l$.

Let

$$A = A_k\lambda^k + A_{k-1}\lambda^{k-1} + \cdots + A_1\lambda + A_0,$$

$$B = B_l\lambda^l + B_{l-1}\lambda^{l-1} + \cdots + B_1\lambda + B_0.$$

Unless $l \leq k$, we may take $Q = Q_1 = 0$, $R = R_1 = A$. Hence we assume $l \leq k$. Since $d(B_l) \neq 0$, the equation $B_lX = A_k$ has a solution $X = C_{k-l}$. Then

$$A - BC_{k-l}\lambda^{k-l}$$

is of degree $k - 1$ at most. Continue as in ordinary long division until a remainder is obtained which is either 0 or of degree $< l$.

Theorem 107.2. If A and B are proper of degrees k and l, respectively, and if $AP_1 = P_2B$, there exist a matrix Q and two matrices R_1 and R_2, which are either 0 or of degrees r_1 and r_2, respectively, such that

$$AR_1 = R_2B, \quad P_1 = QB + R_1, \quad P_2 = AQ + R_2, \quad r_1 < l, r_2 < k.$$

By Theorem 107.1 determine Q_1, Q_2, R_1, and R_2 so that

$$P_2 = AQ_2 + R_2, \quad P_1 = Q_1B + R_1$$

where R_1 is either 0 or of degree $r_1 < l$, and R_2 is either 0 or of degree $r_2 < k$. Then

$$AR_1 - R_2B = A(Q_2 - Q_1)B.$$

The left member is either 0 or of degree $< k + l$, while the right member is either 0 or degree $\geq k + l$.   Hence both members are 0.   Then

$$AR_1 = R_2B,$$

and, since A and B are proper,

$$Q_2 = Q_1 = Q.$$

Theorem 107.3.   If A and B are proper of degree 1 and equivalent, there exist non-singular matrices P and Q with elements in $\mathfrak{F}$ such that $A = PBQ$.

Since A and B are equivalent in $\mathfrak{F}[\lambda]$, there exist matrices P_1 and P_2 whose determinants are units of $\mathfrak{F}[\lambda]$, such that

$$AP_1 = P_2B.$$

Clearly P_1 and P_2 are non-singular.   Since A and B are each of degree 1, the matrices R_1 and R_2 of Theorem 107.2 have elements in $\mathfrak{F}$.   It remains only to show that R_1 and R_2 are non-singular.

Let

$$P_1^{-1} = Q_3A + R_3,$$

where R_3 is either 0 or of degree $r_3 = 0$.   Then

$$I = P_1^{-1}P_1 = (Q_3A + R_3)(QB + R_1)$$

$$= Q_3AQB + Q_3AR_1 + R_3QB + R_3R_1,$$

$$I - R_3R_1 = (Q_3AQ + Q_3R_2 + R_3Q)B.$$

The left member is either 0 or of degree 0 in λ, while the right member is either 0 or of degree ≥ 1 in λ.   Hence each member is 0, $R_3R_1 = I$, $d(R_1) \neq 0$.   Similarly $d(R_2) \neq 0$.   Then

$$A = PBQ, \quad P = R_2, \quad Q = R_1^{-1}.$$

EXERCISES

1. Let

$$A = \begin{bmatrix} 2\lambda^2 + 2\lambda + 1 & 4\lambda - 5 \\ -5 & \lambda^2 + \lambda \end{bmatrix}, \quad B = \begin{bmatrix} \lambda - 1 & \lambda - 5 \\ 2\lambda + 3 & 4 \end{bmatrix}.$$

Find the Q, Q_1, R, and R_1 of Theorem 107.1.

2. $\begin{bmatrix} -3\lambda - 2 & \frac{10}{3}\lambda \\ -4 & -\frac{1}{3}\lambda + 1 \end{bmatrix} = \begin{bmatrix} 1 & \lambda \\ 0 & 1 \end{bmatrix} \begin{bmatrix} \lambda - 2 & 3\lambda \\ -4 & \lambda + 1 \end{bmatrix} \begin{bmatrix} 1 & \frac{1}{3}\lambda \\ 0 & 1 \end{bmatrix}.$

Find matrices with elements free of λ which effect this transformation.

3. Prove that the matrices Q, R, Q_1, R_1 of Theorem 107.1 are unique.

4. In Theorem 107.1, take $B = I\lambda - B_0$. Prove that

$$R = B_0^k A_k + B_0^{k-1} A_{k-1} + \cdots + B_0 A_1 + A_0,$$

$$R_1 = A_k B_0^k + A_{k-1} B_0^{k-1} + \cdots + A_1 B_0 + A_0.$$

5. Let $f(\lambda)$ be the characteristic function of A. Then $f(\lambda)I = \text{adj } (I\lambda - A) \cdot (I\lambda - A)$. Use Exs. 3 and 4 to prove Corollary 101.3.

108. Similarity. Two matrices A and B with elements in a principal ideal ring $\mathfrak{P}$ are said to be *similar* if a unimodular matrix P exists such that

$$A = P^{-1}BP.$$

Theorem 108.1. Every unimodular matrix P determines an automorphism of the matric ring $\mathfrak{M}\mathfrak{P}$.

For, if $A_1 = P^{-1}B_1P$, $A_2 = P^{-1}B_2P$, let

$$A_1 \leftrightarrow B_1, \quad A_2 \leftrightarrow B_2.$$

This is clearly biunique, since $d(P) \neq 0$. Since

$$A_1 + A_2 = P^{-1}(B_1 + B_2)P, \quad A_1A_2 = P^{-1}B_1B_2P,$$

the correspondence is an automorphism relative to both addition and multiplication.

Theorem 108.2. If A and B are similar, they have the same characteristic equations.

For, if $A = P^{-1}BP$,

$$A - \lambda I = P^{-1}(B - \lambda I)P,$$

so that

$$d(A - \lambda I) = d(B - \lambda I).$$

Theorem 108.3. A necessary and sufficient condition that two matrices A and B with coefficients in a field $\mathfrak{F}$ be similar in $\mathfrak{F}$ is that, in the polynomial domain $\mathfrak{F}[\lambda]$, $I\lambda - A$ and $I\lambda - B$ have the same invariant factors.

If $A = P^{-1}BP$, then evidently

$$I\lambda - A = P^{-1}(I\lambda - B)P,$$

so that $I\lambda - A$ and $I\lambda - B$ are equivalent and hence have the same invariant factors by Theorem 105.4.

If conversely, $I\lambda - A$ and $I\lambda - B$ have the same invariant factors, then by Theorem 107.3 there exist non-singular matrices P and Q with elements in $\mathfrak{F}$ such that

$$I\lambda - A = Q(I\lambda - B)P.$$

Hence, on equating coefficients of λ, we have

$$I = QP, \quad A = QBP.$$

Hence $Q = P^{-1}$ so that $A = P^{-1}BP$.

Theorem 108.4. *Let $I\lambda - A$ have the elementary divisors $e_1(\lambda)$, $e_2(\lambda)$, $\cdots$, $e_k(\lambda)$, and let $B_i(\lambda)$ be any matrix of order equal to the degree of $e_i(\lambda)$ which has $e_i(\lambda)$ as its only elementary divisor. Then $I\lambda - A$ is equivalent to*

$$B(\lambda) = B_1(\lambda) \dotplus B_2(\lambda) \dotplus \cdots \dotplus B_k(\lambda).$$

For, if $B_i(\lambda)$ has $e_i(\lambda)$ as its only elementary divisor, then, by Corollary 106.2, $B(\lambda)$ has $e_1(\lambda)$, $e_2(\lambda)$, $\cdots$, $e_k(\lambda)$ as its elementary divisors, and hence is equivalent to $I\lambda - A$.

Theorem 108.5. *Let A be a matrix with elements in any field $\mathfrak{F}$. Then A is similar to*

$$C = C_1 \dotplus C_2 \dotplus \cdots \dotplus C_k,$$

where C_i is the companion matrix of the ith elementary divisor $e_i(\lambda)$ of $I\lambda - A$.

This matrix C is called the *Frobenius normal form* of A.

By Ex. 4, § 102, C_i has $\left| I_i\lambda - C_i \right| = e_i(\lambda) = 0$ as its minimum equation, so that $I_i\lambda - C_i$ has $e_i(\lambda)$ as its only elementary divisor. Thus

$$I\lambda - C = (I_1\lambda - C_1) \dotplus (I_2\lambda - C_2) \dotplus \cdots \dotplus (I_k\lambda - C_k)$$

is equivalent to $I\lambda - A$, and C is similar to A.

Theorem 108.6. *Let A be a matrix with elements in the complex field. Then A is similar to*

$$J = J_1 \dotplus J_2 \dotplus \cdots \dotplus J_k,$$

where J_i is the Jordan matrix of the ith elementary divisor $(\lambda - \lambda_i)^{e_i}$ of $I\lambda - A$.

The matrix J is called the *Jordan normal form* of A.

In the complex field, every polynomial is factorable into linear factors, so that the elementary divisors are of the form $(\lambda - \lambda_i)^{e_i}$. By Ex. 5, § 102, J_i has $\left| I_i\lambda - J_i \right| = (\lambda - \lambda_i)^{e_i} = 0$ as its minimum equation.

$$J_i = \begin{bmatrix} \lambda_i & 1 & 0 & \cdot & \cdot & \cdot & 0 \\ 0 & \lambda_i & 1 & \cdot & \cdot & \cdot & 0 \\ 0 & 0 & \lambda_i & \cdot & \cdot & \cdot & 0 \\ \cdot & \cdot & \cdot & \cdot & \cdot & \cdot & \cdot \\ 0 & 0 & 0 & \cdot & \cdot & \cdot & \lambda_i \end{bmatrix},$$

and so $I_i\lambda - J_i$ has $(\lambda - \lambda_i)^{e_i}$ as it only elementary divisor.   Thus $I\lambda - A$ is equivalent to $I\lambda - J$.

In particular we have shown that every matrix with elements in the complex field is similar to a matrix having only 0's below the main diagonal and having its characteristic roots in the main diagonal.

EXERCISES

1. Show that the matrices

$$\begin{bmatrix} 0 & 1 \\ 8 & 1 \end{bmatrix}, \quad \begin{bmatrix} 16 & -1 \\ 232 & -15 \end{bmatrix}$$

with rational elements are similar.   Find a transforming matrix.   Is it unique?

2. Show that the matrices

$$\begin{bmatrix} 0 & 1 & 0 \\ 0 & 0 & 2 \\ 3 & 4 & 0 \end{bmatrix}, \quad \begin{bmatrix} 3 & 4 & 0 \\ 2 & 4 & 5 \\ 0 & 1 & 0 \end{bmatrix}$$

are similar over $GF(7)$.

3. Return to the exercises of § 100, and show that the characteristic roots of $C_r(A)$ are the $\binom{n}{r}$ products of the characteristic roots of A taken r at a time, equalities among the roots being ignored.

4. Let $x^3 - c_1 x^2 - c_2 x - c_3 = 0$ have the distinct roots ρ_1, ρ_2, ρ_3, and let C be its companion matrix and J its Jordan matrix.   Prove that

$$C = Q^{-1} JQ,$$

where Q is the Vandermonde matrix

$$\begin{bmatrix} 1 & \rho_1 & \rho_1^2 \\ 1 & \rho_2 & \rho_2^2 \\ 1 & \rho_3 & \rho_3^2 \end{bmatrix}.$$

109. Regular representation.   Let

$$f(\lambda) = \lambda^n + a_1\lambda^{n-1} + \cdots + a_n = 0$$

be an equation with coefficients in a field $\mathfrak{F}$ irreducible in $\mathfrak{F}$.   Let ρ be a root of this equation, and define the vector

$$v = (1, \rho, \rho^2, \cdots, \rho^{n-1}).$$

Then
$$\rho v = (\rho, \rho^2, \rho^3, \cdots, \rho^n),$$
$$\rho = 0 \cdot 1 + 1 \cdot \rho + 0 \cdot \rho^2 + \cdots + 0 \cdot \rho^{n-1},$$
$$\rho^2 = 0 \cdot 1 + 0 \cdot \rho + 1 \cdot \rho^2 + \cdots + 0 \cdot \rho^{n-1},$$
$$\cdot \quad \cdot \quad \cdot \quad \cdot \quad \cdot \quad \cdot \quad \cdot \quad \cdot \quad \cdot \quad \cdot \quad \cdot \quad \cdot \quad \cdot$$
$$\rho^n = - a_n \cdot 1 - a_{n-1}\rho - a_{n-2}\rho^2 - \cdots - a_1\rho^{n-1}.$$

That is,

$$\rho v = vR,$$

where

$$R = \begin{bmatrix} 0 & 0 & \cdot & \cdot & \cdot & 0 & -a_n \\ 1 & 0 & \cdot & \cdot & \cdot & 0 & -a_{n-1} \\ 0 & 1 & \cdot & \cdot & \cdot & 0 & -a_{n-2} \\ \cdot & \cdot & \cdot & \cdot & \cdot & \cdot & \cdot \\ 0 & 0 & \cdot & \cdot & \cdot & 1 & -a_1 \end{bmatrix}.$$

Note that R is the companion matrix of $f(\lambda)$.   (See Ex. 4, § 102.)

Theorem 109.1. The correspondence

$$\alpha = c_0 + c_1\rho + \cdots + c_{n-1}\rho^{n-1} \leftrightarrow c_0 I + c_1 R + \cdots + c_{n-1}R^{n-1} = A$$

is biunique, and is an isomorphism under both addition and multiplication.

It is called the *first regular representation* of $\mathfrak{F}(\rho)$ by matrices over $\mathfrak{F}$. We shall first prove that the correspondence

$$\alpha \to A$$

is a homomorphism.   If

$$\alpha v = vA, \quad \beta v = vB,$$

then clearly

$$\alpha v + \beta v = vA + vB,$$

$$(\alpha + \beta)v = v(A + B)$$

by § 94.   Also

$$\alpha\beta v = \alpha vB = vAB$$

by the associative law.

Since $f(\lambda)$ is irreducible, $1, \rho, \rho^2, \cdots, \rho^{n-1}$ are linearly independent, and the elements of ρv are representable in but one way as a linear combination of $1, \rho, \cdots, \rho^{n-1}$. Thus ρ determines R uniquely, and $\Sigma c_i \rho^i$ determines A uniquely.

If two numbers β and γ determine the same matrix, then

$$(\beta - \gamma)v = v \cdot 0 = 0.$$

Then in particular $(\beta - \gamma) \cdot 1 = 0$, so that $\beta = \gamma$, and the correspondence is unique.

By setting up the correspondence

$$v\rho = Sv,$$

we obtain in a similar manner the *second regular representation* of $\mathfrak{F}$ by matrices.

This theorem gives us a third approach to the theory of algebraic numbers. The first approach was obtained by considering the field $Ra(\rho)$ as a subfield of the complex field, and required appeal to the Fundamental Theorem of Algebra. The second method was the Cauchy approach, considering the numbers to be the residues in $Ra[\lambda]$ of $f(\lambda)$. We now have the field $Ra(\rho)$ represented as a commutative matric algebra. This present approach offers many advantages both theoretical and computational.

We now define the *principal equation* of a number

$$\beta = b_0 + b_1\rho + b_2\rho^2 + \cdots + b_{n-1}\rho^{n-1}$$

to be the characteristic equation of the matrix

$$B = b_0I + b_1R + b_2R^2 + \cdots + b_{n-1}R^{n-1}.$$

Clearly $|\lambda I - B| = 0$ is of degree n, and is satisfied by B and hence by β. When β is primitive, that is, satisfies no equation of degree $<n$ with coefficients in $\mathfrak{F}$, it must be true that $|\lambda I - B| = 0$ is the principal equation of β in the sense of § 39.

Whether β is primitive or not, consider the invariant factors

$$h_{n-k}(\lambda), \cdots, h_n(\lambda)$$

of $\lambda I - B$. Now $h_n(\lambda) = 0$ is the minimum equation of B and hence of β. But, since β is in $\mathfrak{F}(\rho)$, its minimum equation is irreducible. Since $h_i(\lambda) \mid h_{i+1}(\lambda)$, every $h_i(\lambda)$ is either 1 or equal to $h_n(\lambda)$. Thus

$$|\lambda I - B| = [h_n(\lambda)]^k,$$

and we have identified our new definition of principal equation with the one given in § 39.

EXERCISES

1. Find the first regular representation of the quadratic field $Ra(\sqrt{m})$, using 1 and $\sqrt{m}$ as basis. Cf. Ex. 5, § 98. Show that, if the number α corresponds to the matrix A, then $N(\alpha) = |A|$.

2. Find by means of § 109 the principal equation of a number (36.2) in the cubic field defined by (36.1). Check the result with (36.4).

3. Find the first regular representation R of a root ρ of the cyclic cubic (37.3). For the cyclic cubic $x^3 - 3x + 1 = 0$, define R' and R'' by substituting R for ρ in (37.4). Prove that

$$R + R' + R'' = 0, \quad RR' + R'R'' + R''R = p, \quad RR'R'' = -q.$$

4. Let $\alpha = x + y\theta$ be an integral number of a quadratic field, and let $A = (a_{rs})$ be its second regular representation. Show that

$$\omega_1 = a_{11} + a_{12}\theta, \quad \omega_2 = a_{21} + a_{22}\theta$$

is a minimal basis for the principal ideal (α). See Ex. 5, § 53.

110. Polynomials in a matrix. A matrix with complex elements which is in the Jordan normal form is a direct sum of matrices of the type

$$J = \begin{bmatrix} \lambda & 1 & 0 & \cdot & \cdot & \cdot & 0 \\ 0 & \lambda & 1 & \cdot & \cdot & \cdot & 0 \\ 0 & 0 & \lambda & \cdot & \cdot & \cdot & 0 \\ \cdot & \cdot & \cdot & \cdot & \cdot & \cdot & \cdot \\ 0 & 0 & 0 & \cdot & \cdot & \cdot & \lambda \end{bmatrix}$$

of order n. That is,

$$J = \lambda I + U,$$

where λI is scalar and U is *nilpotent* of degree n, i.e., $U^n = 0$. For instance, if $n = 4$,

$$U = \begin{bmatrix} 0 & 1 & 0 & 0 \\ 0 & 0 & 1 & 0 \\ 0 & 0 & 0 & 1 \\ 0 & 0 & 0 & 0 \end{bmatrix}, \quad U^2 = \begin{bmatrix} 0 & 0 & 1 & 0 \\ 0 & 0 & 0 & 1 \\ 0 & 0 & 0 & 0 \\ 0 & 0 & 0 & 0 \end{bmatrix}, \quad U^3 = \begin{bmatrix} 0 & 0 & 0 & 1 \\ 0 & 0 & 0 & 0 \\ 0 & 0 & 0 & 0 \\ 0 & 0 & 0 & 0 \end{bmatrix}, \quad U^4 = 0.$$

Now if p is any polynomial, say

$$p(x) = \sum_{i=0}^{m} a_i x^i,$$

then

$$p(J) = \sum_{i=0}^{m} a_i (\lambda I + U)^i$$

$$= \sum_{i=0}^{m} a_i \sum_{j=0}^{i} \binom{i}{j} \lambda^{i-j} U^j, \qquad U^0 = I.$$

Now, for any functions y_{ij},

$$\sum_{i=0}^{m} \sum_{j=0}^{i} y_{ij} = \sum_{j=0}^{m} \sum_{i=j}^{m} y_{ij}.$$

This can be seen immediately by arranging the y's in an array

$$\begin{array}{ccccc} & & & & y_{mm} \\ \cdot & \cdot & \cdot & \cdot & \cdot \\ & & y_{22} & \cdots & y_{m2} \\ & y_{11} & y_{21} & \cdots & y_{m1} \\ y_{00} & y_{10} & y_{20} & \cdots & y_{m0}. \end{array}$$

The first summation is the sum by columns; the second, by rows. Therefore we can write

$$p(J) = \sum_{j=0}^{m} U^j \left[\sum_{i=j}^{m} a_i \binom{i}{j} \lambda^{i-j} \right].$$

But the jth derivative of $p(x)$ is the polynomial

$$p^{(j)}(x) = \sum_{i=j}^{m} a_i i(i-1)(i-2) \cdots (i-j+1)x^{i-j}$$

$$= \sum_{i=j}^{m} a_i j! \binom{i}{j} x^{i-j},$$

so that

(110.1) $\qquad p(J) = \sum_{j=0}^{m} \frac{1}{j!} U^j p^{(j)}(\lambda).$

Thus, suppose that $n = 4$. Then

(110.2) $\qquad p(J) = \begin{bmatrix} p(\lambda) & p'(\lambda) & \dfrac{1}{2}p''(\lambda) & \dfrac{1}{3!}p'''(\lambda) \\ 0 & p(\lambda) & p'(\lambda) & \dfrac{1}{2}p''(\lambda) \\ 0 & 0 & p(\lambda) & p'(\lambda) \\ 0 & 0 & 0 & p(\lambda) \end{bmatrix}.$

Now let A be any matrix with complex elements. It is similar to a direct sum of Jordan matrices, so that there exists a non-singular P such that

$$PAP^{-1} = J_1 + J_2 + \cdots + J_k.$$

Let p be any polynomial. Then

$$P \cdot p(A) \cdot P^{-1} = p(PAP^{-1})$$

$$= p(J_1) + p(J_2) + \cdots + p(J_k),$$

where $p(J_i)$ is a matrix of the type (110.2). Since the characteristic roots of $p(A)$ are the same as those of $P \cdot p(A) \cdot P^{-1}$, we have proved

Theorem 110.1. If $\lambda_1, \lambda_2, \cdots, \lambda_n$ are the complex roots of the characteristic equation of A, then $p(\lambda_1), p(\lambda_2), \cdots, p(\lambda_n)$ are the complex roots of the characteristic equation of $p(A)$, where p is any polynomial.

EXERCISES

1. Theorem 110.1 is useful in applying Tschirnhaus transformations. (See § 40.) Illustrate by finding a cubic equation whose roots are the function $p(\rho) = \rho^3 + \rho^2 + 2$ of the roots of the cubic $x^3 - 3x + 1 = 0$.

2. Solve Ex. 3, § 39, by matric theory.

3. Prove that the characteristic equation of A and the polynomial equation $p(x) = 0$ have a root in common if and only if $|p(A)| = 0$.

4. Find the resultant of

$$x^3 - 18x + 35 = 0, \quad x^2 - x - 30 = 0.$$

5. Find the discriminant of the reduced cubic $x^3 + px + q = 0$. (The discriminant is the resultant of the polynomial and its derivative.)

111. The direct product. Let A and B be matrices, not necessarily of the same order, with elements in a commutative ring $\mathfrak{R}$. If $A = (a_{rs})$ is of order α, and $B = (b_{rs})$ is of order β, we define the *direct product*

(111.1)
$$A \times B = \begin{bmatrix} Ab_{11} & \cdots & Ab_{1\beta} \\ \cdots & \cdots & \cdots \\ Ab_{\beta 1} & \cdots & Ab_{\beta\beta} \end{bmatrix},$$

where Ab_{11} stands for the $\alpha \times \alpha$ array

$$\begin{bmatrix} a_{11}b_{11} & \cdots & a_{1\alpha}b_{11} \\ \cdots & \cdots & \cdots \\ a_{\alpha 1}b_{11} & \cdots & a_{\alpha\alpha}b_{11} \end{bmatrix}.$$

Let $C = A \times B$. If $C = (c_{rs})$, then r and s range from 1 to $\alpha\beta$. Every c_{rs} is the product of an $a_{r_1 s_1}$ by a $b_{r_2 s_2}$, and it can be seen by studying the way in which the direct product is formed that, if

$$c_{rs} = a_{r_1 s_1} b_{r_2 s_2},$$

then

(111.2)
$$r - 1 = \alpha(r_2 - 1) + r_1 - 1, \quad 0 \leqq r_1 - 1 < \alpha,$$
$$s - 1 = \alpha(s_2 - 1) + s_1 - 1, \quad 0 \leqq s_1 - 1 < \alpha.$$

That is, if $r - 1$ is divided by α according to the Euclid algorithm, the quotient is $r_2 - 1$, and the remainder is $r_1 - 1$. The same holds for the column indices. Then every pair r_1, r_2 determines r uniquely, and conversely.

Theorem 111.1. Let A and C be of order α, and B and D of order β. Then

$$(A \times B)(C \times D) = (AC \times BD).$$

For, by (111.2),

$$(A \times B)(C \times D) = (a_{r_1 s_1} b_{r_2 s_2})(c_{r_1 s_1} d_{r_2 s_2}).$$

To multiply these matrices, we set the column index of the first factor equal to the row index of the second factor equal to h, and sum for h. Define h_1 and h_2 by the equation

$$h - 1 = \alpha(h_2 - 1) + h_1 - 1, \qquad 0 \leqq h_1 - 1 < \alpha.$$

As h_1 varies over all integers from 1 to α and h_2 varies over all integers from 1 to β, then h varies over all integers from 1 to $\alpha\beta$. Then

$$(A \times B)(C \times D) = \left(\sum_{h=1}^{\alpha\beta} a_{r_1 h_1} b_{r_2 h_2} c_{h_1 s_1} d_{h_2 s_2} \right)$$

$$= \left(\sum_{h_1=1}^{\alpha} a_{r_1 h_1} c_{h_1 s_1} \sum_{h_2=1}^{\beta} b_{r_2 h_2} d_{h_2 s_2} \right)$$

$$= AC \times BD.$$

Corollary 111.1. *If I_α, I_β are the unit matrices of orders α, β respectively,*

$$A \times B = (A \times I_\beta)(I_\alpha \times B).$$

Theorem 111.2. *If A is of order α and B is of order β,*

$$d(A \times B) = d(A)^\beta d(B)^\alpha.$$

For $A \times I_\beta$ is the direct sum of β matrices, each equal to A, so that $d(A \times I_\beta) = d(A)^\beta$. Moreover, $I_\alpha \times B$ is of the form

$$\begin{bmatrix}
b_{11} & 0 & 0 & \cdots & 0 & b_{12} & 0 & 0 & \cdots & 0 & \cdots \\
0 & b_{11} & 0 & \cdots & 0 & 0 & b_{12} & 0 & \cdots & 0 & \cdots \\
\cdot & \cdot & \cdot & & \cdot & \cdot & \cdot & \cdot & & \cdot & \\
0 & 0 & 0 & \cdots & b_{11} & 0 & 0 & 0 & \cdots & b_{12} & \cdots \\
b_{21} & 0 & 0 & \cdots & 0 & b_{22} & 0 & 0 & \cdots & 0 & \cdots \\
0 & b_{21} & 0 & \cdots & 0 & 0 & b_{22} & 0 & \cdots & 0 & \cdots \\
\cdot & \cdot & \cdot & & \cdot & \cdot & \cdot & \cdot & & \cdot & \\
0 & 0 & 0 & \cdots & b_{21} & 0 & 0 & 0 & \cdots & b_{22} & \cdots \\
\cdot & \cdot & \cdot & & \cdot & \cdot & \cdot & \cdot & & \cdot &
\end{bmatrix}$$

By permuting the rows and columns, this can be put into the form $B \times I_\alpha$, so that here also $d(I_\alpha \times B) = d(B)^\alpha$. The theorem follows from Corollary 111.1.

Theorem 111.3. $(A \times B)^{-1} = A^{-1} \times B^{-1}.$

By Theorem 111.1,

$$(A^{-1} \times B^{-1})(A \times B) = A^{-1}A \times B^{-1}B = I_\alpha \times I_\beta = I_{\alpha\beta}.$$

Theorem 111.4. *If $PAQ = B$ and $RCS = D$, then*

$$(P \times R)(A \times C)(Q \times S) = B \times D.$$

This also follows from two applications of Theorem 111.1.

Corollary 111.4. *If $P^{-1}AP = B$ and $R^{-1}CR = D$, then*

$$(P \times R)^{-1}(A \times C)(P \times R) = B \times D.$$

By the theorem,

$$(P^{-1} \times R^{-1})(A \times C)(P \times R) = B \times D,$$

so that Theorem 111.3 gives the corollary.

Let $\varphi(\xi, \eta) = \Sigma c_{ij}\xi^i\eta^j$ be a polynomial in ξ and η, and define

$$\varphi(A; B) = \sum c_{ij}A^i \times B^j.$$

Theorem 111.5. *The characteristic roots of $\varphi(A; B)$ are the $\alpha\beta$ functions $\varphi(a_p, b_q)$ where the a's are the characteristic roots of A and the b's are those of B.*

As was noted at the end of § 108, we can determine P and Q so that

$$P^{-1}AP = A_1, \quad Q^{-1}BQ = B_1$$

have only 0's below the main diagonal, and hence have their characteristic roots in the main diagonal. This form is preserved under addition, multiplication, scalar multiplication, and direct multiplication. The characteristic roots of $A^i \times B^j$ are the $\alpha\beta$ products $a_p^i b_q^j$, and the characteristic roots of $\varphi(A_1; B_1)$ are the $\alpha\beta$ functions

$$\Sigma c_{ij}a_p^i b_q^j = \varphi(a_p, b_q).$$

But, by Corollary 111.4, $\varphi(A_1; B_1)$ is similar to $\varphi(A; B)$; therefore the theorem is proved.

EXERCISES

1. Find the equation with rational coefficients of degree 6 satisfied by the product $\sqrt{3} \sqrt[3]{2}$. (See Ex. 4, § 40.)

2. Let $f(x) = 0$, $g(x) = 0$ be the respective characteristic equations of A and B. Prove that

$$| A \times I_\beta - I_\alpha \times B |$$

is the resultant of $f(x) = 0$ and $g(x) = 0$.

3. Solve Ex. 4, § 110, by the above method.

4. Prove that the rank of $A \times B$ is equal to the product of the ranks of A and B.

5. Prove that the equation $AXB = C$ has a solution X if and only if the matrix $A \times B^\mathsf{T}$ has the same rank as a certain n^2 by $n^2 + 1$ array obtained by bordering $A \times B^\mathsf{T}$ with the elements of C.

Suggested Readings

Bôcher, M. *Introduction to Higher Algebra.* Macmillan, 1907.

Turnbull, H. W., and Aitken, A. C. *An Introduction to the Theory of Canonical Matrices.* Blackie, London, 1932.

Aitken, A. C. *Determinants and Matrices.* Oliver and Boyd, Edinburgh, 1939.

Dickson, L. E. *Modern Algebraic Theories*, Chapters III–VI. Sanborn, 1926.

MacDuffee, C. C. *The Theory of Matrices.* Springer, Berlin, 1933.

Wedderburn, J. H. M. *Lectures on Matrices.* American Mathematical Society, 1934.

Albert, A. A. *Modern Higher Algebra*, Chapters III, IV, V, X. University of Chicago Press, 1937.

Hasse, H. *Höhere Algebra*, Vol. I. de Gruyter, Berlin, 1926.

van der Waerden, B. L. *Moderne Algebra*, Vol. II, Chapter XV. Springer, Berlin, 1931.

CHAPTER VIII

LINEAR ASSOCIATIVE ALGEBRAS

112. Quaternions. The oldest and best known non-commutative algebra is the algebra of *quaternions*. Let $\mathfrak{F}$ be a field, and let $\mathfrak{Q}$ be the module of all numbers

$$\alpha = a_0 + a_1 i + a_2 j + a_3 k, \qquad a_i \in \mathfrak{F},$$

where it is understood that the numbers i, j, k are commutative with $\mathfrak{F}$, and that all associative and distributive laws hold. It is furthermore assumed that 1, i, j, k are linearly independent with respect to $\mathfrak{F}$. The coefficients a_0, a_1, a_2, a_3 are called the *coördinates* of α.

Multiplication will be defined as soon as it is defined for every pair of basis numbers. Define 1 to be the unit element of multiplication, and define

(112.1) $$i^2 = j^2 = k^2 = -1,$$

$$ij = k, \quad jk = i, \quad ki = j, \quad ji = -k, \quad kj = -i, \quad ik = -j.$$

Theorem 112.1. Quaternion multiplication is associative.

The theorem holds if it holds for the basis numbers. Thus

$$(ij)i = ki = j, \quad i(ji) = i(-k) = j.$$

Since the multiplication table is invariant under the substitution

$$i \to j, \quad j \to k, \quad k \to i,$$

it suffices to verify the associative law for all those products whose left factor is i. We rely on the reader to do this.

We define

$$\bar{\alpha} = 2a_0 - \alpha = a_0 - a_1 i - a_2 j - a_3 k$$

to be the *conjugate* of α. It is clear that the conjugate of $\bar{\alpha}$ is α, and that the conjugate of a sum is equal to the sum of the conjugates.

If we have α and

$$\beta = b_0 + b_1 i + b_2 j + b_3 k,$$

251

it follows from (112.1) that

$$(112.2) \quad \alpha\beta = a_0b_0 - a_1b_1 - a_2b_2 - a_3b_3 + (a_0b_1 + a_1b_0 + a_2b_3 - a_3b_2)i + (a_0b_2 - a_1b_3 + a_2b_0 + a_3b_1)j + (a_0b_3 + a_1b_2 - a_2b_1 + a_3b_0)k.$$

The product $\beta\alpha$ is obtained from the above expression by changing the signs of those products, such as a_1b_2, whose subscripts are unequal and exceed 0, for these products are the coefficients of products such as ij which change sign when the order of multiplication is reversed. The product $\bar{\beta}\bar{\alpha}$ is obtained from $\beta\alpha$ by changing the signs of b_1, b_2, b_3, a_1, a_2, and a_3. The result of combining both of these operations is to change the sign of every product such as a_0b_2 whose subscripts are different, and to leave unchanged a_0b_0, a_1b_1, etc. That is, $\overline{\alpha\beta} = \bar{\beta}\bar{\alpha}$.

A biunique correspondence of a ring with itself which is an automorphism with respect to addition, but such that

$$\alpha \leftrightarrow \alpha', \qquad \beta \leftrightarrow \beta'$$

imply that

$$\alpha\beta \leftrightarrow \beta'\alpha',$$

is called an *anti-automorphism* or *reciprocal automorphism*. We have now proved

Theorem 112.2. The correspondence $\alpha \leftrightarrow \bar{\alpha}$ is an anti-automorphism of $\mathfrak{Q}$.

Let us set $\beta = \bar{\alpha}$ in (112.2). That is, we make the replacement

$$b_0 \to a_0, \quad b_1 \to -a_1, \quad b_2 \to -a_2, \quad b_3 \to -a_3$$

and we have

$$\alpha\bar{\alpha} = a_0^2 + a_1^2 + a_2^2 + a_3^2.$$

This number of $\mathfrak{F}$ we define to be the *norm* of α, and we write

$$N(\alpha) = \alpha\bar{\alpha} = \bar{\alpha}\alpha.$$

Theorem 112.3. The norm of the product of two quaternions is equal to the product of their norms.

For

$$N(\alpha\beta) = \alpha\beta\overline{\alpha\beta} = \alpha\beta\bar{\beta}\bar{\alpha} = \alpha N(\beta)\bar{\alpha} = \alpha\bar{\alpha}N(\beta) = N(\alpha)\cdot N(\beta)\cdot$$

Theorem 112.4. Every quaternion α satisfies the quadratic equation

$$(112.3) \qquad x^2 - 2a_0x + N(\alpha) = 0,$$

which is called the principal equation of α. The conjugate $\bar{\alpha}$ satisfies the same equation.

The equation may be written

$$x^2 - (\alpha + \bar{\alpha})x + \alpha\bar{\alpha} = 0.$$

Let us replace x by α and observe that $\alpha\bar{\alpha} = \bar{\alpha}\alpha$. We have

$$\alpha^2 - \alpha^2 - \bar{\alpha}\alpha + \alpha\bar{\alpha} = 0.$$

Similarly the equation is satisfied when $x \to \bar{\alpha}$.

The middle coefficient

$$T(\alpha) = T(\bar{\alpha}) = \alpha + \bar{\alpha} = 2a_0$$

is called the *trace* of α.

Theorem 112.5. If $N(\alpha) \neq 0$, α has an inverse α^{-1} in $\mathfrak{Q}$ such that $\alpha\alpha^{-1} = \alpha^{-1}\alpha = 1$.

If $N(\alpha) \neq 0$, $\bar{\alpha}/N(\alpha)$ is such a number.

A field is called *formally real* if the equation

$$x_1^2 + x_2^2 + \cdots + x_n^2 = 0$$

implies that $x_1 = x_2 = \cdots = x_n = 0$ for every finite n and every set of x's in the field. Evidently the real field and all its subfields are formally real.

Theorem 112.6. If $\mathfrak{Q}$ is over a formally real field, $N(\alpha) = 0$ implies that $\alpha = 0$.

For $N(\alpha) = a_0^2 + a_1^2 + a_2^2 + a_3^2$.

Corollary 112.6. If $\mathfrak{Q}$ is over a formally real field, every number of $\mathfrak{Q}$ except 0 has a reciprocal.

An algebraic variety (see § 68) for which all the field postulates are known to hold except possibly the commutative law of multiplication is called a *non-commutative field*. The terminology is convenient but not altogether logical, for a field is considered a special instance of a non-commutative field. A non-commutative field having a finite basis relative to a field $\mathfrak{F}$ is also called a *division algebra* over $\mathfrak{F}$, since both left and right division except by 0 are possible and unique. We have proved

Theorem 112.7. If $\mathfrak{Q}$ is over a formally real field, it is a division algebra.

EXERCISES

1. Show that $3 + 5j$ and $3 - 3j + 4k$ have the same principal equation. Can an equation have more solutions in $\mathfrak{Q}$ than its degree?

2. If $\alpha\beta = \alpha\gamma$ and $N(\alpha) \neq 0$, prove that $\beta = \gamma$.

3. If $\mathfrak{F}$ is formally real, prove that the principal equation (112.3) is either irreducible or the square of $x - a_0$.

4. If $\mathfrak{Q}$ is over a field $\mathfrak{F}$ of characteristic $\neq 2$, show that the quaternions α and β are commutative if and only if the rank of the array

$$\begin{bmatrix} a_1 & a_2 & a_3 \\ b_1 & b_2 & b_3 \end{bmatrix}$$

is less than 2.

5. Let δ be any quaternion of norm $\neq 0$. Show that $\alpha \leftrightarrow \delta\alpha\delta^{-1}$ is an automorphism of $\mathfrak{Q}$.

6. If $\mathfrak{F}$ is of characteristic $\neq 2$, and if α is not in $\mathfrak{F}$, show that $\alpha\delta = \delta\bar{\alpha}$ if and only if

$$\delta = d_1i + d_2j + d_3k, \quad a_1d_1 + a_2d_2 + a_3d_3 = 0.$$

Hence show that there always exists a quaternion δ such that $\alpha = \delta\bar{\alpha}\delta^{-1}$.

113. Representations of quaternions. When Sir William Rowan Hamilton, the inventor of quaternions, felt impelled to justify the existence of his non-commutative numbers, he did so by the following scheme.

Let $\mathfrak{Q}$ consist of the quadruples

$$\alpha = (a_0, a_1, a_2, a_3)$$

of numbers of $\mathfrak{F}$. Define

$$(a_0, a_1, a_2, a_3) = (b_0, b_1, b_2, b_3)$$

to mean $a_0 = b_0, a_1 = b_1, a_2 = b_2, a_3 = b_3$. Define addition by the identity

$$(a_0, a_1, a_2, a_3) + (b_0, b_1, b_2, b_3) = (a_0 + b_0, a_1 + b_1, a_2 + b_2, a_3 + b_3),$$

and scalar multiplication by the identity

$$k(a_0, a_1, a_2, a_3) = (ka_0, ka_1, ka_2, ka_3) = (a_0, a_1, a_2, a_3)k.$$

It then follows that

$$\alpha = (a_0, a_1, a_2, a_3) = a_0(1, 0, 0, 0) + a_1(0, 1, 0, 0) + a_2(0, 0, 1, 0) + a_3(0, 0, 0, 1).$$

Call

$$(1, 0, 0, 0) = \epsilon, \quad (0, 1, 0, 0) = i, \quad (0, 0, 1, 0) = j, \quad (0, 0, 0, 1) = k.$$

Then

$$\alpha = a_0\epsilon + a_1i + a_2j + a_3k.$$

Now define multiplication of the basis numbers as in (112.1) so that the subset of numbers $a_0 \epsilon$ are isomorphic with the numbers of $\mathfrak{F}$ under the correspondence

$$a_0 \epsilon \leftrightarrow a_0.$$

Then set $\epsilon = 1$ and obtain the algebra $\mathfrak{Q}$.

Another interesting approach to quaternions is as follows. Consider the total matric algebra $\mathfrak{M}$ of order 2^2 over the complex field C. That is, $\mathfrak{M}$ consists of all numbers

$$a_1 e_{11} + a_2 e_{21} + a_3 e_{12} + a_4 e_{22},$$

where

$$e_{11} = \begin{bmatrix} 1 & 0 \\ 0 & 0 \end{bmatrix}, \qquad e_{21} = \begin{bmatrix} 0 & 0 \\ 1 & 0 \end{bmatrix}, \qquad e_{12} = \begin{bmatrix} 0 & 1 \\ 0 & 0 \end{bmatrix}, \qquad e_{22} = \begin{bmatrix} 0 & 0 \\ 0 & 1 \end{bmatrix}$$

and the a's range over C. It is clear that $e_{11} + e_{22}$ is the unit matrix, the identity of $\mathfrak{M}$.

Let us now make the transformation of basis

$$
\begin{array}{lll}
e_{11} & +e_{22} = 1, \\
-\theta e_{11} & +\theta e_{22} = i, \\
-e_{21} + e_{12} & = j, \\
-\theta e_{21} - \theta e_{12} & = k
\end{array}
$$

(113.1)

where θ is the complex unit, $\theta^2 = -1$. It may be verified that $1, i, j, k$ as so defined satisfy the conditions (112.1). Moreover, equations (113.1) can be solved for the matric units in terms of $1, i, j$, and k, so that the totality of linear combinations of $1, i, j, k$ with complex coefficients coincides with the totality of numbers of the complex total matric algebra $\mathfrak{M}$. We have

Theorem 113.1. The algebra of complex quaternions is the total matric algebra of order 2^2 over the complex field.

It happens that the coefficients in (112.1), the so-called *constants of multiplication*, are all rational numbers. It therefore follows that we may obtain subalgebras of the algebra of complex quaternions by taking as the coefficient field any subfield of the complex field. Thus we obtain the algebra of real quaternions, the algebra of rational quaternions, and many others.

Though the algebra of complex quaternions is a total matric algebra, the same is not true of real or rational quaternions, for the transformation of basis which we used involved the complex unit θ. If $\mathfrak{A}$ is an algebra over a field $\mathfrak{F}$, and if there is a field $\mathfrak{F}' \supset \mathfrak{F}$ such that the algebra $\mathfrak{A}$ over $\mathfrak{F}'$ is total matric, or a direct sum * of total matric algebras, then $\mathfrak{F}'$ is called a *splitting field* for $\mathfrak{A}$. Clearly the complex field is a splitting field for quaternions.

Another representation for quaternions, in terms of matrices which have rational elements but are of order 4, can be obtained by a method similar to that used for fields in § 109.

Let v denote the vector $(1, i, j, k)$.
Then

$$iv = (i, -1, k, -j)$$

and

$$i = 0 \cdot 1 + 1 \cdot i + 0 \cdot j + 0 \cdot k,$$

$$-1 = -1 \cdot 1 + 0 \cdot i + 0 \cdot j + 0 \cdot k,$$

$$k = 0 \cdot 1 + 0 \cdot i + 0 \cdot j + 1 \cdot k,$$

$$-j = 0 \cdot 1 + 0 \cdot i - 1 \cdot j + 0 \cdot k.$$

That is, $iv = vR_1$ where

$$R_1 = \begin{bmatrix} 0 & -1 & 0 & 0 \\ 1 & 0 & 0 & 0 \\ 0 & 0 & 0 & -1 \\ 0 & 0 & 1 & 0 \end{bmatrix}.$$

Similarly we find that $jv = vR_2$ and $kv = vR_3$, where

$$R_2 = \begin{bmatrix} 0 & 0 & -1 & 0 \\ 0 & 0 & 0 & 1 \\ 1 & 0 & 0 & 0 \\ 0 & -1 & 0 & 0 \end{bmatrix}, \quad R_3 = \begin{bmatrix} 0 & 0 & 0 & -1 \\ 0 & 0 & -1 & 0 \\ 0 & 1 & 0 & 0 \\ 1 & 0 & 0 & 0 \end{bmatrix}.$$

As in the proof of Theorem 109.1, it can be shown that the correspondence

$$1 \leftrightarrow I, \quad i \leftrightarrow R_1, \quad j \leftrightarrow R_2, \quad k \leftrightarrow R_3$$

is an isomorphism. This is known as the *first regular representation* of $\mathfrak{Q}$ by means of matrices.

EXERCISES

1. Write out $1, i, j, k$ of (113.1) as matrices, and verify the statement that they satisfy (112.1).

* See § 124.

2. Derive the second regular representation of Ω from the equations

$$vi = S_1 v, \quad vj = S_2 v, \quad vk = S_3 v,$$

where v is now a column vector.

3. Show that the characteristic function of

$$a_0 I + a_1 R_1 + a_2 R_2 + a_3 R_3$$

is equal to the square of the left member of the principal equation (112.3).

4. By the correspondence of § 109,

$$\theta = \sqrt{-1} \leftrightarrow \begin{bmatrix} 0 & -1 \\ 1 & 0 \end{bmatrix}.$$

In (113.1) replace

$$0 \to \begin{bmatrix} 0 & 0 \\ 0 & 0 \end{bmatrix}, \quad 1 \to \begin{bmatrix} 1 & 0 \\ 0 & 1 \end{bmatrix}, \quad \theta \to \begin{bmatrix} 0 & -1 \\ 1 & 0 \end{bmatrix},$$

and show that the resulting 4×4 matrices with rational elements represent Ω.

5. Find a matrix which transforms the second regular representation of Ω into the representation of Ex. 4.

114. Automorphisms and anti-automorphisms. Let Ω be a quaternion algebra over a formally real field $\mathfrak{F}$. A biunique correspondence

$$\alpha \leftrightarrow \alpha', \quad \beta \leftrightarrow \beta', \cdots$$

of the numbers of Ω with themselves is called an *automorphism* if for every α and β

$$\alpha + \beta \leftrightarrow \alpha' + \beta', \quad \alpha\beta \leftrightarrow \alpha'\beta',$$

and an *anti-automorphism* if for every α and β

$$\alpha + \beta \leftrightarrow \alpha' + \beta', \quad \alpha\beta \leftrightarrow \beta'\alpha'.$$

If δ is a fixed number of Ω such that $N(\delta) \neq 0$, it is clear that

$$\alpha \leftrightarrow \delta\alpha\delta^{-1}$$

is an automorphism of Ω. We have seen that the correspondence

$$\alpha \leftrightarrow \bar{\alpha},$$

where $\bar{\alpha}$ is the conjugate of α, is an anti-automorphism. In fact, if $\alpha \leftrightarrow \alpha'$ is an automorphism (or anti-automorphism), then $\alpha \leftrightarrow \bar{\alpha}'$ is an anti-automorphism (or automorphism); therefore the determination of all automorphisms carries with it the determination of all anti-automorphisms, and conversely.

We shall now restrict attention to automorphisms which leave invariant every element of $\mathfrak{F}$. If $\mathfrak{F}$ is the rational field, this is true of every automorphism of $\mathfrak{Q}$. (See Theorem 35.2.)

Theorem 114.1. If $\alpha \leftrightarrow \alpha'$ is an automorphism of $\mathfrak{Q}$, then α and α' satisfy the same principal equation. Moreover, $T(\alpha) = T(\alpha')$, $N(\alpha) = N(\alpha')$.

If it is true that

$$\alpha^2 + p\alpha + q = 0, \qquad\qquad p, q \in \mathfrak{F},$$

and if $\alpha \leftrightarrow \alpha'$ is an automorphism, then $\alpha^2 \leftrightarrow \alpha'^2$, $p\alpha \leftrightarrow p\alpha'$, and

$$\alpha'^2 + p\alpha' + q = 0.$$

Unless α' is in $\mathfrak{F}$ (and therefore α also in $\mathfrak{F}$), this equation is irreducible in Ra, and so it is the principal equation of both α and α'. Then

$$-p = T(\alpha) = T(\alpha'), \quad q = N(\alpha) = N(\alpha').$$

Theorem 114.2. Every automorphism of $\mathfrak{Q}$ is of the type

$$\alpha \leftrightarrow \delta\alpha\delta^{-1}$$

where δ is some fixed number $\neq 0$ of $\mathfrak{Q}$.

Let us suppose that under the given automorphism

$$i \leftrightarrow i', \quad j \leftrightarrow j', \quad k \leftrightarrow k',$$

where i', j', k' obey equations (112.1). Choose

$$(114.1) \qquad \begin{aligned} \delta_1 &= k'j - j'k + i' + i, \\ \delta_2 &= i'k - k'i + j' + j, \\ \delta_3 &= j'i - i'j + k' + k. \end{aligned}$$

We shall show that, for every α in $\mathfrak{Q}$,

$$(114.2) \qquad \alpha'\delta_1 = \delta_1\alpha, \quad \alpha'\delta_2 = \delta_2\alpha, \quad \alpha'\delta_3 = \delta_3\alpha.$$

From the multiplication table (112.1),

$$i'\delta_1 = -j'j - k'k - 1 + i'i, \quad \delta_1 i = -k'k - j'j + i'i - 1.$$

Similarly it may be proved that

$$j'\delta_1 = \delta_1 j, \quad k'\delta_1 = \delta_1 k,$$

so that, for every α in $\mathfrak{Q}$, $\alpha'\delta_1 = \delta_1\alpha$. The other two relations of (114.2) follow from the cyclic permutation

$$i \rightarrow j, \quad j \rightarrow k, \quad k \rightarrow i,$$

which leaves the multiplication table unchanged.

If either $\delta_1 \neq 0$ or $\delta_2 \neq 0$ or $\delta_3 \neq 0$, our theorem is proved. Suppose that $\delta_2 = \delta_3 = 0$. Then

$$j' + j = k'i - i'k,$$

$$\delta_3 = j'i - i'j + i'j' - ji = i'(j' - j) + (j' - j)i = 0,$$

$$j' - j = i'(j' - j)i = k'i + i'k.$$

Consequently $j = -i'k$. On multiplying on the right by k, we have $i = i'$. From cyclic symmetry it follows that $\delta_3 = \delta_1 = 0$ imply that $j = j'$, and $\delta_2 = \delta_1 = 0$ imply that $k = k'$. Thus one of δ_1, δ_2, δ_3 is different from 0 unless the automorphism is the identity. In that case, take $\delta = 1$.

EXERCISES

1. Show that, if $\alpha \leftrightarrow \alpha'$ is an automorphism, $\overline{\alpha}' = \overline{\alpha'}$.

2. Show that $i' = i$ is sufficient in order that $\delta_2 = \delta_3 = 0$.

3. Compute a δ for the automorphisms A_i, A_j, A_k, below.

$$A_i: \quad i \leftrightarrow i, \quad j \leftrightarrow k, \quad k \leftrightarrow -j.$$

4. Compute a δ for the automorphisms B_i, B_j, B_k below:

$$B_i: \quad i \leftrightarrow i, \quad j \leftrightarrow -j, \quad k \leftrightarrow -k.$$

5. Let i_1, j_1, k_1 be $\pm i$, $\pm j$, $\pm k$ in some order. Show that

$$i \leftrightarrow i_1, \quad j \leftrightarrow j_1, \quad k \leftrightarrow k_1$$

is an automorphism or an anti-automorphism according as $i_1 j_1 k_1 = -1$ or $+1$.

6. Show that each of the twenty-four automorphisms of Ex. 5 can be obtained by applying automorphisms of the type of Ex. 3 followed by at most one of the type of Ex. 4.

7. Show that, if α and β satisfy the same principal equation, there exists an automorphism of Ω under which $\alpha \leftrightarrow \beta$.

HINT: Show that $\delta \alpha = \beta \delta$, where $\delta = \alpha - \overline{\beta} = \beta - \overline{\alpha}$. Now see Ex. 6, § 112.

115. Integral quaternions. Let Ω be the algebra of rational quaternions, that is, the set of all numbers

$$(115.1) \qquad\qquad \alpha = a_0 + a_1 i + a_2 j + a_3 k, \qquad\qquad a_i \in Ra.$$

A quaternion is called *integral* if it satisfies some equation of integral type (see § 60) with rational integral coefficients.

Theorem 115.1. The quaternion α is integral if and only if both $T(\alpha)$ and $N(\alpha)$ are rational integers.

Suppose that α satisfies the equation $f(x) = 0$ of integral type. But α also satisfies its principal equation (112.3), and so α satisfies an irreducible equation $m(x) = 0$ which is either linear or quadratic. Then $m(x) \mid f(x)$ by Theorem 38.1. But, by the Gauss Lemma (Theorem 45.3), if $f(x)$ factors, the factors can be so chosen as to be of integral type. Hence $m(x)$ is of integral type. If α is not rational, $m(x) = 0$ is the principal equation of α. If α is rational, $[m(x)]^2 = 0$ is the principal equation. In either case, both $T(\alpha)$ and $N(\alpha)$ are rational integers.

If, conversely, both $N(\alpha)$ and $T(\alpha)$ are rational integers, α satisfies an equation, namely, its principal equation, which is of integral type, and so α is integral.

An *integral domain* of Ω is a set of integral numbers of Ω which is a ring with unit element (see § 68) and which contains four linearly independent numbers. This last restriction is to exclude integral domains, such as $a + bi$ where a and b are rational integers, which are properly integral domains of a subalgebra of Ω.

A *maximal* integral domain is one which is not properly included in another integral domain.

The set of all integral numbers of an algebraic field forms an integral domain, which is therefore the unique maximal integral domain. Unfortunately the set of all integral quaternions is not an integral domain.

Two particular integral domains of quaternions have received much attention and are therefore of interest to us. The first is the set L, called the *Lipschitz integral domain*, which consists of all quaternions

$$\alpha = a_0 + a_1 i + a_2 j + a_3 k,$$

where the a's range over all rational integers. It is evident that $T(\alpha)$ and $N(\alpha)$ are rational integers, so that every number of this set is integral. It is also clear that the set is closed under addition, subtraction, and multiplication, so that it forms a ring. Since L contains $1, i, j, k$, it is of order 4.

The integral domain L is not maximal but is embedded in a maximal integral domain H, called the *Hurwitz integral domain*, which we shall now derive.

If α is integral,

$$T(\alpha) = 2a_0, \quad N(\alpha) = a_0^2 + a_1^2 + a_2^2 + a_3^2$$

must be rational integers. Since $H \supset L$, H must contain $1, i, j, k$, and therefore H must contain $i\alpha, j\alpha, k\alpha$ for every $\alpha \in H$. But

$$T(i\alpha) = -2a_1, \quad T(j\alpha) = -2a_2, \quad T(k\alpha) = -2a_3,$$

and so the doubles of a_0, a_1, a_2, a_3 must be rational integers. Let $2a_i = a_i'$ so that α may be written

$$\alpha = \tfrac{1}{2}(a_0' + a_1'i + a_2'j + a_3'k),$$

where the a''s are rational integers. Then

$$N(\alpha) = \tfrac{1}{4}(a_0'^2 + a_1'^2 + a_2'^2 + a_3'^2).$$

Since $N(\alpha)$ must be a rational integer, we must have

$$a_0'^2 + a_1'^2 + a_2'^2 + a_3'^2 \equiv 0 \qquad \mod 4.$$

Now every square n^2 is congruent to 0 or 1 modulo 4 according as n is even or odd. It must be true, then, that a_0', a_1', a_2', a_3' are either all even or all odd.

We shall define H to be the set of all rational quaternions (115.1) where a_0, a_1, a_2, a_3 are either all integers or all halves of odd integers. If this set constitutes an integral domain, the argument which we have just completed shows that it is maximal, and is the unique maximal set which contains L.

Theorem 115.2. The set H is an integral domain.

We have shown that H consists of integral numbers. To show that it is closed under addition and subtraction, consider

$$\alpha = \tfrac{1}{2}(a_0' + a_1'i + a_2'j + a_3'k), \qquad \beta = \tfrac{1}{2}(b_0' + b_1'i + b_2'j + b_3'k)$$

where the a''s are all even or all odd, and likewise the b''s. If the a''s and b''s are all even or all odd, the sums and differences $a_i' \pm b_i'$ are all even; if the a_i' are all even and the b_i' all odd, or vice versa, the $a_i' \pm b_i'$ are all odd.

We must show that H is closed under multiplication. Let

$$\alpha\beta = \gamma = \tfrac{1}{2}(c_0' + c_1'i + c_2'j + c_3'k).$$

From (112.2),

$$c_0' = \tfrac{1}{2}(a_0'b_0' - a_1'b_1' - a_2'b_2' - a_3'b_3'),$$

$$c_1' = \tfrac{1}{2}(a_0'b_1' + a_1'b_0' + a_2'b_3' - a_3'b_2'),$$

$$c_2' = \tfrac{1}{2}(a_0'b_2' - a_1'b_3' + a_2'b_0' + a_3'b_1'),$$

$$c_3' = \tfrac{1}{2}(a_0'b_3' + a_1'b_2' - a_2'b_1' + a_3'b_0').$$

If the a''s are even, or the b''s are even, each of the c''s is an integer. If all the a''s and all the b''s are odd, each expression in parentheses is the sum of four odd integers, which is even, so again the c''s are integers.

Now $N(\gamma) = N(\alpha) \cdot N(\beta)$, so $N(\gamma)$ is a rational integer. As before,

$$c_0'^2 + c_1'^2 + c_2'^2 + c_3'^2 \equiv 0 \quad \mod 4,$$

so that either all the c''s are even or all are odd.

EXERCISES

1. Show that i and $\frac{3}{5}i + \frac{4}{5}j$ are integral quaternions, but their sum is not.

2. A number of an integral domain is a *unit* if it is a divisor of 1. Show that ϵ is a unit if and only if $N(\epsilon) = +1$.

3. Show that the units of L are eight in number, namely,

$$\pm 1, \ \pm i, \ \pm j, \ \pm k.$$

4. Show that the units of H are 24 in number, and consist of the units of L and in addition the sixteen numbers

$$\pm \tfrac{1}{2} \pm \tfrac{1}{2}i \pm \tfrac{1}{2}j \pm \tfrac{1}{2}k.$$

5. If α is a quaternion of H such that $\alpha^2 = -1$, show that $\alpha = \pm i, \pm j,$ or $\pm k$.

6. Show that the only automorphisms of H are those of Ex. 5, § 114. Show that each of these can be accomplished by using as δ a unit ϵ or a product $(1 + i)\epsilon$.

Hint: There is a unit ϵ_1 such that $1 + j = (1 + i)\epsilon_1$. See Exs. 3, 4, 6, § 114.

116. Quaternion ideals and factorization.* A *left ideal* A of H is a submodule of H such that $HA \subseteq A$. A *right ideal* is a submodule B such that $BH \subseteq B$. An ideal which is both a left and right ideal is called a *two-sided ideal*.

If $\alpha_1, \alpha_2, \cdots, \alpha_n$ are numbers of H not all 0, then the set of all numbers

$$x_1\alpha_1 + x_2\alpha_2 + \cdots + x_n\alpha_n, \qquad\qquad x_i \in H,$$

clearly constitutes a left ideal which will be denoted by the symbol $(\alpha_1, \alpha_2, \cdots, \alpha_n]$. If $n = 1$, the ideal is called *principal*. Thus the principal left ideal $(\alpha]$ consists of all left multiples of the number α.

Theorem 116.1. *If the quaternion ρ is not in H, there exists a quaternion α in H and a quaternion σ not in H such that $\rho = \alpha + \sigma$, $0 < N(\sigma) < 1$.*

Let

$$\rho = r_0 + r_1 i + r_2 j + r_3 k.$$

---

* This paragraph is due to C. G. Latimer, and with his permission is here presented for the first time.

Let a_i be a rational integer nearest to r_i, and write

$$r_i = a_i + s_i, \quad |s_i| \leq \tfrac{1}{2} \qquad (i = 0, 1, 2, 3).$$

Define

$$\alpha = a_0 + a_1 i + a_2 j + a_3 k, \quad \sigma = s_0 + s_1 i + s_2 j + s_3 k.$$

Since ρ is not in H, at least one s_i is $\neq 0$ and the inequality $|s_i| < \tfrac{1}{2}$ holds for at least one subscript. That is,

$$0 < N(\sigma) = s_0^2 + s_1^2 + s_2^2 + s_3^2 < 1.$$

Theorem 116.2. *Every ideal in H is principal.*

The norm of every number $\neq 0$ of the left ideal A is a positive integer. Let d be the smallest positive integer which is the norm of a number of A, and let $d = N(\delta)$, $\delta \in A$. Now if α is any number $\neq 0$ of A, set $\rho = \alpha\delta^{-1} = \alpha\bar{\delta}/d$. If ρ were not in H, we could find by Theorem 116.1 a number $\sigma \neq 0$ such that

$$\rho = \beta + \sigma, \quad 0 < N(\sigma) < 1, \qquad\qquad \beta \in H.$$

This would imply that

$$\alpha = \rho\delta = \beta\delta + \sigma\delta.$$

Since α and $\beta\delta$ are in A, this would imply that $\sigma\delta$ was in A. But

$$N(\sigma\delta) = N(\sigma) \cdot N(\delta) < N(\delta),$$

which is impossible unless $\sigma = 0$. Hence ρ is in H, and $A = (\delta]$. The proof for right ideals is similar.

The definitions of right and left divisors and multiples are precisely the same as those given for matrices in § 104.

Theorem 116.3. *Every finite set of elements $\alpha_1, \alpha_2, \cdots, \alpha_n$ of H, not all 0, has a g.c.r.d., δ, such that*

$$\delta = \xi_1\alpha_1 + \xi_2\alpha_2 + \cdots + \xi_n\alpha_n, \qquad\qquad \xi_i \in H.$$

This g.c.r.d. is unique up to a unit left factor.

The ideal $A = (\alpha_1, \alpha_2, \cdots, \alpha_n]$ is principal, say $A = (\delta]$. Then every number of A, in particular each α_i, is a left multiple of δ, and is representable as a linear combination of the α's. That is,

$$\alpha_i = \eta_i\delta, \quad \delta = \xi_1\alpha_1 + \xi_2\alpha_2 + \cdots + \xi_n\alpha_n, \qquad \eta_i, \xi_i \in H.$$

Thus δ is a g.c.r.d. of $\alpha_1, \alpha_2, \cdots, \alpha_n$.

Suppose that δ_1 is also a g.c.r.d. of $\alpha_1, \alpha_2, \cdots, \alpha_n$. Then

$$\delta = \epsilon\delta_1, \quad \delta_1 = \epsilon_1\delta, \qquad\qquad \epsilon, \epsilon_1 \in H.$$

Then $\delta = \epsilon\epsilon_1\delta$, and, since $\delta \neq 0$, $\epsilon\epsilon_1 = 1$. Thus ϵ and ϵ_1 are units.

A quaternion π is called *prime* if it is not 0 or a unit and every factorization $\pi = \pi_1\pi_2$ implies that π_1 or π_2 is a unit.

Theorem 116.4.   Let $\alpha \in H$ be not divisible by a rational prime, and let

$$N(\alpha) = p_1 p_2 \cdots p_n,$$

where the rational primes p_i are arranged in any fixed order.   Then

$$\alpha = \pi_1\pi_2 \cdots \pi_n, \qquad\qquad N(\pi_i) = p_i$$

where the π's are prime quaternions.

Let p be any one of the p_i, and consider the ideal $P = (p, \alpha]$. By Theorem 116.2 this is principal, and so there exists a quaternion π such that $P = (\pi]$.   Let

$$p = \kappa\pi, \quad \alpha = \lambda\pi, \qquad\qquad \kappa, \lambda \in H.$$

Then

$$N(p) = p^2 = N(\kappa) \cdot N(\pi),$$

so that $N(\pi) = 1$ or p or p^2.

1. Suppose that $N(\pi) = p^2$. Then $N(\kappa) = 1$ so that κ is a unit. Then $p \mid \pi$ and hence $p \mid \alpha$, contrary to assumption. Thus $N(\pi) \neq p^2$.

2. Suppose $N(\pi) = 1$. Since $\pi \in P$, $1 = \pi\bar{\pi} \in P$ so that P is the unit ideal.   Then there exist numbers μ and ν such that

$$1 = \mu p + \nu\alpha, \qquad\qquad \mu, \nu \in H.$$

Then $\nu\alpha = 1 - \mu p$, so that

$$N(\nu\alpha) = (1 - \mu p)(1 - \bar{\mu}p) = 1 - pT(\mu) + p^2N(\mu).$$

But $\mu \in H$, so that $T(\mu)$ and $N(\mu)$ are rational integers.   Hence

$$N(\nu\alpha) = N(\nu) \cdot N(\alpha) \equiv 1 \qquad \mathrm{mod}\, p.$$

This is impossible, since $N(\alpha) \equiv 0 \bmod p$.   Thus $N(\pi) \neq 1$.

It has now been proved that $N(\pi) = p$. Take $p = p_n$, and denote a corresponding π by π_n.   Then

$$\alpha = \alpha_1\pi_n, \quad N(\alpha_1) = p_1 p_2 \cdots p_{n-1}, \quad N(\pi_n) = p_n.$$

As before, we find a π_{n-1} such that

$$\alpha_1 = \alpha_2\pi_{n-1}, \quad N(\alpha_2) = p_1 p_2 \cdots p_{n-2}, \quad N(\pi_{n-1}) = p_{n-1}.$$

Continuing, we have the theorem.

Let ϵ_i be units and let

$$\alpha = \pi_1\pi_2 \cdots \pi_n.$$

It is obvious that 1's in the form $\epsilon_i \bar{\epsilon}_i$ can be inserted between every two π's, thus yielding another factorization

$$\alpha = \pi_1 \epsilon_1 \cdot \bar{\epsilon}_1 \pi_2 \epsilon_2 \cdot \bar{\epsilon}_2 \pi_3 \epsilon_3 \cdots \bar{\epsilon}_{n-1} \pi_n.$$

We shall say that these two factorizations of α are *the same except for unit factors*. If $\tau = \epsilon_1 \pi \epsilon_2$, where ϵ_1 and ϵ_2 are units, we shall say that τ and π are *associated* or are *associates*.

Theorem 116.5. Let α have no rational prime factor. For a given ordering of the rational primes in the factorization of $N(\alpha)$, the factorization of α into prime factors is unique except for unit factors.

Suppose that

$$N(\alpha) = p_1 p_2 \cdots p_n, \quad \alpha = \pi_1 \pi_2 \cdots \pi_n = \tau_1 \tau_2 \cdots \tau_n,$$

$$N(\pi_i) = N(\tau_i) = p_i.$$

Suppose that the π's are obtained in the manner of Theorem 116.4 so that π_n is a g.c.r.d. of α and p_n. Since τ_n is also a common right divisor of α and p_n, τ_n is a right divisor of π_n. Let

$$\pi_n = \epsilon_{n-1} \tau_n, \quad N(\pi_n) = N(\epsilon_{n-1}) \cdot N(\tau_n).$$

But $N(\pi_n) = N(\tau_n) \neq 0$ so that $N(\epsilon_{n-1}) = 1$ and ϵ_{n-1} is a unit. Then

$$\tau_n = \bar{\epsilon}_{n-1} \pi_n,$$

where $\bar{\epsilon}_{n-1}$ is a unit. Thus

$$\alpha_1 = \pi_1 \pi_2 \cdots \pi_{n-1} = \tau_1 \tau_2 \cdots \tau_{n-1} \bar{\epsilon}_{n-1}.$$

If $n > 2$, we proceed as before to show that

$$\tau_{n-1} \bar{\epsilon}_{n-1} = \bar{\epsilon}_{n-2} \pi_{n-1},$$

or

$$\tau_{n-1} = \bar{\epsilon}_{n-2} \pi_{n-1} \epsilon_{n-1} \qquad\qquad N(\epsilon_{n-1}) = 1.$$

We continue until the theorem is proved.

EXERCISES

1. If α is divisible by the rational prime p, show that $p^2 \mid N(\alpha)$. Use the example $\alpha = 3 + 4i$ to show that the converse is not true.

2. If $\beta \neq 0$ and α are two numbers of H, show that there exist numbers κ and ρ in H such that

$$\alpha = \kappa\beta + \rho, \qquad\qquad N(\rho) < N(\beta).$$

3. Show that there exists a euclidean algorithm for finding a g.c.r.d. of two quaternions of H. Thus give another proof of Theorem 116.2.

4. Find a g.c.r.d. of the quaternions $10 + 11i$ and 17.

5. Show that

$$- 5 + 12i + 4j + 6k = (3 - 2i)(-3 + 2i + 2k)$$

$$= (2 - 3i + 2k)(-2 + i - 2j + 2k),$$

and that the factors with the same norm are not associated.

117. Factorization of rational primes. A quaternion α of H whose coördinates are the integers a_i, or the halves $a_i'/2$ where all the a_i' are odd, is clearly divisible by the odd prime p if p divides every a_i or every a_i'. If a quaternion of H is multiplied by the odd prime p, p must then appear as a divisor of every a_i or every a_i', and so the converse holds. If α has integral coördinates all of which are even or all of which are odd, then $2 \mid \alpha$. Conversely, the product of 2 by any $\alpha \in H$ has integral coördinates all of which are even or all are odd.

Every quaternion of H can be written as a product of rational primes by a quaternion with no rational prime factor. As the factorization of quaternions with no rational prime factor was completely treated in Theorem 116.4, the factorization theory of integral quaternions will be complete when we have shown how a rational prime can be factored.

Lemma 117. *The congruence*

$$(117.1) \qquad\qquad x^2 + y^2 + 1 \equiv 0 \qquad \mod p$$

has solutions in rational integers for every rational prime p.

If $p = 2$, $x \equiv 1$, $y \equiv 0$ is a solution.

If p is odd and -1 is a quadratic residue modulo p (see § 17), there exists an integer x_1 such that $x_1^2 \equiv -1 \mod p$. Then $x \equiv x_1$, $y \equiv 0$ is a solution of (117.1).

If p is odd and -1 is a quadratic non-residue modulo p, consider the sequence of integers

$$p - 1, \quad p - 2, \cdots, 2, 1.$$

Since $p - 1 \equiv -1$, the first is a non-residue modulo p. The last is a residue. Let a be the first residue in this sequence, so that $a + 1$ is a non-residue. Then $-a - 1$ is a residue by Theorem 17.2. Suppose that

$$x_1^2 \equiv a, \quad y_1^2 \equiv -a - 1 \qquad \mod p.$$

Then

$$x_1^2 + y_1^2 + 1 \equiv 0 \qquad \mod p.$$

Theorem 117.1. *A positive prime p is a product $\pi\bar{\pi}$ of a prime quaternion and its conjugate.*

Let p be any positive prime. Let x_1, y_1 be a solution of (117.1), and define

$$\sigma = x_1 + y_1 i + j, \qquad p \mid N(\sigma).$$

Since the coefficient of j is odd and that of k is even, σ is divisible by no rational prime. By Theorem 116.4 there exists a prime quaternion π such that

$$\sigma = \pi\tau, \quad N(\pi) = \pi\bar{\pi} = p,$$

which proves the theorem.

Theorem 117.2. Every quaternion of H has an associate all of whose coördinates are rational integers.

Consider

$$\alpha = \tfrac{1}{2}(a_0 + a_1 i + a_2 j + a_3 k),$$

where the a's are odd integers. Then

$$a_i \equiv r_i \qquad \text{mod } 4. \qquad\qquad r_i = +1 \text{ or } -1.$$

Set

$$\epsilon = \tfrac{1}{2}(r_0 + r_1 i + r_2 j + r_3 k).$$

By Ex. 4, § 115, ϵ is a unit. Since $a_i - r_i \equiv 0$ mod 4, the quaternion

$$\rho = \tfrac{1}{4}(a_0 - r_0) + \tfrac{1}{4}(a_1 - r_1)i + \tfrac{1}{4}(a_2 - r_2)j + \tfrac{1}{4}(a_3 - r_3)k$$

has rational integral coördinates. But $2\rho = \alpha - \epsilon$, and so we have

$$\alpha\bar{\epsilon} - \epsilon\bar{\epsilon} = 2\rho\bar{\epsilon}.$$

The coördinates of $2\rho\bar{\epsilon}$ are integers, and $\epsilon\bar{\epsilon} = N(\epsilon) = 1$. Thus $\bar{\epsilon}$ is a unit for which

$$\alpha\bar{\epsilon} = 2\rho\bar{\epsilon} + 1$$

has integral coördinates.

Corollary 117.2. Every positive prime can be written as a product of two conjugate prime quaternions whose coördinates are rational integers.

Theorem 117.3. Every positive integer can be written as a sum of four squares of rational integers.

Let the positive integer n be written

$$n = p_1 p_2 \cdots p_k,$$

where the p's are positive primes. Let

$$p_i = \pi_i \bar{\pi}_i, \qquad N(\pi_i) = p_i,$$

where the π_i are prime quaternions with integral coördinates. Consider the quaternion

$$\sigma = \pi_1 \pi_2 \cdots \pi_k = s_0 + s_1 i + s_2 j + s_3 k.$$

Since the coördinates of each π_i are rational integers, the s_i are rational integers. But

$$n = p_1 p_2 \cdots p_k = N(\pi_1) N(\pi_2) \cdots N(\pi_k) = N(\sigma)$$
$$= s_0^2 + s_1^2 + s_2^2 + s_3^2.$$

EXERCISES

1. Find by trial all the ways of representing each of the following numbers as a sum of four squares: 12, 13, 17, 35.

2. Factor 13 into a product of two prime quaternions in two ways which are not "the same except for unit factors."

3. In an algebraic integral domain in which every ideal is principal, factorization into primes is unique. (Cf. Theorems 67.7 and 69.3.) Show exactly where the proof of the unique factorization theorem breaks down for quaternions.

4. Using the notation of Theorem 117.1, prove that $\pi = (\sigma, p]$.

5. Resolve 23 into a sum of four squares by a method which involves no guessing but does employ the index tables of § 16.

118. Division algebras. Let $\mathfrak{D}$ be any division algebra of order n with unit element 1 over a field $\mathfrak{F}$. Then $\mathfrak{D}$ consists of all numbers

$$\alpha = a_1 \epsilon_1 + a_2 \epsilon_2 + \cdots + a_n \epsilon_n, \qquad\qquad a_i \in \mathfrak{F}$$

where $\epsilon_1 = 1$, $\epsilon_2, \cdots, \epsilon_n$ are linearly independent with respect to $\mathfrak{F}$, every ϵ_i is commutative with $\mathfrak{F}$, every product $\epsilon_i \epsilon_j$ is in $\mathfrak{D}$, and $(\epsilon_i \epsilon_j) \epsilon_k = \epsilon_i (\epsilon_j \epsilon_k)$, and every number $\neq 0$ of $\mathfrak{D}$ has an inverse in $\mathfrak{D}$. The numbers $\epsilon_1, \epsilon_2, \cdots, \epsilon_n$ are called a *set of basis numbers*.

Since every number of $\mathfrak{D}$ is a linear combination of n numbers, it follows that every set of $n + 1$ numbers such as

$$1, \alpha, \alpha^2, \cdots, \alpha^n$$

are linearly dependent with respect to $\mathfrak{F}$. Thus every number α of $\mathfrak{D}$ satisfies an equation with coefficients in $\mathfrak{F}$ of degree n. Hence every α satisfies a *minimum equation* with coefficients in $\mathfrak{F}$ of smallest possible degree.

Theorem 118.1. Let α satisfy the minimum equation $m(x) = 0$ of degree r. Then all polynomials in α form a subfield of $\mathfrak{D}$ of order r.

Since $m(x)$ is of degree r and is minimal,

$$1, \alpha, \alpha^2, \cdots, \alpha^{r-1}$$

are linearly independent, and all numbers

$$\rho = a_0 + a_1\alpha + a_2\alpha^2 + \cdots + a_{r-1}\alpha^{r-1}, \qquad a_i \in \mathfrak{F}$$

clearly form a commutative subalgebra $\mathfrak{A}$ of $\mathfrak{D}$. Every such ρ except 0 has an inverse in $\mathfrak{D}$. We have only to show that ρ^{-1} is in $\mathfrak{A}$.

Since the powers $1, \rho, \rho^2, \cdots, \rho^r$ are all in $\mathfrak{A}$, they are linearly dependent. Then, as before, ρ satisfies an equation of minimum degree,

$$c_0 + c_1\rho + c_2\rho^2 + \cdots + c_s\rho^s = 0, \qquad c_s \neq 0, s \leqq r.$$

That is,

$$\rho(c_1 + c_2\rho + \cdots + c_s\rho^{s-1}) = -c_0.$$

Now $c_0 \neq 0$, for, if it were zero, the fact that ρ has an inverse in $\mathfrak{D}$ would imply that

$$c_1 + c_2\rho + \cdots + c_s\rho^{s-1} = 0,$$

whereas s was minimal. Hence

$$\rho^{-1} = \frac{-(c_1 + c_2\rho + \cdots + c_s\rho^{s-1})}{c_0},$$

which is in $\mathfrak{A}$.

Now let $\mathfrak{D}_4$ be a division algebra of order 4 which is actually not commutative. Let

$$\alpha = a_1 + a_2\epsilon_2 + a_3\epsilon_3 + a_4\epsilon_4, \qquad a_i \in \mathfrak{F}$$

be any one of its numbers. As we have seen, α satisfies a minimum equation $m(x) = 0$ of degree $r \leqq 4$. If this equation were of degree 4 for some α, then $1, \alpha, \alpha^2, \alpha^3$ would be linearly independent, and hence would form a basis for $\mathfrak{D}_4$. Then every two numbers of $\mathfrak{D}_4$ would be commutative, contrary to assumption. Thus $r \leqq 3$.

In fact, $r < 3$. For, let β be a number of $\mathfrak{D}_4$ which is not representable as a polynomial in α. Clearly β exists, for otherwise $\mathfrak{D}_4$ would be commutative. If the minimum equation of α were of degree 3, then $1, \alpha, \alpha^2, \beta$ would be linearly independent and would form a basis for $\mathfrak{D}_4$. In particular we should have

$$\alpha\beta = k_0 + k_1\alpha + k_2\alpha^2 + k_3\beta,$$

$$(\alpha - k_3)\beta = k_0 + k_1\alpha + k_2\alpha^2.$$

Since α does not satisfy a linear equation, $\alpha - k_3 \neq 0$ and has an inverse which, by Theorem 118.1, is a polynomial in α. Thus β is a polynomial in α, contrary to its choice. We have proved

Theorem 118.2. Every number of $\mathfrak{D}_4$ which is not in $\mathfrak{F}$ has a quadratic equation for its minimum equation.

Let α be a number of $\mathfrak{D}_4$ which is not in $\mathfrak{F}$. Then 1 and α form a basis for a subfield $\mathfrak{A}$ of $\mathfrak{D}_4$. Since $\mathfrak{D}_4$ is of order 4, there exists another number β of $\mathfrak{D}_4$ which is not in $\mathfrak{A}$; then β is not in $\mathfrak{F}$, and the minimum equation of β is also quadratic, and 1 and β generate another subfield $\mathfrak{B}$ of $\mathfrak{D}_4$.

The numbers 1, α, β, $\alpha\beta$ are linearly independent with respect to $\mathfrak{F}$. For, if there existed a relation

$$k_0 + k_1\alpha + k_2\beta + k_3\alpha\beta = 0, \qquad\qquad k_i \in \mathfrak{F},$$

it would follow that

$$(k_2 + k_3\alpha)\beta = - k_0 - k_1\alpha.$$

Unless $k_2 = k_3$ were zero, $k_2 + k_3\alpha$ would have an inverse in $\mathfrak{A}$ (Theorem 118.1) so that β would be in $\mathfrak{A}$, contrary to its choice. But, on the other hand, if $k_2 = k_3 = 0$, then also $k_0 = k_1 = 0$, for 1 and α are linearly independent. Thus 1, α, β, $\alpha\beta$ are linearly independent, and we have proved

Theorem 118.3. A basis 1, α, β, $\alpha\beta$ may be chosen for $\mathfrak{D}_4$, where α and β satisfy quadratic equations.

If it were true that $\alpha\beta = \beta\alpha$, the algebra $\mathfrak{D}_4$ would be commutative, contrary to assumption. Define

$$\beta^* = \alpha^{-1}\beta\alpha$$

so that

$$\beta\alpha = \alpha\beta^*, \qquad\qquad \beta^* \neq \beta.$$

It then follows that

$$\beta^2\alpha = \beta\alpha\beta^* = \alpha\beta^{*2}.$$

Hence, if $m(x) = b_0 + b_1x + x^2 = 0$ is the minimum equation of β,

$$m(\beta)\cdot\alpha = \alpha\cdot m(\beta^*) = 0,$$

so that β^* is also a root of $m(x) = 0$.

If we knew that β^* were in the quadratic field $\mathfrak{B}$, it would follow that $\beta^* = \bar\beta$, the ordinary conjugate of β in $\mathfrak{B}$. But we do not know that β^* is in $\mathfrak{B}$, and indeed it may not be. We shall see, however, that it is possible so to choose α and β that this is true.

EXERCISES

1. Show that every set of n linearly independent numbers of $\mathfrak{D}$ constitute a basis for $\mathfrak{D}$.

2. Show that, if the distinct numbers α and β of $\mathfrak{D}_4$ satisfy the same binomial equation $x^2 = a$, there exists a number τ of $\mathfrak{D}_4$ such that $\tau^{-1}\beta\tau = - \alpha$.

HINT: Set $\alpha - \beta = \gamma$, and form $\alpha\gamma + \gamma\beta$.

3. Show that if $\mathfrak{F}$ is of characteristic $\neq 2$, and if there exists a τ such that $\tau^{-1}\alpha\tau = -\alpha$, then α satisfies a pure quadratic $x^2 = a$.

4. Show that, if the distinct numbers α and β satisfy the same quadratic equation and are commutative, their sum is in $\mathfrak{F}$.

HINT: Use the identity $\alpha^2 - \beta^2 = (\alpha - \beta)(\alpha + \beta) - \alpha\beta + \beta\alpha$.

5. Show that, if $\mathfrak{F}$ is of characteristic $\neq 2$, a transformation $\alpha' = \alpha + h$ can be applied so that α' satisfies a pure quadratic equation.

119. Generalized quaternions.

Let $\mathfrak{D}_4$ be a division algebra of order 4, which is actually not commutative, over a field $\mathfrak{F}$ whose characteristic is $\neq 2$. By Theorem 118.3, there exists a basis 1, α, β, $\alpha\beta$, where α is any number of $\mathfrak{D}_4$ not in $\mathfrak{F}$, and β is any number not representable as a polynomial in α.

By Ex. 5, § 118, a number $j = \beta + h$ exists which satisfies a pure quadratic equation $j^2 = b$. Then j is not a polynomial in α, and 1, α, j, αj constitute a basis for $\mathfrak{D}_4$.

We have seen that j and

$$j^* = \alpha^{-1}j\alpha$$

are distinct and satisfy the same quadratic equation $j^2 = b$. Then, by Ex. 2, § 118, there exists a number τ such that

$$\tau^{-1}j^*\tau = -j = \tau^{-1}\alpha^{-1}j\alpha\tau.$$

Let us denote $\alpha\tau$ by i. Now i is not in $\mathfrak{F}$, for this would imply that $-j = j$. Hence we may use i in place of α. It will remain true that j is not a polynomial in i for the same reason. Then 1, i, j, ij constitute a basis for $\mathfrak{D}_4$.

Now $-j = i^{-1}ji$ implies that $-i = jij^{-1}$, and so by Ex. 3, § 118, i also satisfies a pure quadratic equation. Thus we have the complete multiplication table for $\mathfrak{D}_4$ given by

$$(119.1) \qquad i^2 = a, \quad j^2 = b, \quad ji = -ij, \qquad\qquad a, b \in \mathfrak{F}.$$

We have now obtained a normalized basis which every $\mathfrak{D}_4$ must possess. It is not evident (or true) however, that a division algebra $\mathfrak{D}_4$ exists for every choice of a and b in (119.1). In fact, if either a or b is a square in $\mathfrak{F}$, clearly $\mathfrak{D}_4$ does not exist. Even this restriction is not enough.

Theorem 119.1. If b is not the norm of any number in the quadratic field $\mathfrak{F}(i)$, then (119.1) determines a division algebra.

Every number α of $\mathfrak{D}_4$ may be written

$$\alpha = a_0 + a_1 i + a_2 j + a_3 ij$$
$$= (a_0 + a_1 i) + (a_2 + a_3 i)j.$$

If $a_2 + a_3 i = 0$, α is in $\mathfrak{F}(i)$. Then α has an inverse in $\mathfrak{F}(i)$ unless $\alpha = 0$, and hence has an inverse in $\mathfrak{D}_4$.

Now suppose that $a_2 + a_3 i \neq 0$. We shall first show that there exists a number γ such that

$$\alpha = (a_2 + a_3 i)\gamma.$$

The first factor is in $\mathfrak{F}(i)$ and not 0, and so it has an inverse. If we can show that γ always has an inverse, it will follow that α has an inverse, and $\mathfrak{D}_4$ is a division algebra.

Assume a γ of the form

$$\gamma = c_1 + c_2 i + j,$$

where c_1 and c_2 are to be determined in $\mathfrak{F}$. Then

$$\alpha = a_0 + a_1 i + a_2 j + a_3 ij$$
$$= (a_2 c_1 + a_3 c_2 a) + (a_2 c_2 + a_3 c_1)i + a_2 j + a_3 ij.$$

Thus c_1 and c_2 must be determined from the equations

$$a_2 c_1 + a_3 c_2 a = a_0,$$
$$a_3 c_1 + a_2 c_2 = a_1.$$

These numbers c_1 and c_2 can be determined if the determinant is not 0, that is, if

$$a_2^2 - a_3^2 a = N(a_2 + a_3 i) \neq 0.$$

But $a_2 + a_3 i \neq 0$, and so $N(a_2 + a_3 i) \neq 0$, and γ exists.

We must now show that γ has an inverse. Consider

$$(c_1 + c_2 i + j)(c_1 - c_2 i - j) = c_1^2 - ac_2^2 - b.$$

If this is $\neq 0$, then

$$\gamma^{-1} = \frac{c_1 - c_2 i - j}{c_1^2 - ac_2^2 - b}.$$

But $c_1^2 - ac_2^2 - b = 0$ means that

$$b = c_1^2 - ac_2^2 = N(c_1 + c_2 i).$$

Hence, if no number $c_1 + c_2 i$ of $\mathfrak{F}(i)$ exists whose norm is b, then we may be sure that γ has an inverse, and hence α has an inverse.

EXERCISES

1. If $\mathfrak{D}_4$ has a basis determined by (119.1), prove that it also has a basis determined by

$$i'^2 = l^2 a, \quad j'^2 = m^2 b, \quad j'i' = -i'j', \qquad a, b \in \mathfrak{F},$$

where l and m are any numbers of $\mathfrak{F}$ not 0.

2. Prove that the algebra of ordinary quaternions is the only division algebra of order 4 over the real field which is not commutative.

3. Defining conjugate as in § 112, prove that, in any generalized quaternion algebra, the conjugate of the product of two numbers is equal to the product of the conjugates taken in reverse order.

4. Defining norm as in § 112, prove that, in any generalized quaternion algebra, the norm of a product is equal to the product of the norms.

5. Let $\alpha = a_0 + a_1 i + (a_2 + a_3 i)j$ be in $\mathfrak{D}_4$. Let

$$a_0 + a_1 i \leftrightarrow A, \quad a_0 - a_1 i \leftrightarrow A', \quad a_2 + a_3 i \leftrightarrow B, \quad a_2 - a_3 i \leftrightarrow B'$$

under the correspondence of § 109. Show that

$$\alpha \leftrightarrow \begin{bmatrix} A & B \\ bB' & A' \end{bmatrix}$$

is the second regular representation of $\mathfrak{D}_4$. (Cf. Ex. 2, § 113.)

6. Prove that every commutative division algebra over a field $\mathfrak{F}$ is an algebraic extension of $\mathfrak{F}$.

120. Cyclic algebras.* By taking account of the suggestions furnished by a study of generalized quaternions, we may proceed to develop a large class of non-commutative associative algebras, many of which are division algebras.

Let $f(x) = 0$ be a cyclic equation of degree n with coefficients in $\mathfrak{F}$. (See § 47.) It is irreducible, and, if α is one of its roots, all its roots can be written

$$\alpha, \theta(\alpha), \quad \theta^2(\alpha), \cdots, \theta^{n-1}(\alpha),$$

where θ is a polynomial with coefficients in $\mathfrak{F}$, and θ^2 means the iterate $\theta[\theta(\alpha)]$. Let $y^n = b$ be a binomial equation which is irreducible in $\mathfrak{F}$, and let β be one of its roots. This equation is cyclic in $\mathfrak{F}(\rho)$ where ρ is an nth root of unity. (See § 47.)

Let us consider the set of all linear combinations of the n^2 numbers

$$(120.1) \quad 1, \alpha, \alpha^2, \cdots, \alpha^{n-1}, \beta, \beta\alpha, \beta\alpha^2, \cdots, \beta\alpha^{n-1}, \cdots,$$

$$\beta^{n-1}\alpha, \beta^{n-1}\alpha^2, \cdots, \beta^{n-1}\alpha^{n-1}$$

with coefficients in the field $\mathfrak{F}$. The "product" of two numbers such as $\beta\alpha$ is purely formal, and really means nothing more than the ordered pair (β, α).

We shall make a linear algebra out of this module by defining the product of any two of these basis numbers as a linear combination of them. We define

$$\alpha\beta = \beta \cdot \theta(\alpha)$$

* Also called Dickson algebras, in honor of their discoverer, L. E. Dickson.

and assume the associative law. We shall see that the product of every two basis numbers is now uniquely defined. Thus

$$\alpha^2\beta = \alpha\beta\cdot\theta(\alpha) = \beta\cdot[\theta(\alpha)]^2,$$

and, for any polynomial φ,

$$\varphi(\alpha)\cdot\beta = \beta\cdot\varphi[\theta(\alpha)].$$

We shall prove by induction that

(120.2) $$\varphi(\alpha)\cdot\beta^r = \beta^r\cdot\varphi[\theta^r(\alpha)],$$

which has been shown to hold for $r = 1$. By the associative law,

$$\varphi(\alpha)\cdot\beta^r = \{\varphi(\alpha)\cdot\beta^{r-1}\}\beta.$$

By the induction hypothesis we have

$$\begin{aligned}
\varphi(\alpha)\cdot\beta^r &= \{\beta^{r-1}\cdot\varphi[\theta^{r-1}(\alpha)]\}\beta \\
&= \beta^{r-1}\{\varphi[\theta^{r-1}(\alpha)]\beta\} \\
&= \beta^{r-1}\{\beta\cdot\varphi[\theta^{r-1}(\theta\alpha)]\} \\
&= \beta^r\cdot\varphi[\theta^r(\alpha)].
\end{aligned}$$

Theorem 120.1. *The module whose basis is (120.1) is closed under multiplication.*

For clearly the product of any two numbers of (120.1) can be written as a power of β multiplied on the right by a polynomial in α. By the relation $\beta^n = b$, this power of β can be made $< n$. By the relation $f(\alpha) = 0$ of degree n, the polynomial in α can be replaced by one whose degree is $< n$. The resulting expression for the product of two basis numbers is a linear combination of the basis numbers.

We have shown that, if the associative law holds, then (120.2) holds. Conversely, we may prove

Theorem 120.2. *Multiplication in the module (120.1) is associative if it is defined by (120.2).*

For

$$\begin{aligned}
[\beta^i\alpha^j\cdot\beta^k\alpha^l]\beta^p\alpha^q &= \beta^{i+k}[\theta^k(\alpha)]^j\alpha^l\cdot\beta^p\alpha^q \\
&= \beta^{i+k+p}[\theta^{k+p}(\alpha)]^j[\theta^p(\alpha)]^l\alpha^q.
\end{aligned}$$

On the other hand,

$$\begin{aligned}
\beta^i\alpha^j[\beta^k\alpha^l\cdot\beta^p\alpha^q] &= \beta^i\alpha^j\beta^{k+p}[\theta^p(\alpha)]^l\alpha^q \\
&= \beta^{i+k+p}[\theta^{k+p}(\alpha)]^j[\theta^p(\alpha)]^l\alpha^q.
\end{aligned}$$

These results are identical and give identical residues after being reduced modulo $\beta^n - b$ and $f(\alpha)$.

EXERCISES

1. If $\mathfrak{D}$ is a division algebra of order n over the real field Re, prove that a basis 1, ϵ_1, ϵ_2, $\cdots$, ϵ_{n-1} may be so chosen that $\epsilon_i^2 = -1$.

2. Show that the only division algebra of order 2 over Re is the complex field C.

3. Show that there exists no division algebra of order 3 over Re.

HINT: Let $i^2 = j^2 = -1$. Show that $ij = a_0 + a_1 i + a_2 j$ implies that $a_1^2 = -1$.

4. If the basis numbers of $\mathfrak{D}$ over Re are such that $\epsilon_i^2 = -1$, show that $\epsilon_i \epsilon_j + \epsilon_j \epsilon_i \subset Re$.

HINT: Both $\epsilon_i + \epsilon_j$ and $\epsilon_i - \epsilon_j$ satisfy quadratic equations.

5. If a division algebra over Re has the basis 1, ϵ_1, ϵ_2, ϵ_3, $\cdots$, where the ϵ's are normalized as in Exs. 1 and 4, show that ϵ_2 may be replaced by ϵ_2' such that $\epsilon_1 \epsilon_2' + \epsilon_2' \epsilon_1 = 0$.

HINT: Set $\epsilon_2' = (\epsilon_2 + c\epsilon_1)/\sqrt{1 - c^2}$, where $\epsilon_1 \epsilon_2 + \epsilon_2 \epsilon_1 = 2c$.

6. Show that there exists no division algebra over Re of order > 4.

HINT: Take a basis as in Ex. 5 with $\epsilon_3 = \epsilon_1 \epsilon_2$, $\epsilon_i \epsilon_j + \epsilon_j \epsilon_i = a_{ij}$, $a_{12} = 0$. Show that this implies that $-2\epsilon_4 = a_{14}\epsilon_1 + a_{24}\epsilon_2 + a_{34}\epsilon_3$.

121. Cyclic algebras of order nine. We shall now consider the cyclic algebras of order 9 over the rational field Ra. Every rational cyclic cubic (see (37.3)) is given by

$$(121.1) \qquad x^3 - 3(r^2 + 3s^2)x + 2r(r^2 + 3s^2) = 0.$$

Let α be one of its roots (see (37.4)). Then

$$\theta(\alpha) = -\frac{1}{s}(r^2 + 3s^2) + \frac{r - s}{2s}\alpha + \frac{1}{2s}\alpha^2,$$

and $\theta^2(\alpha) = \theta[\theta(\alpha)]$ are the other two roots. Let β be a root of the equation

$$y^3 = b,$$

where b is rational but not a rational cube.

Theorem 121.1. A cyclic algebra $\mathfrak{D}$ of order 9 over the rational field Ra is a division algebra if b is not the norm of a number of $Ra(\alpha)$.

The algebra $\mathfrak{D}$ has the basis

$$1, \alpha, \alpha^2, \beta, \beta\alpha, \beta\alpha^2, \beta^2, \beta^2\alpha, \beta^2\alpha^2.$$

Every number of $\mathfrak{D}$ can be written

$$\chi = \kappa(\alpha) + \beta\lambda(\alpha) + \beta^2\mu(\alpha),$$

where
$$\kappa(\alpha) = x_0 + x_1\alpha + x_2\alpha^2, \quad \lambda(\alpha) = x_3 + x_4\alpha + x_5\alpha^2,$$
$$\mu(\alpha) = x_6 + x_7\alpha + x_8\alpha^2.$$

We need to show that every $\chi \neq 0$ has an inverse.

Case I. $\mu(\alpha) = \lambda(\alpha) = 0$, $\kappa(\alpha) \neq 0$. Since $\kappa(\alpha)$ has an inverse in the field $Ra(\alpha)$, χ has an inverse in $\mathfrak{D}$.

Case II. $\mu(\alpha) = 0$, $\lambda(\alpha) \neq 0$. Write
$$-\kappa(\alpha) \cdot \lambda^{-1}(\alpha) = \nu(\alpha).$$
Then
$$[\beta - \nu(\alpha)]\lambda(\alpha) = [\beta + \kappa(\alpha) \cdot \lambda^{-1}(\alpha)]\lambda(\alpha) = \chi,$$
so that χ has an inverse if $\beta - \nu(\alpha)$ has one. But, if we write θ for $\theta(\alpha)$ and θ^2 for $\theta[\theta(\alpha)]$, we have

$$[\beta - \nu(\alpha)][\beta^2 + \beta \cdot \nu(\theta^2) + \nu(\theta) \cdot \nu(\theta^2)] = \beta^3 + \beta^2 \cdot \nu(\theta^2)$$
$$+ \beta \cdot \nu(\theta) \cdot \nu(\theta^2) - \nu(\alpha) \cdot \beta^2 - \nu(\alpha) \cdot \beta \cdot \nu(\theta^2) - \nu(\alpha) \cdot \nu(\theta) \cdot \nu(\theta^2).$$

But, by (120.2),
$$\nu(\alpha) \cdot \beta^2 = \beta^2 \cdot \nu(\theta^2), \quad \nu(\alpha) \cdot \beta = \beta \cdot \nu(\theta),$$

and so the above expression is equal to

(121.2) $$\qquad b - \nu(\alpha) \cdot \nu(\theta) \cdot \nu(\theta^2).$$

But $\nu(\theta)$ and $\nu(\theta^2)$ are the conjugates of $\nu(\alpha)$ in the cubic field $Ra(\alpha)$; therefore this last product is equal to the norm of $\nu(\alpha)$ and is rational. Since b is not equal to the norm of any number in $Ra(\alpha)$, (121.2) is not 0. Hence in this case $\beta - \nu(\alpha)$ has an inverse, and so does χ.

Case III. $\mu(\alpha) \neq 0$. Write

(121.3) $$\qquad \chi \cdot \mu^{-1}(\alpha) = \sigma(\alpha) + \beta \cdot \tau(\alpha) + \beta^2,$$

where
$$\sigma(\alpha) = \kappa(\alpha) \cdot \mu^{-1}(\alpha), \quad \tau(\alpha) = \lambda(\alpha) \cdot \mu^{-1}(\alpha).$$

Then χ has an inverse if the right member of (121.3) has an inverse. But

$$[\beta - \tau(\theta)][\sigma(\alpha) + \beta \cdot \tau(\alpha) + \beta^2]$$
$$= \beta \cdot \sigma(\alpha) + \beta^2 \cdot \tau(\alpha) + \beta^3 - \tau(\theta) \cdot \sigma(\alpha) - \tau(\theta) \cdot \beta \cdot \tau(\alpha) - \tau(\theta) \cdot \beta^2$$
$$= \beta \cdot \sigma(\alpha) + \beta^2 \cdot \tau(\alpha) + b - \tau(\theta) \cdot \sigma(\alpha) - \beta \cdot \tau(\theta^2) \cdot \tau(\alpha) - \beta^2 \cdot \tau(\alpha)$$
$$= \beta \cdot [\sigma(\alpha) - \tau(\theta^2) \cdot \tau(\alpha)] + b - \tau(\theta) \cdot \sigma(\alpha)$$
$$= \beta \cdot \zeta(\alpha) + \xi(\alpha),$$

where the meanings of $\zeta(\alpha)$ and $\xi(\alpha)$ are evident. The right-hand member could be 0 only if

$$\sigma(\alpha) - \tau(\theta^2)\cdot\tau(\alpha) = 0, \quad b - \tau(\theta)\cdot\sigma(\alpha) = 0.$$

This gives, upon eliminating $\sigma(\alpha)$,

$$b = \tau(\theta)\cdot\tau(\theta^2)\cdot\tau(\alpha) = N(\tau(\alpha)).$$

This is impossible, since b is not a norm.   Now, by Case II, $\beta\cdot\zeta(\alpha) + \xi(\alpha)$ has an inverse in $\mathfrak{D}$. Therefore (121.3) has the inverse

$$[\beta\cdot\zeta(\alpha) + \xi(\alpha)]^{-1}[\beta - \tau(\theta)].$$

Finally, χ has an inverse.

EXERCISES

1. Let α be a root of the irreducible equation $x^3 + px + q = 0$, where p and q are odd integers. Let $\xi = a_0 + a_1\alpha + a_2\alpha^2$, where a_0, a_1, a_2 are rational integers. Prove that

$$N(\xi) \equiv 1 + (a_0 + 1)(a_1 + 1)(a_2 + 1) \qquad \mod 2.$$

(See (36.4).)

2. Prove that $N(\xi)$ in Ex. 1 either is odd or is divisible by 8.

3. Prove that no even integer not divisible by 8 is the norm of any number of $Ra(\alpha)$, where α is defined as in Ex. 1.

4. Show that

$$\alpha^3 - 3\alpha + 1 = 0, \quad \beta^3 = 2, \quad \alpha\beta = \beta(\alpha^2 - 2)$$

define a division algebra of order 9 over Ra. Find its complete multiplication table. See Ex. 2, § 37.

122. Linear algebras with a unit element. In § 112 we defined a non-commutative field as an algebraic variety for which all the field postulates except the commutative law of multiplication were assumed to hold. A non-commutative field with a finite basis relative to some field $\mathfrak{F}$ was called a division algebra.

If we discard not only the commutative law of multiplication, but also the assumption that every element except 0 has an inverse with respect to multiplication, we obtain a variety which in § 68 was called a ring with unit element.

Let $\mathfrak{R}i$ be a ring with unit element 1. If $\mathfrak{R}i$ contains a field $\mathfrak{F}$ every number of which is commutative with every number of $\mathfrak{R}i$ and a finite number n of numbers ϵ_1, ϵ_2, $\cdots$, ϵ_n such that every number of $\mathfrak{R}i$ can be written in the form

$$a_1\epsilon_1 + a_2\epsilon_2 + \cdots + a_n\epsilon_n, \qquad a_i \in \mathfrak{F},$$

we shall call $\mathfrak{R}i$ a *finite linear associative algebra with unit element over* $\mathfrak{F}$, or briefly, an *algebra with unit element*.

We may assume that the *basis numbers* ϵ_1, ϵ_2, $\cdots$, ϵ_n are linearly independent, for a dependence relation among them would imply the existence of a basis consisting of fewer than n numbers. If the basis numbers are linearly independent and n in number, the algebra is said to be of *order n* over $\mathfrak{F}$.

We have already encountered many instances of such algebras with unit element. Algebraic fields (§ 38) and, in fact, algebraic extensions of any field (§ 78) can be considered as commutative division algebras. Quaternions, and indeed all cyclic algebras (§ 120), whether they are division algebras or not, come under this classification. Also, all total matric algebras (§ 98) are included.

If $\mathfrak{A}$ is an algebra with unit element over $\mathfrak{F}$ with basis ϵ_1, ϵ_2, $\cdots$, ϵ_n, then any n numbers of $\mathfrak{A}$ which are linearly independent with respect to $\mathfrak{F}$ can be taken as a basis for $\mathfrak{A}$. For, let

$$\epsilon_i' = a_{i1}\epsilon_1 + a_{i2}\epsilon_2 + \cdots + a_{in}\epsilon_n, \qquad (i = 1, 2, \cdots, n)$$

be n such numbers. If the determinant $|\,a_{rs}\,|$ were 0, there would be a linear relation among its rows, and so the ϵ_1', ϵ_2', $\cdots$, ϵ_n' would be linearly dependent, contrary to assumption. Since this determinant is $\neq 0$, the equations can be solved for the ϵ_i in terms of the ϵ_i', so that every number of $\mathfrak{A}$ can be written as a linear combination of ϵ_1', ϵ_2', $\cdots$, ϵ_n'.

Since $\mathfrak{A}$ is a ring, the product of every two numbers of $\mathfrak{A}$ is in $\mathfrak{A}$, in notation, $\mathfrak{A}^2 \subseteq \mathfrak{A}$. In particular,

$$(122.1) \qquad \epsilon_i\epsilon_j = c_{ij1}\epsilon_1 + c_{ij2}\epsilon_2 + \cdots + c_{ijn}\epsilon_n, \qquad c_{ijk} \in \mathfrak{F}.$$

We shall call the n^3 numbers c_{ijk} the *constants of multiplication* of $\mathfrak{A}$. They, together with the distributive law, determine uniquely the product of every two numbers of $\mathfrak{A}$.

The constants of multiplication cannot be arbitrarily assigned, for multiplication in $\mathfrak{A}$ was assumed to be associative. For every i, j, k, it must be true that

$$\epsilon_i(\epsilon_j\epsilon_k) = (\epsilon_i\epsilon_j)\epsilon_k.$$

That is,

$$\epsilon_i\sum_h c_{jkh}\epsilon_h = \sum_h c_{ijh}\epsilon_h\epsilon_k,$$

$$\sum_{h,\,l} c_{jkh}c_{ihl}\epsilon_l = \sum_{h,\,l} c_{ijh}c_{hkl}\epsilon_l.$$

Since the ϵ's are linearly independent, this implies that

$$(122.2) \qquad \sum_h c_{jkh}c_{ihl} = \sum_h c_{ijh}c_{hkl} \qquad (i, j, k, l = 1, 2, \cdots, n).$$

These n^4 equations are necessary and sufficient in order that the n^3 constants of multiplication define an associative algebra of order n.

EXERCISES

1. Show that the following algebra is associative, and find its constants of multiplication.

	ϵ_1	ϵ_2	ϵ_3
ϵ_1	ϵ_1	ϵ_2	ϵ_3
ϵ_2	ϵ_2	ϵ_1	ϵ_3
ϵ_3	ϵ_3	ϵ_3	0 ·

Is it commutative?   Is it a division algebra?

2. Treat similarly the algebra

	ϵ_1	ϵ_2	ϵ_3	ϵ_4
ϵ_1	ϵ_1	ϵ_2	ϵ_3	ϵ_4
ϵ_2	ϵ_2	0	0	ϵ_2
ϵ_3	ϵ_3	0	0	ϵ_3
ϵ_4	ϵ_4	$-\epsilon_2$	ϵ_3	ϵ_1 ·

3. Let δ_{rs} be Kronecker's delta.   That is, δ_{rr} is the unit element of $\mathfrak{F}$, while $\delta_{rs} = 0$ if $r \neq s$.   Prove that every total matric algebra of order n^2 over $\mathfrak{F}$ has a basis

$$\epsilon_{11}, \ \epsilon_{12}, \ \cdots, \ \epsilon_{1n}, \ \epsilon_{21}, \ \cdots, \ \epsilon_{nn}, \quad \epsilon_{ij} = (\delta_{ri}\delta_{sj}),$$

and that $\epsilon_{ij}\epsilon_{kl} = \delta_{jk}\epsilon_{il}$.

4. Show that the unit element of an algebra is unique.

5. Prove that, if an element $\alpha \in \mathfrak{A}$ has a unique right inverse β ($\alpha\beta =$ unit element ϵ), then β is also a left inverse.

HINT: $\alpha(\beta + \beta\alpha - \epsilon) = \epsilon$.

123. The regular representations.   Let $\mathfrak{A}$ be an algebra with basis $\epsilon_1, \ \epsilon_2, \ \cdots, \ \epsilon_n,$ where ϵ_1 is a unit element, and with multiplication table

(122.1).   As in § 113, we denote by v the vector $(\epsilon_1, \epsilon_2, \cdots, \epsilon_n)$.   Then

$$\epsilon_i v = (\epsilon_i \epsilon_1, \epsilon_i \epsilon_2, \cdots, \epsilon_i \epsilon_n) = (\Sigma c_{i1k}\epsilon_k, \Sigma c_{i2k}\epsilon_k, \cdots, \Sigma c_{ink}\epsilon_k)$$

$$= (\epsilon_1, \epsilon_2, \cdots, \epsilon_n) \begin{bmatrix} c_{i11} & c_{i21} & \cdots & c_{in1} \\ c_{i12} & c_{i22} & \cdots & c_{in2} \\ \cdot & \cdot & \cdot & \cdot \\ c_{i1n} & c_{i2n} & \cdots & c_{inn} \end{bmatrix} = v(c_{isr}).$$

We define the n matrices $R_1, R_2, \cdots, R_n$ by

$$R_i = (c_{isr}) \qquad (i = 1, 2, \cdots, n),$$

where, as usual, r is the row index and s the column index.   If

$$\alpha = a_1 \epsilon_1 + a_2 \epsilon_2 + \cdots + a_n \epsilon_n$$

is any number of $\mathfrak{A}$, we define

$$R(\alpha) = a_1 R_1 + a_2 R_2 + \cdots + a_n R_n.$$

It is evident that

$$\alpha v = a_1 \epsilon_1 v + a_2 \epsilon_2 v + \cdots + a_n \epsilon_n v$$

$$= v a_1 R_1 + v a_2 R_2 + \cdots + v a_n R_n = v R(\alpha).$$

That the correspondence

$$\alpha \to R(\alpha)$$

is a homomorphism with respect to addition follows immediately from the definition of $R(\alpha)$.   Furthermore,

$$(\alpha\beta)v = \alpha(\beta v) = \alpha[v \cdot R(\beta)] = (\alpha v) \cdot R(\beta)$$

$$= [v \cdot R(\alpha)] \cdot R(\beta) = v \cdot [R(\alpha) \cdot R(\beta)].$$

Hence

$$\alpha\beta \to R(\alpha) \cdot R(\beta),$$

and so the correspondence is also a homomorphism with respect to multiplication.

Suppose that two numbers α and β determine the same matrix $R(\alpha)$. Then

$$(\alpha - \beta)v = v \cdot 0 = 0.$$

The first 0 is a matrix, the second is a vector.   But $\mathfrak{A}$ has the unit element ϵ_1, so that

$$\alpha - \beta = (\alpha - \beta)\epsilon_1 = 0, \quad \alpha = \beta.$$

Hence the correspondence $\alpha \leftrightarrow R(\alpha)$ is biunique and is an isomorphism.

This correspondence is called the *first regular representation* of $\mathfrak{A}$ by matrices.

By writing v as a column vector, we may proceed similarly to find

$$v\epsilon_i = S_i v, \quad S_i = (c_{ris}).$$

These S-matrices are also linearly independent with respect to $\mathfrak{F}$, and they furnish the *second regular representation* of $\mathfrak{A}$ by matrices.

Another approach to these regular representations is interesting in showing their close relationship to the associativity conditions (122.2). By a mere interchange of subscripts and order of factors, these may be written in either of the two forms

$$\sum_h c_{ihr} c_{jsh} = \sum_h c_{ijh} c_{hsr},$$

$$\sum_h c_{rih} c_{hjs} = \sum_h c_{ijh} c_{rhs} \qquad (i, j, r, s = 1, 2, \cdots, n).$$

For every i and j, form the matrices in which the members of the above equations stand in row r and column s. Then the first of the above equations becomes

$$R_i R_j = \sum_h c_{ijh} R_h,$$

and the second becomes

$$S_i S_j = \sum_h c_{ijh} S_h \qquad (i, j = 1, 2, \cdots, n).$$

The homomorphisms $\epsilon_i \rightarrow R_i$, $\epsilon_i \rightarrow S_i$ with respect to multiplication are thus established in another way.

It is now possible to use some of the theory of matrices to establish theorems about algebras.

That every number α of $\mathfrak{A}$ satisfies some equation of degree n with coefficients in $\mathfrak{F}$ is obvious, for

$$1, \alpha, \alpha^2, \cdots, \alpha^n$$

constitute $n + 1$ numbers of $\mathfrak{A}$, which must be linearly dependent.

Theorem 123.1. *Every number α of $\mathfrak{A}$ satisfies its first characteristic equation*

$$f_1(x) = \left| xI - R(\alpha) \right| = 0,$$

and its second characteristic equation

$$f_2(x) = \left| xI - S(\alpha) \right| = 0.$$

Since α satisfies an equation of degree n, it must satisfy some equation

$m(x) = 0$ of minimum degree $r \leqq n$. Since this will have to be the equation of lowest degree satisfied by $R(\alpha)$, and also the equation of lowest degree satisfied by $S(\alpha)$, it is the common minimum equation of both these matrices. By Theorem 102.3, we know that the distinct irreducible factors of the characteristic and minimum functions of a matrix are the same. Hence we have

Theorem 123.2. The distinct irreducible factors of $f_1(x)$, $f_2(x)$, and $m(x)$ are the same.

EXERCISES

1. Find the matrices $R_1, R_2, R_3, S_1, S_2, S_3$ which represent the algebra of Ex. 1, § 122, from the definitions $R_i = (c_{isr})$, $S_i = (c_{ris})$.

2. Find the first regular representation of the algebra of Ex. 2, § 122, by forming $\alpha v = v R(\alpha)$, $\alpha = a_1 \epsilon_1 + \cdots + a_4 \epsilon_4$.

3. The principal equation of an algebra is the equation of lowest degree satisfied by the "general number," i.e., the number whose coefficients are independent variables over $\mathfrak{F}$. Find the principal equations of the algebras of Exercises 1 and 2.

124. Direct sums. Suppose that $\mathfrak{B}$ and $\mathfrak{C}$ are two algebras with unit elements defined over a field $\mathfrak{F}$. Consider the set $\mathfrak{A}$ of all number pairs (β, γ) where β is in $\mathfrak{B}$ and γ is in $\mathfrak{C}$. We shall define equality by the statement that

$$(\beta_1, \gamma_1) = (\beta_2, \gamma_2)$$

means that $\beta_1 = \beta_2$ and $\gamma_1 = \gamma_2$. We define addition by the identity

$$(\beta_1, \gamma_1) + (\beta_2, \gamma_2) = (\beta_1 + \beta_2, \gamma_1 + \gamma_2),$$

and multiplication by the identity

$$(\beta_1, \gamma_1) \times (\beta_2, \gamma_2) = (\beta_1 \beta_2, \gamma_1 \gamma_2).$$

The correspondences

$$(\beta, 0) \leftrightarrow \beta, \quad (0, \gamma) \leftrightarrow \gamma$$

are obviously biunique, and it follows directly from the definitions of addition and multiplication that they are isomorphisms. Thus the set $\mathfrak{A}$ contains subsets isomorphic with $\mathfrak{B}$ and $\mathfrak{C}$. We shall henceforth write β for the number $(\beta, 0)$ of $\mathfrak{A}$, and γ for the number $(0, \gamma)$ of $\mathfrak{A}$. In this sense the sum $\beta + \gamma$ and the product $\beta\gamma$ have meanings. In fact,

$$\beta + \gamma = (\beta, \gamma), \quad \beta\gamma = 0.$$

The mathematical system $\mathfrak{A}$ is called the *direct sum* of $\mathfrak{B}$ and $\mathfrak{C}$, and is written $\mathfrak{A} = \mathfrak{B} + \mathfrak{C}$.

Theorem 124.1. *The direct sum of two algebras with unit elements is an algebra with unit element.* *The unit element of the direct sum is the sum of the unit elements of the components.* *The order of the direct sum is the sum of the orders of the components.*

The ring postulates (§ 68) are readily verified for $\mathfrak{A}$ from the definitions of addition and multiplication. If η is the unit element of $\mathfrak{B}$, and ζ that of $\mathfrak{C}$, then

$$(\eta, \zeta)(\beta, \gamma) = (\eta\beta, \zeta\gamma) = (\beta, \gamma) = (\beta, \gamma)(\eta, \zeta),$$

so that $\mathfrak{A}$ has the unit element $\epsilon = \eta + \zeta$. Since every element of $\mathfrak{A}$ is expressible uniquely as the sum of a number of $\mathfrak{B}$ and a number of $\mathfrak{C}$, the order of $\mathfrak{A}$ is the sum of the orders of $\mathfrak{B}$ and $\mathfrak{C}$.

If every number of an algebra $\mathfrak{A}$ can be written as a sum of a number of a subalgebra $\mathfrak{B}$ and a number of a subalgebra $\mathfrak{C}$, we call $\mathfrak{A}$ a *sum* of $\mathfrak{B}$ and $\mathfrak{C}$, and write $\mathfrak{A} = \mathfrak{B} + \mathfrak{C}$. The *product* $\mathfrak{BC}$ is the set of all products of a number of $\mathfrak{B}$ as left factor, by a number of $\mathfrak{C}$ as right factor. The *intersection* $\mathfrak{B} \wedge \mathfrak{C}$ is the set of all numbers common to $\mathfrak{B}$ and $\mathfrak{C}$.

Theorem 124.2. *If $\mathfrak{A}$ contains two proper subalgebras $\mathfrak{B}$ and $\mathfrak{C}$, and if*

$$\mathfrak{A} = \mathfrak{B} + \mathfrak{C}. \quad \mathfrak{BC} = \mathfrak{CB} = 0, \quad \mathfrak{B} \wedge \mathfrak{C} = 0,$$

then

$$\mathfrak{A} \cong \mathfrak{B} + \mathfrak{C}.$$

Let

$$\alpha = \beta_1 + \gamma_1 = \beta_2 + \gamma_2, \quad \beta_1, \beta_2 \in \mathfrak{B}, \quad \gamma_1, \gamma_2 \in \mathfrak{C}.$$

Then

$$\beta_1 - \beta_2 = \gamma_2 - \gamma_1$$

is in $\mathfrak{B} \wedge \mathfrak{C}$, which is 0, and so $\beta_1 = \beta_2$ and $\gamma_1 = \gamma_2$. That is, the representation of α as the sum of a number of $\mathfrak{B}$ and a number of $\mathfrak{C}$ is unique. Hence the order of $\mathfrak{A}$ is equal to the order of $\mathfrak{B} + \mathfrak{C}$, and the correspondence

$$\beta + \gamma \leftrightarrow (\beta, \gamma) \qquad\qquad \beta \in \mathfrak{B}, \gamma \in \mathfrak{C}$$

is an isomorphism under both addition and multiplication.

EXERCISES

1. Show that, if $\mathfrak{B}$ has a basis $\eta_1, \eta_2, \cdots, \eta_m$, and $\mathfrak{C}$ has a basis $\zeta_1, \zeta_2, \cdots, \zeta_n$, then $\eta_1, \eta_2, \cdots, \eta_m, \zeta_1, \zeta_2, \cdots, \zeta_n$ is a basis for $\mathfrak{B} + \mathfrak{C}$.

2. Show that, if the basis for $\mathfrak{B} + \mathfrak{C}$ is chosen as in Ex. 1, the matrices of the first regular representation of $\mathfrak{B} + \mathfrak{C}$ are the direct sums (§ 106) of the regular representations of $\mathfrak{B}$ and $\mathfrak{C}$. That is, if $\alpha = \beta + \gamma, \beta \in \mathfrak{B}, \gamma \in \mathfrak{C}$, then $R(\alpha) = R(\beta) + R(\gamma)$.

125. Idempotent elements and invariant subalgebras. An element ι of an algebra $\mathfrak{A}$ with unit element is called *idempotent* if $\iota^2 = \iota$. The unit element of $\mathfrak{A}$ is, of course, idempotent, and so is 0. In the total matric algebra of order 4, the matrix

$$\begin{bmatrix} 1 & 0 \\ 0 & 0 \end{bmatrix}$$

is idempotent, and is neither the unit element nor 0.

The following transformation will be called a *Peirce transformation.*[*] Let ι be any idempotent element of $\mathfrak{A}$, and α any number of $\mathfrak{A}$. Define

$$(125.1) \qquad\qquad \alpha' = \alpha - \iota\alpha - \alpha\iota + \iota\alpha\iota.$$

Theorem 125.1. The Peirce transformation carries $\mathfrak{A}$ into a subalgebra $\mathfrak{C}$.

Let $\mathfrak{C}$ be the set of numbers of $\mathfrak{A}$ which is obtained by applying the Peirce transformation to every number of $\mathfrak{A}$. We may notice that $\iota' = 0$, and that, for every number α' in $\mathfrak{C}$,

$$\iota\alpha' = \iota\alpha - \iota^2\alpha - \iota\alpha\iota + \iota^2\alpha\iota = 0, \qquad\qquad \alpha'\iota = 0.$$

Furthermore, $(\alpha')' = \alpha'$, so that every number of $\mathfrak{C}$ is left invariant by (125.1).

If α_1 and α_2 are two numbers of $\mathfrak{A}$, then evidently

$$(125.2) \qquad\qquad (\alpha_1 + \alpha_2)' = \alpha'_1 + \alpha'_2.$$

It is easily shown that

$$(125.3) \qquad\qquad \alpha'_1\alpha'_2 = (\alpha_1\alpha_2)' - (\alpha_1\iota\alpha_2)'.$$

Therefore the sum and the product of two numbers of $\mathfrak{C}$ are again in $\mathfrak{C}$.

If ϵ is the unit element of $\mathfrak{A}$,

$$\epsilon' = \epsilon - \iota\epsilon - \epsilon\iota + \iota\epsilon\iota = \epsilon - \iota - \iota + \iota = \epsilon - \iota,$$

and

$$\epsilon'\alpha' = \epsilon\alpha' - \iota\alpha' = \alpha', \quad \alpha'\epsilon' = \alpha'.$$

Hence ϵ' is the unit element of $\mathfrak{C}$.

If ι is the unit element of $\mathfrak{A}$, then clearly $\mathfrak{C} = 0$. If $\iota = 0$, then $\mathfrak{C} = \mathfrak{A}$. In other cases, $\mathfrak{C}$ is a proper subalgebra of $\mathfrak{A}$.

It was seen in Chapter II in the study of finite groups that a subgroup had little significance in the structure theory unless it was invariant. The same is true in the structure theory of algebras.

Let $\mathfrak{A}$ be an algebra with unit element, and $\mathfrak{B}$ a subalgebra with

---

[*] First used by Benjamin Peirce.

unit element. If every product in either order of an element of $\mathfrak{A}$ by an element of $\mathfrak{B}$ is in $\mathfrak{B}$—in notation, $\mathfrak{AB} \subseteq \mathfrak{B}$, $\mathfrak{BA} \subseteq \mathfrak{B}$—then $\mathfrak{B}$ is an *invariant subalgebra* of $\mathfrak{A}$.

Theorem 125.2.   If ι is the unit element of an invariant subalgebra $\mathfrak{B}$ of $\mathfrak{A}$, the Peirce transformation defines a ring homomorphism of $\mathfrak{A}$ into the subalgebra $\mathfrak{C}$.

If $\iota \in \mathfrak{B}$, and $\mathfrak{B}$ is invariant, then $\alpha_1 \iota \alpha_2 \in \mathfrak{B}$. But for any number $\beta \in \mathfrak{B}$,

$$\beta' = \beta - \beta - \beta + \beta = 0,$$

so that $(\alpha_1 \iota \alpha_2)' = 0$, and (125.3) reduces to

$$\alpha_1' \alpha_2' = (\alpha_1 \alpha_2)'.$$

This, together with (125.2), proves the assertion in the theorem.

Theorem 125.3.   If ι is the unit element of an invariant subalgebra $\mathfrak{B}$, and if the corresponding Peirce transformation carries $\mathfrak{A}$ into $\mathfrak{C}$, then $\mathfrak{A} = \mathfrak{B} + \mathfrak{C}$.

From (125.1),

$$\alpha' = \alpha - \iota\alpha - \alpha\iota + \iota\alpha\iota.$$

Since $\mathfrak{B}$ is invariant in $\mathfrak{A}$, $-\iota\alpha - \alpha\iota + \iota\alpha\iota$ is in $\mathfrak{B}$. Thus

$$\alpha = \alpha' + \beta,$$

where α' is in $\mathfrak{C}$ and β is in $\mathfrak{B}$. Then

$$\mathfrak{A} = \mathfrak{B} + \mathfrak{C}.$$

If β is in $\mathfrak{B}$, and $\gamma = \alpha'$ is in $\mathfrak{C}$,

$$\beta\gamma = \beta\alpha - \beta\iota\alpha - \beta\alpha\iota + \beta\iota\alpha\iota$$
$$= \beta\alpha - \beta\alpha - \beta\alpha\iota + \beta\alpha\iota = 0,$$

since ι is a unit element for $\mathfrak{B}$. Thus $\mathfrak{BC} = 0$, and similarly $\mathfrak{CB} = 0$.

Suppose that β is in both $\mathfrak{B}$ and $\mathfrak{C}$. Since $\beta \in \mathfrak{B}$, $\beta' = 0$. Since $\beta \in \mathfrak{C}$, $\beta' = \beta$. Thus $\beta = 0$. The theorem now follows from Theorem 124.2.

Lemma 125.4.   If $\mathfrak{B}$ and $\mathfrak{C}$ are invariant subalgebras with unit elements of the algebra $\mathfrak{A}$ with unit element, then $\mathfrak{B} \wedge \mathfrak{C} = \mathfrak{BC}$, and $\mathfrak{B} \wedge \mathfrak{C}$ is an invariant subalgebra of $\mathfrak{A}$ whose unit element is the product of the unit elements of $\mathfrak{B}$ and $\mathfrak{C}$.

Since $\mathfrak{B}$ and $\mathfrak{C}$ are both invariant, $\mathfrak{BC} \subseteq \mathfrak{B}$, $\mathfrak{BC} \subseteq \mathfrak{C}$, and so $\mathfrak{BC} \subseteq \mathfrak{B} \wedge \mathfrak{C}$. Since $\mathfrak{C}$ has a unit element, every element of $\mathfrak{B} \wedge \mathfrak{C}$

can be written as a product of a number (itself) of $\mathfrak{B}$ by a number (the unit element) of $\mathfrak{C}$, and so $\mathfrak{B} \wedge \mathfrak{C} \subseteq \mathfrak{B}\mathfrak{C}$. Hence $\mathfrak{B} \wedge \mathfrak{C} = \mathfrak{B}\mathfrak{C}$.

It is clear that, if β and γ belong to both $\mathfrak{B}$ and $\mathfrak{C}$, so do their sum and product. Since $\mathfrak{B}$ and $\mathfrak{C}$ are invariant in $\mathfrak{A}$,

$$\mathfrak{A}(\mathfrak{B}\mathfrak{C}) = (\mathfrak{A}\mathfrak{B})\mathfrak{C} \subseteq \mathfrak{B}\mathfrak{C}, \quad (\mathfrak{B}\mathfrak{C})\mathfrak{A} = \mathfrak{B}(\mathfrak{C}\mathfrak{A}) \subseteq \mathfrak{B}\mathfrak{C},$$

so $\mathfrak{B}\mathfrak{C}$ is invariant in $\mathfrak{A}$.

If η is the unit element of $\mathfrak{B}$, and ζ that of $\mathfrak{C}$, and if β belongs to both $\mathfrak{B}$ and $\mathfrak{C}$, then

$$\eta\zeta\beta = \eta\beta = \beta, \quad \beta\eta\zeta = \beta\zeta = \beta,$$

and so $\eta\zeta$ is a unit element for $\mathfrak{B} \wedge \mathfrak{C}$.

An algebra with unit element is called *irreducible* if it has no proper invariant subalgebra with unit element.

Theorem 125.4. Every algebra with unit element can be expressed in exactly one way, apart from arrangements of the components, as a direct sum of irreducible algebras.

If $\mathfrak{A}$ is reducible, it has an invariant subalgebra with unit element, and so by Theorem 125.3, $\mathfrak{A}$ can be written as a direct sum of algebras with unit elements. Each is of order less than the order of $\mathfrak{A}$. Unless each component is irreducible, it can be replaced by a direct sum of algebras of lower orders. Since $\mathfrak{A}$ is of finite order, it can be expressed as a direct sum of irreducible algebras.

Suppose that

$$\mathfrak{A} = \mathfrak{B}_1 + \mathfrak{B}_2 + \cdots + \mathfrak{B}_k = \mathfrak{C}_1 + \mathfrak{C}_2 + \cdots + \mathfrak{C}_l,$$

where each of the component algebras is irreducible. Let η_i be the unit element of $\mathfrak{B}_i$ and ϵ that of $\mathfrak{A}$. Then, by Theorem 124.1,

$$\epsilon = \eta_1 + \cdots + \eta_k,$$

and

$$\mathfrak{C}_j = \epsilon\mathfrak{C}_j = \eta_1\mathfrak{C}_j + \cdots + \eta_k\mathfrak{C}_j \neq 0.$$

Hence there is at least one unit element η_i such that $\eta_i\mathfrak{C}_j \neq 0$. Now $\mathfrak{B}_i$ and $\mathfrak{C}_j$ are both invariant in $\mathfrak{A}$, so that

$$\eta_i\mathfrak{C}_j \subseteq \mathfrak{B}_i, \quad \eta_i\mathfrak{C}_j \subseteq \mathfrak{C}_j, \quad \eta_i\mathfrak{C}_j \subseteq \mathfrak{B}_i \wedge \mathfrak{C}_j.$$

Hence $\mathfrak{B}_i \wedge \mathfrak{C}_j \neq 0$, and by the lemma, $\mathfrak{B}_i \wedge \mathfrak{C}_j$ is an invariant subalgebra of $\mathfrak{A}$. It is therefore an invariant subalgebra of both $\mathfrak{B}_i$ and $\mathfrak{C}_j$. But $\mathfrak{B}_i$ and $\mathfrak{C}_j$ are irreducible, and so $\mathfrak{B}_i \wedge \mathfrak{C}_j = \mathfrak{B}_i = \mathfrak{C}_j$. Since the $\mathfrak{B}_i$ are all distinct, and also the $\mathfrak{C}_i$, the two decompositions are the same except possibly for order.

EXERCISES

1. The algebra $\mathfrak{A}$:

	ϵ_1	ϵ_2	ϵ_3
ϵ_1	ϵ_1	ϵ_2	$\epsilon_1 - \epsilon_2$
ϵ_2	ϵ_2	$-\epsilon_1$	$\epsilon_1 + \epsilon_2$
ϵ_3	$\epsilon_1 - \epsilon_2$	$\epsilon_1 + \epsilon_2$	$-\epsilon_1 - \epsilon_2 + \epsilon_3$

has the invariant subalgebra (ϵ_1, ϵ_2). Apply a Peirce transformation, and express $\mathfrak{A}$ as a direct sum of two irreducible algebras.

2. Find an invariant subalgebra of the algebra of Ex. 1, § 122, and write this algebra as a direct sum.

3. Show that the Peirce transformation determines a linear transformation by means of which the basis numbers of $\mathfrak{C}$ (Theorem 125.2) are expressed in terms of the basis numbers of $\mathfrak{A}$. Illustrate with the last exercise.

4. If $\epsilon_1, \epsilon_2, \cdots, \epsilon_h$ are a basis for a subalgebra $\mathfrak{B}$ of the algebra $\mathfrak{A}$ with basis $\epsilon_1, \epsilon_2, \cdots, \epsilon_n$, show that, for $i \leqq h$, every matrix S_i has the form

$$\left[\begin{array}{c|c} & \begin{matrix} 0 \cdots 0 \\ \cdot \ \cdot \ \cdot \ \cdot \ \cdot \\ 0 \cdots 0 \end{matrix} \\ \hline & \end{array} \right].$$

5. If, in Ex. 4, $\mathfrak{B}$ is an invariant subalgebra of $\mathfrak{A}$, the matrices S_i have the forms

$$\left[\begin{array}{c|c} & \begin{matrix} 0 \cdots 0 \\ \cdot \ \cdot \ \cdot \ \cdot \ \cdot \\ 0 \cdots 0 \end{matrix} \\ \hline \begin{matrix} 0 \cdots 0 \\ \cdot \ \cdot \ \cdot \ \cdot \ \cdot \\ 0 \cdots 0 \end{matrix} & \end{array} \right] \text{ for } i \leqq h, \qquad \left[\begin{array}{c|c} & \begin{matrix} 0 \cdots 0 \\ \cdot \ \cdot \ \cdot \ \cdot \ \cdot \\ 0 \cdots 0 \end{matrix} \\ \hline & \end{array} \right] \text{ for } i > h.$$

126. Direct products. Suppose that $\mathfrak{B}$ is an algebra with the $\mathfrak{F}$-basis

$$\epsilon_1, \epsilon_2, \cdots, \epsilon_m, \qquad \epsilon_i \epsilon_j = \sum c_{ijk} \epsilon_k,$$

where ϵ_1 is the unit element, and that $\mathfrak{C}$ is an algebra with the $\mathfrak{F}$-basis

$$\eta_1, \eta_2, \cdots, \eta_n, \qquad \eta_i \eta_j = \sum c'_{ijk} \eta_k,$$

where η_1 is the unit element. Consider the mn ordered pairs (ϵ_i, η_j), and the $\mathfrak{F}$-module $\mathfrak{A}$ composed of all numbers

$$\sum a_{ij}(\epsilon_i, \eta_j), \qquad\qquad a_{ij} \in \mathfrak{F}.$$

These pairs are defined to be linearly independent over $\mathfrak{F}$, which is the same as saying that two numbers of $\mathfrak{A}$ are equal if and only if corresponding coefficients are equal. The product of two numbers of $\mathfrak{A}$ is defined by the distributive law and the multiplication table

(126.1) $$(\epsilon_i, \eta_j)(\epsilon_k, \eta_l) = \sum_{p,\,q} c_{ikp}c'_{jlq}(\epsilon_p, \eta_q).$$

As a special instance of the definition of multiplication, we have

$$(\epsilon_i, \eta_1)(\epsilon_k, \eta_1) = \sum_{p} c_{ikp}(\epsilon_p, \eta_1),$$

so that the numbers $\Sigma a_i(\epsilon_i, \eta_1)$ form a subalgebra of $\mathfrak{A}$ isomorphic with $\mathfrak{B}$. Similarly the numbers $\Sigma b_j(\epsilon_1, \eta_j)$ form a subalgebra of $\mathfrak{A}$ isomorphic with $\mathfrak{C}$. Also

$$(\epsilon_i, \eta_1)(\epsilon_1, \eta_l) = (\epsilon_i, \eta_l) = (\epsilon_1, \eta_l)(\epsilon_i, \eta_1).$$

Hence, if we use the notation ϵ_i for (ϵ_i, η_1) and η_l for (ϵ_1, η_l), then $\epsilon_i \eta_l$ will mean (ϵ_i, η_l). Thus we have embedded the algebras $\mathfrak{B}$ and $\mathfrak{C}$ in an algebra $\mathfrak{A}$, that is, we have constructed an algebra $\mathfrak{A}$ which contains subalgebras which are isomorphic with $\mathfrak{B}$ and $\mathfrak{C}$. This algebra $\mathfrak{A}$ is called the *direct product* of $\mathfrak{B}$ and $\mathfrak{C}$, and is written $\mathfrak{A} = \mathfrak{B} \times \mathfrak{C}$.

In the new notation, we may say that $\mathfrak{A}$ consists of all numbers

$$\sum a_{ij}\epsilon_i\eta_j, \qquad\qquad a_{ij} \in \mathfrak{F}$$

where, as was noted above, $\epsilon_i\eta_j = \eta_j\epsilon_i$. That is, $\mathfrak{A}$ consists of all numbers

$$c_1\eta_1 + c_2\eta_2 + \cdots + c_n\eta_n, \qquad c_j = \sum a_{ij}\epsilon_i,$$

and also of all numbers

$$b_1\epsilon_1 + b_2\epsilon_2 + \cdots + b_m\epsilon_m, \qquad b_i = \sum a_{ij}\eta_j.$$

Thus it is possible to consider the direct product $\mathfrak{B} \times \mathfrak{C}$ of two algebras over $\mathfrak{F}$ either as the algebra $\mathfrak{C}$ with the coefficient field $\mathfrak{F}$ extended to the algebra $\mathfrak{B}$, or as the algebra $\mathfrak{B}$ with $\mathfrak{F}$ extended to $\mathfrak{C}$.

Theorem 126.1. If an algebra $\mathfrak{A}$ with unit element contains two subalgebras $\mathfrak{B}$ and $\mathfrak{C}$, each with unit element, such that every number of $\mathfrak{B}$ is *commutative with every number of* $\mathfrak{C}$, *and if the order of* $\mathfrak{BC}$ *is equal to the product of the orders of* $\mathfrak{B}$ *and* $\mathfrak{C}$, *then*

$$\mathfrak{BC} \cong \mathfrak{B} \times \mathfrak{C}.$$

Let $\mathfrak{B}$ have the $\mathfrak{F}$-basis $\epsilon_1, \epsilon_2, \cdots, \epsilon_m$, where ϵ_1 is the unit element, and let $\mathfrak{C}$ have the $\mathfrak{F}$-basis $\eta_1, \eta_2, \cdots, \eta_n$, where η_1 is the unit element. Set up the correspondence

$$\epsilon_i \eta_j \leftrightarrow (\epsilon_i, \eta_j).$$

Since the order of $\mathfrak{BC}$ is equal to the product of the orders of $\mathfrak{B}$ and $\mathfrak{C}$, there can be no linear relation

$$\sum a_{ij} \epsilon_i \eta_j = 0$$

unless every a_{ij} is 0. Hence the above correspondence is biunique. Clearly the correspondence

$$\mathfrak{BC} \cong \mathfrak{B} \times \mathfrak{C}$$

is an isomorphism relative to addition. Since every $\mathfrak{B}$ is commutative with every $\mathfrak{C}$, we may use the notation at the beginning of the paragraph to obtain

$$\epsilon_i \eta_j \cdot \epsilon_k \eta_l = \epsilon_i \epsilon_k \cdot \eta_j \eta_l = \sum c_{ikp} c'_{jlq} \epsilon_p \eta_q.$$

A comparison with (126.1) shows the isomorphism with respect to multiplication.

An important instance of the direct product is an algebra $\mathfrak{B} \times \mathfrak{M}$, where $\mathfrak{M}$ is a total matric algebra (§ 98). If $\mathfrak{P}$ is any prime field, the total matric algebra $\mathfrak{M}$ of order n^2 consists of all $n \times n$ matrices with elements in $\mathfrak{P}$. This algebra possesses a basis $\epsilon_{11}, \cdots, \epsilon_{nn}$ where ϵ_{ij} is the 0 matrix with the element in row i and column j replaced by 1. The multiplication table is

$$\epsilon_{ij} \epsilon_{kl} = \delta_{jk} \epsilon_{il}, \qquad \delta_{jk} = \text{Kronecker's delta}.$$

(See Ex. 3, § 122.) Hence each of the constants of multiplication is 0 or 1. Now let $\mathfrak{B}$ be any algebra over a field containing the prime field $\mathfrak{P}$. The direct product $\mathfrak{B} \times \mathfrak{M}$ consists, then, of all $n \times n$ matrices whose elements are numbers of $\mathfrak{B}$. Such algebras were considered in § 98.

EXERCISES

1. Let $\mathfrak{B}$ be the field of complex numbers $a + bi$ over Ra. Find the multiplication table of the direct product of $\mathfrak{B}$ with itself.

2. Show that $\mathfrak{B} \times \mathfrak{M}$ cannot be a division algebra if $\mathfrak{M}$ is of order > 1.

3. Show that the direct product of two total matric algebras is a total matric algebra.

127. Linear algebras. The term *linear algebra* in the widest sense in which it is used is applied to a linear form module, over a field, for which a multiplication is defined. We shall consider only algebras which have a finite basis relative to a field and which are associative. Such algebras include those considered in §§ 122–126 and also others which may not have a unit element.

Since the unit element is not postulated, it may not be true that the algebra contains a subalgebra isomorphic with the coefficient field. For that reason it is necessary to postulate the operation of scalar multiplication, as well as multiplication within the algebra $\mathfrak{A}$.

Let us assume, then, that $\mathfrak{A}$ is a ring (see § 68) and $\mathfrak{F}$ is a field. Let $\alpha, \beta, \gamma, \cdots$ be elements of $\mathfrak{A}$, and $a, b, c, \cdots$ numbers of $\mathfrak{F}$. We shall assume that:

1. $a\alpha$ is in $\mathfrak{A}$, and $a\alpha = \alpha a$.
2. $a(\alpha + \beta) = a\alpha + a\beta$.
3. $\alpha(a + b) = \alpha a + \alpha b$.
4. $1\alpha = \alpha$, where 1 is the unit element of $\mathfrak{F}$.
5. The associative law
$$x(yz) = (xy)z$$

holds where x, y, z are elements of $\mathfrak{A}$ or $\mathfrak{F}$, indiscriminately.

It is now established that $\mathfrak{A}$ is an $\mathfrak{F}$-module. We assume, further, that it is a finite $\mathfrak{F}$-module. That is,

6. There exist in $\mathfrak{A}$ a finite number of elements $\epsilon_1, \epsilon_2, \cdots, \epsilon_n$ such that every number of $\mathfrak{A}$ can be written uniquely

$$\alpha = a_1\epsilon_1 + a_2\epsilon_2 + \cdots + a_n\epsilon_n, \qquad a_i \in \mathfrak{F}.$$

The number n of elements in a linearly independent basis is called the *order* of $\mathfrak{A}$.

As in § 122, we define the *constants of multiplication* c_{ijk} by the relation

$$\epsilon_i\epsilon_j = \sum c_{ijk}\epsilon_k, \qquad c_{ijk} \in \mathfrak{F}.$$

Since $\mathfrak{A}$ is associative, the n^3 numbers c_{ijk} are subject to the n^4 conditions (122.2).

The lack of a unit element introduces many complications. For instance, while the matrices R_i and S_i can be defined as in § 123, they are not always linearly independent, and hence do not always represent the algebra. Frequently they do, however, and it may even happen that the R_i are linearly independent and not the S_i or vice versa. A matric representation in terms of n matrices, each with $n + 1$ rows and columns, can always be secured by the following device. Adjoin to the algebra $\mathfrak{A}$ another basis number ϵ_0 such that $\epsilon_i = \epsilon_0\epsilon_i = \epsilon_i\epsilon_0$ for every ϵ_i. This new algebra $\mathfrak{A}^*$ of order $n + 1$ has the unit element ϵ_0, and its first matrices

$$R_0, R_1, R_2, \cdots, R_n$$

are linearly independent. The set obtained by neglecting R_0 is closed under multiplication and represents $\mathfrak{A}$. We may proceed similarly with the S-matrices.

As an extreme example of algebras without a unit element, we may mention the *zero algebras*, in which every constant of multiplication is 0. The associativity conditions are trivially satisfied. The product of every two numbers of the algebra is zero — in notation, $\mathfrak{A}^2 = 0$.

An algebra is called *nilpotent* if some power of it is zero. If r is the smallest exponent for which $\mathfrak{A}^r = 0$, then $\mathfrak{A}$ is nilpotent of *index r*. This means that r is the smallest integer such that

$$\alpha_1 \alpha_2 \cdots \alpha_r = 0$$

for *every* product of r factors from $\mathfrak{A}$. If $\mathfrak{A}$ has a unit element, it is clearly not nilpotent, for no power of the unit element is 0.

EXERCISES

1. Show that the algebra

	ϵ_1	ϵ_2
ϵ_1	ϵ_2	0
ϵ_2	0	0

over Ra is nilpotent of index 3.

2. Consider the algebra

	ϵ_1	ϵ_2
ϵ_1	ϵ_1	0
ϵ_2	ϵ_2	0

over Ra. Show that it is represented by its R-matrices but not by its S-matrices.

3. Adjoin a unit element ϵ_0 to the algebra of Ex. 1, and thus obtain two 3×3 matrices which represent the algebra.

4. Consider the algebra $\mathfrak{A}$:

	ϵ_1	ϵ_2	ϵ_3
ϵ_1	ϵ_1	0	ϵ_3
ϵ_2	0	ϵ_2	0
ϵ_3	0	ϵ_3	0

over Ra. Find all its idempotent elements. Is one of these a unit element? What is the effect upon $\mathfrak{A}$ of the Peirce transformations based upon each of these idempotents?

5. Show that the R-matrices, and also the S-matrices, are linearly independent and hence represent the algebra $\mathfrak{A}$, if $\mathfrak{A}$ contains a single number which is not a proper divisor of zero. (See § 68.)

128. Ideals. As in § 125, a subalgebra $\mathfrak{B}$ of $\mathfrak{A}$ is called *invariant* in $\mathfrak{A}$ if $\mathfrak{B}\mathfrak{A} \subseteq \mathfrak{B}$ and $\mathfrak{A}\mathfrak{B} \subseteq \mathfrak{B}$. In this case, $\mathfrak{B}$ may not have a unit element. The close analogy of this concept with that of ideal in an algebraic domain (§ 65) is at once apparent. The analogy is even closer to the left and right ideals of the domain H of integral quaternions (§ 116).

Let $\mathfrak{A}$ be a linear algebra. A *left ideal* $\mathfrak{L}$ of $\mathfrak{A}$ is a submodule of $\mathfrak{A}$ such that $\mathfrak{A}\mathfrak{L} \subseteq \mathfrak{L}$. A *right ideal* $\mathfrak{R}$ is a submodule such that $\mathfrak{R}\mathfrak{A} \subseteq \mathfrak{R}$. A module which is both a left ideal and a right ideal is called a *two-sided ideal* or an *invariant subalgebra*.

In all previous instances, we have defined ideal only in an integral domain, and every ideal was of the same order as the domain. In the present instance, every ideal of $\mathfrak{A}$ except $\mathfrak{A}$ itself is of lower order than $\mathfrak{A}$. We have not excluded 0 from being an ideal.

Let $\mathfrak{A}$ be an algebra, and let $\mathfrak{J}$ be a two-sided ideal of $\mathfrak{A}$. Two numbers are called *congruent* modulo $\mathfrak{J}$ if their difference is in $\mathfrak{J}$. That is, the two statements

$$\alpha \equiv \beta \mod \mathfrak{J}, \qquad \alpha - \beta \in \mathfrak{J},$$

mean the same thing.

Theorem 128.1. *If $\mathfrak{J}$ is a two-sided ideal of $\mathfrak{A}$, the elements of $\mathfrak{A}$ modulo $\mathfrak{J}$ constitute an algebra $\mathfrak{A}/\mathfrak{J}$,* called the difference algebra.*

Suppose that

$$\alpha \equiv \beta, \quad \gamma \equiv \delta \mod \mathfrak{J}.$$

Then

$$\alpha = \beta + i_1, \quad \gamma = \delta + i_2, \qquad\qquad i_1, i_2 \in \mathfrak{J},$$

so that

$$\alpha + \gamma = \beta + \delta + i_1 + i_2, \quad \alpha + \gamma \equiv \beta + \delta \mod \mathfrak{J}.$$

Also,

$$\alpha\gamma = \beta\delta + \beta i_2 + i_1\delta + i_1 i_2.$$

Since $\mathfrak{J}$ is a two-sided ideal,

$$\beta i_2 + i_1\delta + i_1 i_2 \in \mathfrak{J},$$

so that

$$\alpha\gamma \equiv \beta\delta \mod \mathfrak{J}.$$

---

* Also written $\mathfrak{A} - \mathfrak{J}$ in some books. The concept is analogous to that of quotient group. (See § 26.)

Thus $\mathfrak{A}/\mathfrak{J}$ is closed under addition and multiplication. Similarly it is closed under scalar multiplication, and all the assumptions of § 127 follow readily.

It must not be assumed that $\mathfrak{A}/\mathfrak{J}$ is isomorphic with a subalgebra of $\mathfrak{A}$, although this is frequently true. Let a basis for $\mathfrak{A}$,

$$\epsilon_1, \ \epsilon_2, \ \cdots, \ \epsilon_k, \ \epsilon_{k+1}, \ \cdots, \ \epsilon_n,$$

be so chosen that $\epsilon_{k+1}, \ \cdots, \ \epsilon_n$ constitute a basis for $\mathfrak{J}$. Then

$$\alpha = a_1\epsilon_1 + \cdots + a_n\epsilon_n \equiv a_1\epsilon_1 + \cdots + a_k\epsilon_k \qquad \mathrm{mod}\ \mathfrak{J}.$$

The product of two numbers

$$\alpha = a_1\epsilon_1 + \cdots + a_k\epsilon_k, \quad \beta = b_1\epsilon_1 + \cdots + b_k\epsilon_k$$

in $\mathfrak{A}/\mathfrak{J}$ is not usually the same as their product in $\mathfrak{A}$, for the latter will ordinarily involve the basis numbers $\epsilon_{k+1}, \ \cdots, \ \epsilon_n$ as well as the numbers $\epsilon_1 \cdots, \ \epsilon_k$. By cutting off all but the terms in $\epsilon_1, \ \cdots, \ \epsilon_k$, we obtain the product $\alpha\beta$ in $\mathfrak{A}/\mathfrak{J}$.

If $\mathfrak{A}$ has a unit element, however, and $\mathfrak{B}$ is an ideal with unit element, then we have shown that there exists an algebra $\mathfrak{C}$ with unit element such that $\mathfrak{A} = \mathfrak{B} + \mathfrak{C}$. Then both $\mathfrak{B}$ and $\mathfrak{C}$ are invariant in $\mathfrak{A}$, and

$$\frac{\mathfrak{A}}{\mathfrak{B}} \cong \mathfrak{C}, \quad \frac{\mathfrak{A}}{\mathfrak{C}} \cong \mathfrak{B}.$$

EXERCISES

1. Consider the algebra of Ex. 1, § 125. Let $(\epsilon_1, \epsilon_2) = \mathfrak{J}$, and find $\mathfrak{A}/\mathfrak{J}$. Compare the result with that of the exercise mentioned.

2. The algebra of Ex. 4, § 127, contains the ideal (ϵ_3) which does not contain a unit element. Show that $\mathfrak{A}$ is a sum of (ϵ_3) and another subalgebra, but is not their direct sum.

3. If $\epsilon_1, \ \epsilon_2, \ \cdots, \ \epsilon_h$ are a basis for a left ideal $\mathfrak{L}$ of the algebra $\mathfrak{A}$ with basis $\epsilon_1, \ \epsilon_2, \ \cdots, \ \epsilon_n$, what forms do the S-matrices assume? (See Ex. 5, § 125.) Do the same for a right ideal $\mathfrak{R}$.

4. Show that the algebra of Ex. 2, § 127, has infinitely many right unit elements but no left unit elements. (The number ϵ is a right unit element if $\alpha\epsilon = \alpha$ for every α.)

5. Prove that, if $\mathfrak{A}$ has a unique right unit element ϵ, then ϵ is a unit element. HINT: $\beta(\epsilon\alpha - \alpha + \epsilon) = \beta$.

129. The radical. Suppose that $\mathfrak{K}$ and $\mathfrak{J}$ are two two-sided ideals in an algebra $\mathfrak{A}$ of order n over a field $\mathfrak{F}$. Suppose that $\mathfrak{K}$ has an $\mathfrak{F}$-basis $\alpha_1, \alpha_2, \ \cdots, \ \alpha_p$, and that $\mathfrak{J}$ has an $\mathfrak{F}$-basis $\beta_1, \beta_2, \ \cdots, \ \beta_q$. The *union* of the two ideals, written either $(\Re, \Im)$ or $\Re \vee \Im$, consists of all numbers which are linear combinations with coefficients in $\Im$ of the numbers

$$\alpha_1, \alpha_2, \cdots, \alpha_p, \beta_1, \beta_2, \cdots, \beta_q.$$

If $\Re$ and $\Im$ are ideals, it is clear that $(\Re, \Im)$ is an ideal.

Either $\Re \subseteq \Im$, or at least one α is linearly independent of the β's. Hence the order of $(\Re, \Im)$ is greater than the orders of both $\Re$ and $\Im$, or else one of these ideals is a subideal of the other.

Now suppose that both $\Re$ and $\Im$ are nilpotent ideals, $\Re^k = 0$, $\Im^i = 0$. We have

Theorem 129.1.   The union of two nilpotent ideals is a nilpotent ideal.

The union $(\Re, \Im)$ consists of all numbers $\kappa + \iota$, where $\kappa \in \Re$, $\iota \in \Im$. Consider the product

$$\prod (\kappa_p + \iota_p) \qquad (p = 1, 2, \cdots, k + i - 1),$$

where the κ_p are in $\Re$ and the ι_p are in $\Im$. Every term in the expansion of this product contains either at least k factors in $\Re$ or at least i factors in $\Im$. In either case, this term is 0, since both $\Re$ and $\Im$ are invariant. Hence $(\Re, \Im)$ is nilpotent of index $\leq k + i$.

Theorem 129.2.   Every nilpotent ideal is contained in a unique maximal nilpotent ideal.

Let $\Re$ and $\Im$ be two nilpotent ideals, neither of which is a subideal of the other. Their union is a nilpotent ideal, of higher order than either $\Re$ or $\Im$, which contains both $\Re$ and $\Im$. Since the algebra $\Im$ is of finite order, in a finite number of steps we reach a nilpotent ideal which contains every other nilpotent ideal.

This unique maximal nilpotent ideal is called the *radical* of $\Im$. It will be denoted by $\Re$. It is the union of all nilpotent ideals of $\Im$. An algebra which contains no nilpotent ideal other than 0 is called *semi-simple*. If it contains no ideal other than 0, it is *simple*.

Theorem 129.3.   If $\Re$ is the radical of $\Im$, $\Im/\Re$ is semi-simple.

Let $\Re$ be nilpotent of index r. Let $\Im/\Re$ contain a nilpotent ideal $\overline{\Re}$ of index s. Denote by $\Re_1$ the set of all numbers of $\Im$ which are congruent modulo $\Re$ to the numbers of $\overline{\Re}$. That is, the elements of $\overline{\Re}$ are the elements of $\Re_1$ modulo $\Re$.

Let ρ_1 and ρ_2 be any two numbers of $\Re_1$, and let α be any number of $\Im$. Let

$$\rho_1 \equiv \bar\rho_1, \quad \rho_2 \equiv \bar\rho_2, \quad \alpha \equiv \bar\alpha \qquad \mathrm{mod} \ \Re.$$

Then $\rho_1 + \rho_2$, $\alpha\rho_1$, and $\rho_1\alpha$ are in $\mathfrak{R}_1$, since $\bar{\rho}_1 + \bar{\rho}_2$, $\bar{\alpha}\bar{\rho}_1$ and $\bar{\rho}_1\bar{\alpha}$ are in the ideal $\bar{\mathfrak{R}}$ of $\mathfrak{A}/\mathfrak{R}$. Hence $\mathfrak{R}_1$ is a two-sided ideal of $\mathfrak{A}$.

To show that $\mathfrak{R}_1$ is nilpotent, form the product $\rho_1\rho_2 \cdots \rho_s$ of any s numbers of $\mathfrak{R}_1$. Then

$$\rho_1\rho_2 \cdots \rho_s \equiv \bar{\rho}_1\bar{\rho}_2 \cdots \bar{\rho}_s \qquad \mathrm{mod}\ \mathfrak{R}.$$

But $\bar{\mathfrak{R}}$ is of index s, and so this product is congruent to 0 modulo $\mathfrak{R}$, that is, it is in $\mathfrak{R}$. But $\mathfrak{R}$ is of index r in $\mathfrak{A}$, so that any product of rs numbers of $\mathfrak{R}_1$ is equal to 0 in $\mathfrak{A}$. Hence $\mathfrak{R}_1$ is nilpotent in $\mathfrak{A}$ of index $\leqq rs$. Since $\mathfrak{R}_1$ is nilpotent, and $\mathfrak{R}$ is the radical, $\mathfrak{R}_1 \subseteq \mathfrak{R}$. Hence $\mathfrak{R}_1 \equiv 0 \bmod \mathfrak{R}$, and $\bar{\mathfrak{R}} = 0$ in $\mathfrak{A}/\mathfrak{R}$. Thus $\mathfrak{A}/\mathfrak{R}$ is semi-simple.

We shall conclude our brief sketch of the structure of linear algebras by stating without proof the main results in the structure theory of linear algebras:

Every linear algebra $\mathfrak{A}$ which contains a nilpotent ideal $\neq 0$ has a radical $\mathfrak{R}$, and $\mathfrak{A}/\mathfrak{R}$ is semi-simple and contains a unit element. Every semi-simple algebra is uniquely expressible as a direct sum of simple algebras, each with a unit element. Every simple algebra is the direct product of a division algebra and a total matric algebra. Every division algebra over an algebraic field is cyclic.

EXERCISES

1. Consider the algebra of Ex. 2, § 122, over Ra. What is its radical? Find the multiplication table of $\mathfrak{A}/\mathfrak{R}$. Is $\mathfrak{A}/\mathfrak{R}$ isomorphic with a subalgebra of $\mathfrak{A}$?

2. Consider the algebra $\mathfrak{A}$:

	ϵ_1	ϵ_2	ϵ_3	ϵ_4
ϵ_1	0	0	0	ϵ_1
ϵ_2	0	ϵ_1	0	ϵ_2
ϵ_3	0	0	ϵ_1	ϵ_3
ϵ_4	ϵ_1	ϵ_2	ϵ_3	ϵ_4

Then $\mathfrak{R} = (\epsilon_1)$ is a nilpotent invariant subalgebra. What is the multiplication table of $\mathfrak{A}/\mathfrak{R}$? What is the radical of $\mathfrak{A}/\mathfrak{R}$? Use the method in the proof of Theorem 129.3 to find the radical $\mathfrak{R}$ of $\mathfrak{A}$. Is $\mathfrak{A}/\mathfrak{R}$ isomorphic with a subalgebra of $\mathfrak{A}$?

3. If the semi-simple algebra $\mathfrak{A}/\mathfrak{R}$ remains semi-simple for every algebraic extension of $\mathfrak{F}$, then $\mathfrak{A}$ contains a subalgebra $\mathfrak{A}^*$ isomorphic with $\mathfrak{A}/\mathfrak{R}$ so that $\mathfrak{A} = \mathfrak{A}^* + \mathfrak{R}$. This is not a direct sum, for, although $\mathfrak{A}^*\mathfrak{R} \subseteq \mathfrak{R}$, $\mathfrak{R}\mathfrak{A}^* \subseteq \mathfrak{R}$, these products are not usually 0. Illustrate this isomorphism with the algebras of Exs. 1, 2.

4. Let $\mathfrak{F}$ be the field $GF(2, \lambda)$, that is, the field of all rational functions of the indeterminate λ with coefficients 0 or 1 mod 2. Let $\mathfrak{A}$ be the algebra over $\mathfrak{F}$ with multiplication table

	ϵ_1	ϵ_2	ϵ_3	ϵ_4
ϵ_1	ϵ_1	ϵ_2	ϵ_3	ϵ_4
ϵ_2	ϵ_2	$\lambda\epsilon_1 + \epsilon_3 + \epsilon_4$	ϵ_4	$\lambda\epsilon_3$
ϵ_3	ϵ_3	ϵ_4	0	0
ϵ_4	ϵ_4	$\lambda\epsilon_3$	0	0.

Show that the radical is $\mathfrak{R} = (\epsilon_3, \epsilon_4)$, and that $\mathfrak{A}/\mathfrak{R}$ has the multiplication table

	$\bar{\epsilon}_1$	$\bar{\epsilon}_2$
$\bar{\epsilon}_1$	$\bar{\epsilon}_1$	$\bar{\epsilon}_2$
$\bar{\epsilon}_2$	$\bar{\epsilon}_2$	$\lambda\bar{\epsilon}_1$.

Show that the only idempotents in $\mathfrak{A}$ are 0 and ϵ_1. Show that there exists no number $\alpha \in \mathfrak{A}$ such that $\alpha^2 = \lambda\epsilon_1$, and hence that $\mathfrak{A}$ contains no subalgebra isomorphic with $\mathfrak{A}/\mathfrak{R}$.

Suggested Readings

Dickson, L. E. *Linear Algebras*. Cambridge University Press, 1914.

Dickson, L. E. *Algebras and Their Arithmetics*. University of Chicago Press, 1923.

Dickson, L. E. *Algebren und ihre Zahlentheorie*. Füssli, Zurich, 1927.

Hurwitz, A. *Vorlesungen über die Zahlentheorie der Quaternionen*. Springer, Berlin, 1919.

Wedderburn, J. H. M. "On Hypercomplex Numbers." *Proceedings of the London Mathematical Society*, Series II, Vol. 6 (1907), pp. 77–118.

Albert, A. A. *Structure of Algebras*. American Mathematical Society, New York, 1939.

van der Waerden, B. L. *Moderne Algebra*, Vol. II, Chapter XVI. Springer, Berlin, 1931.

Deuring, M. *Algebren*. Springer, Berlin, 1935.

THE LETTERS OF THE GREEK ALPHABET, WITH THEIR NAMES

A	α	alpha	I ι	iota	P ρ	rho
B	β	beta	K κ	kappa	Σ σ s	sigma
Γ	γ	gamma	Λ λ	lambda	T τ	tau
Δ	δ	delta	M μ	mu	Υ υ	upsilon
E	ε	epsilon	N ν	nu	Φ φ φ	phi
Z	ζ	zeta	Ξ ξ	xi	X χ	chi
H	η	eta	O o	omicron	Ψ ψ	psi
Θ ϑ θ		theta	Π π	pi	Ω ω	omega

GERMAN ALPHABET AND HANDWRITING

German Type	Handwriting	Roman Type	Name	German Type	Handwriting	Roman Type	Name
A,a		A, a	ah	N,n		N,n	n
B,b		B, b	bay	O,o		O,o	o
C,c		C, c	tsay	P,p		P,p	pay
D,d		D, d	day	Q,q		Q,q	koo
E,e		E, e	eh	R,r		R,r	air
F,f		F, f	f	S,ſ,s		S,s	s
G,g		G, g	gay	T,t		T,t	tay
H,h		H, h	hah	U,u		U,u	oo
I,i		I, i	e	V,v		V,v	fow
J,j		J, j	yot	W,w		W,w	vay
K,k		K, k	kah	X,x		X,x	ix
L,l		L, l	l	Y,y		Y,y	ipsilon
M,m		M,m	m	Z,z		Z,z	tset
				_ ß		ß,ss	s-tset

Reproduced with the publisher's permission from *First Book in German* by E. W. Bagster-Collins, Macmillan, 1914.

INDEX

SYMBOLS